The Onset of Stuttering

THE ONSET OF STUTTERING

Research Findings and Implications

Wendell Johnson and Associates

RICHARD M. BOEHMLER

W. GRANT DAHLSTROM

FREDERIC L. DARLEY

LEONARD D. GOODSTEIN

JOSEPH A. KOOLS

JAMES N. NEELLEY

WILLIAM F. PRATHER

DOROTHY SHERMAN

CAROLYN G. THURMAN

WILLIAM D. TROTTER

DEAN WILLIAMS

MARTIN A. YOUNG

UNIVERSITY OF MINNESOTA PRESS, Minneapolis

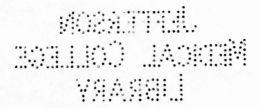

Preface

THE program of research reported in this volume consisted of three related investigations — designated for convenience of reference as Studies I, II, and III — conducted from 1934 to 1957. The institutional settings and sponsorship of this research are described in detail in the text and footnotes of Chapter 1. The investigations were carried out at the University of Iowa and Study III was done with the cooperation of the University of Minnesota and Northwestern University. The investigative procedures employed are also described in Chapter 1; the findings are presented in the Summary Table in Appendix A and in Chapters 2–8, and they are summarized in Chapter 9; the conclusions are developed in Chapter 10. A brief résumé is to be found at the end of Chapter 10. The full reports of Studies I and II, abstracted in Chapters 1 and 2 of this volume, are to be found in Chapters 3 and 4 of *Stuttering in Children and Adults: Thirty Years of Research at the University of Iowa,* edited by the writer with the assistance of Ralph M. Leutenegger, and published in 1955 by the University of Minnesota Press.

The efforts represented by this book have been shared by many persons. The names of those who contributed most substantially to the research and the writing of the report are listed opposite the title page. Frederic L. Darley served as a consultant and supervised the training of the interviewers in Study III; moreover, he did Study II, as doctoral research for the most part, and a considerable portion of Chapter 2 has been taken from his previously published account of that investigation. Richard Boehmler served for two years as work supervisor of Study III; he also did a considerable number of interviews, collected and analyzed a large proportion of the children's speech samples that are discussed in Chapter 8, carried out much of the statistical processing of the data, and prepared a preliminary draft of certain parts of Chapters 1, 3, 4, 5, 6, and 8. Carolyn Gustafson Thurman was an interviewer throughout Study III, assisted with the

v

training and supervising of other interviewers, and checked the coding of interview data for IBM punching. Other interviewers in Study III were Beulah Rohrlich, Janet Way, Aviva Epstein, Bernard Stoll, and Charles Robins. Ralph Leutenegger assisted in securing subjects for Study III.

William D. Trotter served as work supervisor of Study III during the period when preliminary drafts of the report were being prepared. Dorothy Sherman was a consultant for Study III, served as the major statistical adviser, and gave a considerable part of the manuscript a critical reading. Don Lewis contributed valuable counsel concerning statistical treatment of data in Study II, and this advice was followed also in Study III. Martin A. Young did approximately a third of the follow-up interviews reported in Chapter 6, checked statistical operations, personally carried out a substantial share of the processing of the data, prepared the table in Appendix B, and served as a statistical consultant. James N. Neelley did the larger share of the follow-up interviews and assisted the writer clinically and administratively in ways that made the preparation of the report possible. W. Grant Dahlstrom and Leonard D. Goodstein served successively as psychological consultants for Study III and were responsible for the part of the research reported in Chapter 7. Dean Williams spent much time with the writer in discussion of the clinical and theoretical implications of the data, read the manuscript critically, and contributed importantly to the point of view employed in interpretation of the findings.

Forrest Lee Brissey, James V. Frick, and Dean Williams assisted in the preliminary work in refining the procedure employed in the recording of children's speech samples and in making some of the recordings used in the present study, and Joseph Kools analyzed a considerable proportion of these speech samples and prepared drafts of the tables and certain portions of related material utilized in writing Chapter 8. Robert Duffy also assisted with analysis of the speech samples.

Consultants for Study III, in addition to James F. Curtis, Frederic L. Darley, Leonard D. Goodstein, Dorothy Sherman, and D. C. Spriestersbach of the University of Iowa, were W. Grant Dahlstrom and Earl D. Schubert, then of the University of Iowa; Spencer F. Brown, M.D., then of the University of Minnesota; Bryng Bryngelson and Ernest H. Henrikson of the University of Minnesota; and Charles Elliott, then of Northwestern University. Administrative work of major importance was performed by James F. Curtis, head of the Department of Speech Pathology and Audiology, University of Iowa, since 1956, and D. C. Spriestersbach, who rendered a particularly valuable administrative service in relation to the organization and early development of Study

III. Jayne Zeman and Phyllis Irwin gave essential administrative assistance during most of the period in which the report was being drafted.

Expressions of appreciation for assistance in locating subjects for the three investigations are due particularly to the following: the late W. A. WinterStein, then director of the Division of Special Education of the Iowa State Department of Public Instruction; Spencer F. Brown, M.D., then of the Department of Pediatrics, University Hospital, Bryng Bryngelson, professor of speech, Ernest H. Henrikson, director of the Speech Clinic, and E. W. Ziebarth, then head of the department of Speech, all of the University of Minnesota; Harold Westlake, director of the Speech Clinic, and Charles Elliott, then of the Speech Clinic staff, both of Northwestern University; Margaret Hall Powers, director of the Bureau of Physically Handicapped Children and Division of Speech Correction, Chicago, Illinois, Public Schools; Buford Garner, superintendent, Iowa City, Iowa, Public Schools; Roger Lienke, then director of the Iowa State Services for Crippled Children, Iowa City; R. R. Remboldt, director of the University Hospital School for Severely Handicapped Children, Iowa City; Boyd McCandless, director, and Orvis C. Irwin and Ruth Updegraff of the staff of the Iowa Child Welfare Research Station, University of Iowa; and many other interested colleagues and friends.

William F. Prather performed an extraordinary amount of work in checking tabulations and computations, particularly those represented in the Summary Table in Appendix A, and in assisting with the analysis of the data. A number of the tables were prepared with the help of Eileen Seigel. Carol Chinn Strange contributed impressively to the assembling of the Summary Table in Appendix A and did a major share of the typing of some of the drafts of the manuscript. Christina Sturdevant assisted with typing and performed certain of the tabulations in the preparation of the Summary Table.

Phyllis Irwin carried major responsibility for typing the final draft and readying the manuscript for the publisher. Special acknowledgment is made of the extraordinary craftsmanship displayed by Mrs. Irwin in preparing the special typescript used for reproducing the extensive tabular materials in the appendixes. Margaret Seemuth also did a considerable part of the typing, and others who assisted with preparation of the manuscript included Marjorie Albee, Ann Collins Laursen, Beverly Johnson, Barbara Schindler, Christine Holloway, Beulah Rohrlich, Dorothy Becker, Catherine Cheyne, Claryce Uhl, Marilyn Veglahn, and Barbara Miller. Phyllis Irwin, Beverly Johnson, Linda Jean Hill Eberline, Ann Collins Laursen, Jo Ann Osmundson, and Bonnie McConnell assisted with proofreading and preparation of the index.

To all whose names have been mentioned, to the parents and children who served as subjects and informants, to the many students and professional colleagues in addition to those named who were helpful in countless ways, a deeply sincere expression of appreciation is extended.

In the full reports of Studies I and II in *Stuttering in Children and Adults: Thirty Years of Research at the University of Iowa*, acknowledgments are made of the support and assistance of persons who contributed to those phases of the total program. The Foreword and Chapter 1 of that book contain a historical account of the stuttering research program at the University of Iowa in which there is a calling of the roll of the persons, so far as they are known to the writer, who were responsible for the initiation, several decades ago, of the research adventure in the course of which this investigation of the onset of the problem of stuttering came to be made.

Substantial portions of Chapters 3 and 4 of *Stuttering in Children and Adults* are reprinted or summarized in Chapters 1 and 2 of this book by arrangement with the University of Minnesota Press. Appleton-Century-Crofts granted permission to adapt in Chapter 1 a passage from *Handbook of Speech Pathology*, 1956, edited by Lee Edward Travis, and Harper and Brothers granted permission to reproduce in Chapter 3 a passage from *Speech Handicapped School Children*, revised edition, 1956. Chapter 7 is reprinted, in extended form and with editorial adaptations, from the *Journal of Consulting Psychology*, with the permission of the American Psychological Association. Passages from "Listener Evaluations of Speech Interruptions," by Dean E. Williams and Louise R. Kent, are reprinted in Chapter 10, with the permission of the American Speech and Hearing Association. The cooperation of these publishers is acknowledged with gratitude. The writer is also pleased to thank the publishers and authors who have granted permission to quote or adapt material from sources specified in the relevant footnotes.

John Ervin, Jr., Jeanne Sinnen, and Janet Salisbury, of the University of Minnesota Press, exercised degrees of competence, skill in communication, and patience and understanding that transformed the labor attendant upon publication of this book into a pleasant and rewarding experience.

The research of Study III, and the publication of *Stuttering in Children and Adults*, and of the present volume, have been made possible by grants from the Louis W. and Maud Hill Family Foundation.

The enlightened interest and support of A. A. Heckman, executive director, and the members of the Board of the Foundation are respectfully and gratefully acknowledged.

This attempt to indicate backgrounds and to acknowledge collaboration and assistance is, of course, both heartening and sobering. Like any other such undertaking, it must end by making wholly clear that in searching for the sources of one's evolving questions and ever-emerging answers, one moves in a gathering company along a trail that winds its many-vistaed way from the fantasy of I to the reality of We.

And in the present reality of We there are places that are special for Edna and Katy Lou and for Nick and Karen and Julie.

WENDELL JOHNSON

Iowa City
August 1958

Contents

LIST OF TABLES

The Onset of Stuttering

CHAPTER 1

Problem, Plan, and Purpose

THE story of stuttering may be viewed as a sort of miniature history of human thought. Engrossing as is the problem of stuttering itself, it scarcely equals, as a source of fascination, the thinking about it that has been carried on since the earliest recorded references to it. In this, as in many another contest with mystery, men have persuaded themselves nearly always to prefer the contentment of honored belief to the adventure of disciplined doubt.

The opening chapters of the story have never been found, and the trustworthiness of possible conjecture concerning them is limited. So it is that in our attempt to understand the origins of stuttering we are hindered, as we are in trying to discover and to comprehend the other facets of humanity's early stirrings. We cannot be certain, first of all, that stuttering, as we understand the word's meaning, was known to those comparatively modern folk whom we in the Western world call the ancients — the Greeks and other Mediterranean peoples in the few centuries before and after the beginnings of the Christian era. Recent exploration of this matter has yielded information that serves to alert sensitive and discriminating investigators to the possibility, if not indeed the likelihood, of variations in the notions and the facts represented by terms such as "stuttering" and "speech impediment" from language to language and from age to age.* There are other reasons also, such as lack of adequate records and apparent inconsistencies in available documents, for very considerable restraint in drawing conclusions as to what the relevant historical facts may have been.

A dramatic example of the need for alertness to ambiguity in cur-

---

* See John J. Morgenstern, "Psychological and Social Factors in Children's Stammering," a Ph.D. dissertation completed at the University of Edinburgh, 1953, under the direction of Professor James Drever. The historical information and considerations reviewed by Morgenstern suggest that the stuttering problem may be, to some degree at least, part of the price we have paid for civilization as represented by the Renaissance in Western culture and corresponding developments in other parts of the world. While there is need, of course, for more research, Morgenstern's work in this area has been provocative.

rent versions of ancient events is seen in the story of Demosthenes. It has long been a part of our accepted historical lore that Demosthenes stammered or stuttered as a youth, and overcame his impediment of speech by standing on the seashore and, with pebbles under his tongue, shouting above the roar of the waves. By these heroic means, so legend has it, he achieved the fluency and skill, if not the wisdom, he later displayed to the undying glory of Athens as the greatest orator among the Greeks. And although the legend seems unlikely to lose favor after its long career of distinguished service in the cause of human inspiration, such evidence as modern scholarship has yielded appears to indicate that Demosthenes lisped and was concerned with improving his breath control but probably did not stutter as we understand the term. Certainly he underwent very considerable training, which involved speaking before mirrors, breathing exercises of various sorts, and running uphill — or something like a present-day prize fighter's "road work." Moreover, his education and his native endowments were considerable, and it seems clear that his rise to oratorical heights is to be attributed to many influences in addition to any effects he may have gained from pebbles used orally or otherwise.*

Traditional Views

If we are content to base our thinking principally upon the more adequate knowledge of the past few centuries, we may reasonably hazard the general proposition that in the main those concerned with stuttering have attributed it to some alleged flaw or other in either the soma or the psyche of the speaker. In doing so they have made use of what we may most reasonably take to be the traditional pattern of human thought, at least in Western culture. This pattern may be represented quite simply by the form "A causes B." It is a pattern that we use with the ease, and so with the relative thoughtlessness, of thoroughly accustomed habit. As basically folk thinking it represents in varying degrees the kind of thinking we do whenever we do not think overly much about the thinking we do.

Applied to the problem of stuttering, it prompts us to say that there is a something (A) which exists within or as a part of the physical body, or the psyche or personality, of a human being, and

* George R. R. Pflaum, "The Voice Training of the Orators in Antiquity up to the Time of Quintilian" (unpublished Ph.D. dissertation, Cornell University, 1924), a translation from the German of Armin Krumbacher's *Die Stimmbildung Der Redner Im Altertum Biss Auf Die Zeit Quintilianus* (Paderborn: F. Schöningh, 1920). The statement made here is based, according to Pflaum, on material attributed by Krumbacher to Demetrius of Phalerum, who, according to Plutarch, *Demosthenes*, Chapter 11, obtained his information about the voice training of Demosthenes from Demosthenes himself. See Pflaum (89, pp. 27–33).

4

which causes, or manifests itself as, stuttering (B). B, the stuttering, is assumed in this way of thinking to be a symptom or sign of A, whatever A may be. And whatever A may be, or whatever it may be imagined to be, it is presented as though it were essentially constant, as though it were separate and distinct from B, and presumably, as usually set forth, as though it were unaffected by B. There exists, that is to say, a one-way relationship between A and B. Meanwhile, the antecedents, or origins, or causes of A are either not acknowledged or are vaguely indicated as residing in some sort of alleged genetic predisposition, or tissue deficiency, or pathology, or neurotic motivation, or in an environment that is presumably inadequate or disturbing in some loosely designated, or unidentified, respects.

Meanwhile, the phenomena that are alleged to be the effects of this presumably unvarying and constant cause are themselves intermittent and conspicuously variable. Moreover, these effects (B) are observed to have effects of their own, and the question arises necessarily as to the means by which the supposed cause (A) might conceivably be isolated from the consequences of its own presumed effects. In regarding stuttering as a symptom of a neurosis, for example, it is, we may assume, logically necessary to maintain a clear distinction between what is taken to be stuttering and what is to be viewed as neurosis; to verify the stuttering as an effect of the neurosis, while establishing the neurosis as basic to, rather than as fully or partially a consequence of, the stuttering; and to account for observed variations in the effect, stuttering, by reference to variations in the cause, the neurosis — if, indeed, such a neurosis, and such variations of it, are to be observed. That is to say, should variations in the neurosis, if any, be noted, their explanatory significance would necessarily depend upon their correspondence to variations in the stuttering. Whether or not such correspondence were to be demonstrated, the variations in the neurosis would need to be accounted for by reference to a presumably more basic cause, variations in which would need to be explained, in turn, by reference to a cause still more basic, and so on without apparent end. Otherwise, since it is to be granted that a varying effect may not be accounted for by reference to an unvarying cause, the theory "A causes B," in the specified form "neurosis causes stuttering," is necessarily to be rejected, as is any other specified form of the "A causes B" sort of theory, such as "an inherited predisposition causes stuttering," that is not logically defensible.*

* These comments are adapted with permission of Appleton-Century-Crofts from the author's fuller statement on the theory of stuttering in Johnson (59).

The Onset of Stuttering

Generally speaking, particular hypotheses derived from this basic pattern have "explained" stuttering, as has been indicated, as evidence of either a fault in the physical structure of the speaker or a flaw in the speaker's personality. Either explanation is a pointing toward the speaker, rather than the listener, or the interaction between listener and speaker, as the site of the trouble and of the factors functionally related to it. Viewed closely, either explanation appears, in fact, to identify the problem of stuttering as one involving speech considered as an expressive, even a sheer motor, process. A growing body of research findings (59, 61, 62, 127), including a considerable proportion of those reported in this book, implies meanwhile that the problem involves an interrelation between speaker and auditor. The problem would appear to concern not only speaking but listening as well, and in the interaction between these two processes, as they are carried on by one and the same person, or by two or more persons, the ways of perceiving and evaluating the speaking that is done would seem to be functionally related to the manner in which it is done.

The essential purpose of the present investigation has been to gather substantially more of the facts to be explained before yielding further to the manifestly human compulsion to make explanations. The research has been motivated, in part, by an uneasy feeling that in our traditional attempts to explain to each other the stuttering we have not understood — to adapt Professor Robert Oppenheimer's humbling phrase — we have tended to divorce our desire to explain from our curiosity about what there is, in fact, to be understood. The attempt has accordingly been made in the present research to minimize, or to make explicit, any preconceptions with respect to what the facts to be explained ought to be — to take as little for granted as possible concerning, for example, what children who come to be regarded as stutterers are like otherwise, and what sorts of parents or homes they have, or concerning what it is that children do in speaking or in other aspects of their behavior that others or the children themselves regard as stuttering, or concerning the circumstances under which certain children come to be thought of as stutterers.

Basic Questions

This research has been addressed to these basic questions:

What firsthand descriptions are made of whatever it is that is alleged to be the problem of stuttering at the point in time at which it is said to be beginning or to have begun?

From what specific informants are such firsthand descriptions of the beginnings of the problem obtainable?

6

When, with reference to the ages of such persons as are said to be stuttering or to have begun to stutter, did the alleged problem of stuttering begin?

What accounts are obtainable concerning the circumstances under which the problem of stuttering reportedly arose in given cases?

What reactions were and are made by the person who is said to be stuttering or by others, particularly that person's parents, to the alleged stuttering?

What descriptive accounts are obtainable concerning the development or course of the problem of stuttering, as reported, in relation to presumably relevant circumstances?

Are there differences, discernible by means of the methods used, between children regarded as stutterers and children not so regarded?

Are there differences, discernible by means of the methods used, between parents who regard their children as stutterers and parents who do not so regard their children?

These questions are worded with an eye to the distinction to be made between events and reports of events — to the differences, that is, between descriptive accounts and inferences derived from them, on the one hand, and whatever they are presumably accounts of and inferences about, on the other. It may seem too obvious to mention, and yet it is much too important to overlook, that in this book, as in any other, what are presented are necessarily reports of, statements about, and inferences concerning some alleged events, rather than the observed or observable events themselves. Confronted with words only, we may not avoid a varying degree of uncertainty as to what the facts are, or were, to which the words presumably refer. We were as painstaking as we knew how to be at the time in phrasing our questions, in presenting them to the informants, and in recording the informants' responses. Such confidence as this may afford the reader is to be tempered by the realization that there is a provocative similarity between a person's response to his own past — or to his own child's past — and his response to a Rorschach ink blot, for example. Just as in part he describes the ink blot and in part he describes that which he himself projects into the ink blot, so in recounting his own or his child's history a person tells partly fact and for the rest an account compounded of wish and dread, of schooled assumption and inadvertent belief, of sheer confusion and imagination, of memory both too sparse and too abundant. An appreciation of this would seem to be essential to an evaluation of its probable importance in specific instances. This precaution indicated, we may proceed in accordance with it to examine the report to be made of the present investigation.

The Onset of Stuttering

Studies I, II, and III

The research under consideration has extended from 1934 to the present writing and has involved three studies, which will be designated for convenience of reference in this report by means of Roman numerals I, II, and III.* The first of these, Study I, was carried on from 1934 to 1940 and was reported by Johnson in condensed form in 1942 (57) and in full in 1955 (62, pp. 37–73). It was a study of forty-six allegedly stuttering children and forty-six allegedly nonstuttering children of essentially like sex, age, and intelligence level, and of the parents of these children. Interviews with parents were the chief source of data.

In this initial study there were thirty-two male and fourteen female stutterers and thirty-three male and thirteen female nonstutterers. The ages of the stutterers ranged from two years, two months, twenty-three days to nine years, three months, twelve days, with a median of four years, two months; the ages of the nonstutterers ranged from two years, two months, twenty-four days to nine years, ten months, one day, with a median of four years, five months, sixteen days. The stutterers' I.Q.'s ranged from 80 to 159, with a median of 114; the nonstutterers' I.Q.'s ranged from 95 to 158, with a median of 116.† In Study I socioeconomic class was not controlled; the socioeconomic status of the nonstuttering group was possibly slightly higher than that of the stuttering group, and it may most reasonably be estimated that both groups were drawn predominantly from the middle class.

* In planning the various phases of this research, we have attempted as a matter of course to benefit from work previously reported, particularly that of Despert (27, 28), Johnson (56), LaFollette (71), Moncur (84), Wood (132), and Hood, Shank, and Williamson (55). These are among the investigations most relevant to the purposes and procedures of the present research that were available at the time this research was formulated. More recent work, including that published in the *Journal of Speech and Hearing Disorders* and elsewhere while this book was being prepared for publication, has been carefully noted. Information concerning current studies, as yet unpublished, has been taken into consideration so far as possible. In a less highly specific but yet significant sense much of the general body of published work dealing with stuttering and related or similar problems, and with investigative procedure, particularly the methodology of case study, is relevant to a consideration of the problems and objectives of the present research, and the attempt has been made to use pertinent publications and information of whatever sort.

† In testing intelligence of the stutterers the following tests were used: Stanford Revision of the Binet-Simon Intelligence Scale, 1916 and 1937, Forms L and M; Minnesota Preschool Scale; Kuhlmann Revision of the Binet-Simon Intelligence Scale; Kuhlmann-Anderson Group Intelligence Test; Pintner Non-Language Primary Mental Test; Merrill-Palmer Scale of Mental Tests; Otis Classification Test (Form A, for grades 4 to 8); and Detroit Advanced First Grade Intelligence Test. The Kuhlmann-Anderson and the 1916 and 1937 editions of the Stanford Revision of the Binet-Simon Intelligence Scale were used in testing the nonstutterers. The scores from these various tests were converted into I.Q.'s for purposes of approximate group description and comparison.

Out of this original study a further stage of investigation was developed and this was carried forward from 1948 to 1952, primarily as a doctoral dissertation by Darley (24, pp. 74–153). This investigation, Study II, involved fifty children who were regarded by their parents as stutterers and fifty children of essentially like sex, age, and socioeconomic level of family who were not so regarded by their parents. In each case the mother and father were interviewed independently by means of a comprehensive 846-item interview in essential accordance with the interviewing principles and procedure developed by Kinsey (67), with responses coded for purposes of quantitative analysis.

All the subjects in Study II, as in Study I, were Caucasian. In each group in Study II there were thirty-nine boys and eleven girls. Matching with reference to chronological age was effected within the limits of a maximal discrepancy of six months. Ages of the stutterers ranged from two years, four months to fourteen years, four months, with a mean of eight years, eight months; ages of the nonstutterers ranged from two years, two months to fourteen years, with a mean of nine years. The two groups of families were matched in socioeconomic status, and of the 100 families in both groups 38 per cent were classified as lower-middle, 38 per cent as upper-middle, and 4 per cent as upper class, with only 20 per cent in the classes designated as upper-lower (18 per cent) and lower-lower (2 per cent).* Of Darley's fifty stuttering children forty-six were given the Revised Stanford-Binet Scale, Form L, and four were given the Wechsler-Bellevue Intelligence Scale, Form I; the distribution of I.Q.'s of these fifty subjects was compared with that of the general population as reported by Wechsler (118). The chi-square test did not indicate a statistically significant difference between the two distributions. The stutterers' I.Q.'s ranged from 54 to 162; 56 per cent were between 92 and 115, 26 per cent were higher than 115, and 18 per cent were lower than 92. Darley found it impractical to administer intelligence tests to his control subjects. More detailed data from Study II are to be found in the Summary Table in Appendix A.

Study III, which has not been reported previously, was conducted during the period from 1952 to 1957, and included an additional 150 allegedly stuttering children and 150 allegedly nonstuttering children, matched as in the second study for sex, age, and socioeconomic status of the family. In each group 107, or 71 per cent, were boys and 43, or 29 per cent, were girls. This sex ratio, approximately 2.5 to 1, is nearly identical with the distribution of 70 per cent male to 30 per cent fe-

* Use was made of the classificatory system presented by Warner, Meeker, and Eels in *Social Class in America* (117).

male subjects in the stuttering group in Study I. It is a bit below that which obtained in Study II, in which 78 per cent were boys and 22 per cent were girls, slightly more than 3.5 to 1. All these figures are a bit below the modal value, approximately 4 to 1, of the ratios summarized by Schuell (97).

The experimental group in Study III ranged in age from 27 to 96 months at the time the mother was interviewed. The mean age was 59.9 months, or approximately five years. The control group, matched for age with the experimental group, ranged in age from 28 to 103 months, with a mean age of 60.2 months.* The interview developed for Study II, somewhat revised, was used in interviewing fathers and mothers independently. The interview, in the form in which it was used in Study III, is reproduced in Appendix A; items used in Study II but not in Study III are not included in the Summary Table, and the differences between the two versions of the instrument in the wording of specific questions are indicated. The number of mothers and of fathers who gave each specified response to each item in Study II and in Study III, respectively, is shown in the Summary Table, except, as has been stated, for items used in Study II but not in Study III.

Definitions of "Stutterer" and "Nonstutterer"

A fundamental decision that had to be made before this research program could be launched was concerned with the criteria to be used in differentiating "children who stutter" from "children who do not stutter." It is to be appreciated that there is no standard operational definition of "stuttering" or "stutterer." Generally speaking, the word "stuttering" signifies a judgment made by a listener (who may be the speaker as well) concerning something the speaker is presumably doing or has done; the word "stuttering" is not unambiguously descriptive of the speaker's behavior. In view of the lack of clear procedural precedents for deciding how children are to be sorted into "stuttering" and "nonstuttering" groups and the importance of the bases on which this decision was made in these investigations, the exact relevant wordings employed in the two previously published reports are here reproduced. In the report of Study I this statement was made:

* It will be noted that the age difference between the two oldest children in the two groups was seven months. This was the only instance in which the matching for age was not within six months. The age difference of this pair was a week over the six-month criterion because of a delay in interviewing the parents. The mean absolute difference in age between members of matched pairs was two months and eleven days, but the difference in mean ages of the two groups was, as has been indicated, only three tenths of a month.

Care was taken to avoid so far as possible the influence of any prejudices of the investigators with regard to the definitions of "stutterer" and "nonstutterer." Everything considered, the most defensible procedure appeared to be that of placing in the stuttering group children who were referred to the clinic as stutterers. The referral was accompanied in every case by a request for remedial advice and help. Care was taken never to suggest to parents or teachers that a given child was a stutterer when he had not been recognized as such by them. The original diagnosis of stuttering was never made by the investigators. The original diagnoses were made as follows: twenty-two cases by both parents more or less simultaneously so far as could be determined; fourteen by the mother only (the father, if living or residing in the home, subsequently concurred in the diagnosis in every instance); three by a preschool teacher; two by a kindergarten teacher; and one each by a grandmother, a first-grade teacher, a speech correction teacher, a neighbor, and a graduate student in the University of Iowa Department of Speech who was living in the home of one of the children.

A child was accepted as a nonstutterer only if the parents, teachers, and others associated with the child regarded him unquestionably as a nonstutterer. If anyone at all regarded a given child as a stutterer, that child was excluded from the nonstuttering group. That a child may have been regarded as a stutterer by someone at some time previous to this study was taken to be irrelevant. As a matter of fact, after the forty-six children had been selected as nonstutterers beyond the question of anyone who knew them at the time of the study, it was found that six of them had at some time been regarded by someone as stutterers. To the investigators it seemed that exclusion of these six children would have begged one of the questions under investigation. That is, the decision to exclude them would have implied that any child who did not stutter, but who had been suspected previously by someone of being a stutterer, was necessarily the same as a child who was definitely regarded as a stutterer at the time of the study — that "once a stutterer, always a stutterer." The fact that a nonstuttering child was at one time, but not at the time of the investigation, suspected of being a stutterer was taken to be simply part of the case history data concerning him, just as it was regarded as part of the case history data concerning a stuttering child that he was at one time, but not at the time of the study, regarded as a nonstutterer. The most legitimate conditions of our investigation appeared to have been fulfilled when it was established that the nonstutterers were definitely classified as such by the persons intimately acquainted and concerned with them, and that they were approximately matched with the stutterers as to chronological age, sex, and I.Q. (62, pp. 39–40) *

* The statement also contains this indication of the reasoning employed: "Our intention was to avoid any 'loading' of the data that might have resulted from formulating our extensional definitions of 'stutterer' and 'nonstutterer' on the basis of any assumptions which, for purposes of this study, must be regarded as unestablished. The assumption that a 'nonstutterer' is an individual who has never been suspected of 'stuttering,' or that anyone who has ever been suspected by anyone of being a

The Onset of Stuttering

In the report of Study II the following statement appears:

For the purpose of this study, any child was considered a stutterer who (1) showed unmistakable anxiety-tension reactions in relation to his speech nonfluencies; or (2) had been or was currently regarded as a stutterer; or (3) declared himself to be a stutterer. These criteria have been discussed by Johnson.† Acceptance of a child as a case appropriate for this study did not, therefore, rest upon the requirement that he manifest tense nonfluencies in speech with accompanying anxiety. The fact that his family had been concerned enough about his nonfluencies to label them and to seek professional help was sufficient warrant for use of the case in the study.

Forty of the fifty stutterers were selected for this study as their parents brought them to the Iowa Outpatient Speech Clinic to obtain diagnosis and recommendations for therapy. Of all the stuttering cases brought to the clinic between June 1948 and July 1949, those children of fourteen years or under who were accompanied by both parents were used in the study. Of the remaining ten cases, five were found in the Des Moines public schools by a public school speech correctionist, and five came to the attention of field nurses of the Iowa State Services for Crippled Children, who arranged for them to come with their parents to field clinics held in various Iowa towns, where the interviews were conducted . . . .

Each of the fifty families in the experimental group was matched with a family having a child of like age and sex who did not stutter. An age discrepancy of six months was allowed . . .

A third basis was used for matching, namely, socioeconomic status of the child's family. . . . The instrument used to accomplish the desired matching on the basis of socioeconomic class was the Index of Status Characteristics developed by W. Lloyd Warner and his associates [117] . . .

It is of interest to note that in the interviewing of the control group parents, although none considered his child to be a stutterer or to have a speech deviation which he was willing to label stuttering, at least one parent of each of seven children pointed out to the interviewer that the child had been observed at one time to be nonfluent to a noticeable degree.‡ Following are typical comments: "We noted occasional halting, some repeating"; "He thought faster than he could talk and repeated"; "We were advised it was not stuttering"; "Some repeating and blocking were noted while he was living with his grand-

'stutterer' is by virtue of that fact still a 'stutterer' is such an assumption." In Study II this essential policy was also followed, but in Study III it was not. Although granting that the position stated here is a strong one, the investigators in designing Study III concluded that still more rigorous comparisons of alleged stutterers and alleged nonstutterers could be achieved by excluding so far as possible from the latter any persons who had ever been regarded as stutterers.

† Wendell Johnson, *et al., Speech Handicapped School Children* (New York: Harper, 1948), pp. 213–215. The relevant corresponding passage, considerably recast and expanded, is to be found on pp. 260–264 of the second edition, revised, 1956 (61).

‡ It is to be considered that in Study II the criteria used in classifying a child as a nonstutterer were essentially the same as those employed in Study I.

mother"; "We noticed him repeating at age three, said nothing about it, and it dropped out." (24, pp. 79–80, 142*)

In Study III, reported here for the first time, a child was accepted for inclusion in the group of stutterers (experimental group) if he or she met the following criteria:

1. The child's family belonged to the Caucasian classification. (In view of the small numbers of subjects belonging to other classifications who might have been available, this criterion was employed as a means of avoiding a type of heterogeneity of sample that might have had effects very difficult to evaluate.)

2. The child was without gross sensory or motor impairment, specifically marked visual or auditory deficiency, cerebral palsy, or other crippling physical disability. (The purpose of this criterion was to avoid possibly complicating effects of the evaluative reactions of children and parents to such disabilities, had they been present.)

3. The child was considered to be a stutterer by at least one parent. It was not specified that there must be agreement of other adults (doctor, speech correctionist, teacher, etc.) with the parent or parents that the child was stuttering.

4. The average duration of the stuttering, according to the reports of the father and mother, had not been over thirty-six months. (An attempt was made to interview the parents as soon as possible after onset in order to obtain as accurate an account as possible of the circumstances surrounding the onset and of the details of the early development of the problem.)

5. Both natural parents were available and living together or, if the child was adopted, he had been adopted into the family to be interviewed before attaining the age of six months. (This criterion was included with a view to ensuring uniformity as well as maximal thoroughness and reliability in securing case history data.)

A child was accepted for inclusion in the control group of non-stutterers if he or she satisfied criteria 1, 2, and 5 above, and in addition, met the following matching criteria:†

1. The child had never been considered as a stutterer by his parents.

2. The child was not more than six months older or younger than his or her experimental group counterpart.

3. The child was of the same sex as his or her experimental group counterpart.

4. The child's family fell in the same socioeconomic class, as deter-

*See this source (pp. 74–153) for a more detailed statement.

† These, except for no. 1, were the same criteria as were used in Study II. In Study I the matching criteria, as has been indicated, were sex, age, and intelligence.

mined by the Warner, Meeker, and Eels "Index of Status Characteristics" (117), as its experimental group counterpart.

Care was exercised, particularly in Study III, to ensure that families selected for the control group were taken from a population not markedly different from that represented by the experimental group with regard to "relevant sophistications." That is, the attempt was made not to select control families predominantly from special populations that might be expected to know a good deal more than most families about the nature and development of stuttering, or about alternative theories and practices in child care and training. For example, the effort was made to avoid biasing the control sample by inclusion of an excessive proportion of parents who were speech pathologists or who belonged to child study groups. A special effort was also made to obtain control cases from areas other than Iowa City since a relatively large proportion of Iowa City parents may know of the research program and the clinical services for stutterers that have been carried on at the University of Iowa during the past thirty years and thus have more than an average degree of sophistication about stuttering. A large number of the control cases were obtained from communities within an hour's drive of Iowa City as well as from the Minneapolis–St. Paul area.

Children whose speech was characterized by apparently functional articulation errors were not, on that basis alone, excluded from either the experimental or the control groups in any of these studies.

Sources of Case Material

The allegedly stuttering subjects in Study I were drawn from Iowa with the exception of three from Minnesota; all the control subjects in Study I were from Iowa. In Study II the subjects were classified according to geographical area; all hundred parents in the experimental group were drawn from midwestern United States, and ninety-four were native to this region; of the hundred control group parents, fifty were from the midwestern, twenty-eight from the southern (mostly the Washington, D.C., area), and fifteen from the northeastern section of the United States. The experimental cases in Study III were drawn mainly from Iowa, Illinois, and Minnesota, through the clinical facilities of the University of Iowa, Northwestern University, and the University of Minnesota. These cases were referred mainly by speech therapists, physicians, child welfare workers, special education teachers, and other school personnel. Some families were self-referred.

The participation of the parents and children in these studies was requested on the basis of the contribution they would be making to-

14

ward improved understanding of the problem of stuttering. In addition, all the experimental group cases in Study I and Study II and the experimental group cases in Study III who were referred to the investigators in Iowa and Illinois were offered clinical assistance. In the Minnesota area it did not prove practicable in the course of Study III to offer direct clinical service, although in cases referred by speech therapists the therapists were given certain information that was intended to be helpful to them in working with the children or in counseling the parents.

In Study I all the experimental group parents were interviewed in their homes, and in addition several of the parents visited the University of Iowa Speech Clinic on one or more occasions. The number of interviews per stuttering case ranged from two to nineteen, with a median of four. Most of the experimental group parents in Study II were interviewed in the University of Iowa Speech Clinic. In Study III practically all the parents in the Minnesota area were interviewed in their homes. In Iowa the interviews took place at the University of Iowa Speech Clinic, and in Illinois most of the interviews were carried out at the Northwestern University Speech Clinic. Nearly all the interviews of control group parents in all three studies were conducted in their homes.

The control group subjects in Study III, as noted above, were drawn mostly from the states of Iowa and Minnesota. Assistance in finding control subjects was secured through parent-teacher associations and church groups, from physicians, teachers, school administrators, and other interested persons, and names were obtained from public school records, preschool enrollment lists, and birth records in newspapers. The control group parents were appealed to in this as in the other two studies on the basis of the contribution they would make to increased knowledge about stuttering, and, in addition, the majority of the control group parents in Study III, as well as four sets of control group parents in Study II, were reimbursed at the rate of one dollar per hour to help compensate them for the time they contributed.

Interviewing Procedures

The investigative procedures used in Study I are indicated in the following passage from the report of that study:

In setting up the procedure to be followed in this study several . . . considerations were . . . emphasized. Since interview and case-study techniques were clearly indicated, certain precautions were taken to minimize the usual shortcomings of such techniques when used as research tools. First, it was desirable that the stuttering cases to be studied should be those in whom stuttering was of recent origin. Adult

15

stutterers, or their parents, are rarely able to recall in relatively great detail the beginnings of their problems. The degree to which we were successful in this connection is shown by the fact that the median interval between date of onset of stuttering and date of first interview was five months and eighteen days. In 25 per cent of the cases this interval was two months or less, and in 75 per cent of the cases it was thirteen months or less. The shortest interval between onset and first interview was four days. In one case the interval was five years and two months, and this case was used because the information that could be obtained seemed to be unusually detailed and dependable.

Second, a fairly long period of observation in each stuttering case studied was considered desirable. The median period of observation for these cases was two years and four months. The range was from five to fifty-one months, the 25th percentile was seventeen and a half months, and the 75th percentile was thirty-six months.

Third, an attempt was made to check the information obtained by carrying out more than one interview in each stuttering case. This made for greater thoroughness and the detection of apparent misinformation, differences of statement among persons interviewed, etc. The number of interviews per stuttering case ranged from two to nineteen. The median number was four, the 25th percentile was three, and the 75th percentile was six. A total of 247 interviews were made in studying the forty-six stutterers. In twenty-eight cases supplementary data were obtained by correspondence.

Fourth, an effort was made to counteract the conscious and unconscious biases and assumptions peculiar to each interviewer. This factor is of particular importance in such a study as this one because of the number of controversial points to which the data are relevant. For this reason, more than one interviewer was assigned to each stuttering case. The number of interviewers per stuttering case ranged from two to five. The median number was three. In each of six cases there were two interviewers, in twenty-three cases three, in thirteen cases four, and in four cases there were five different interviewers. In the study as a whole seventeen different interviewers were involved; all held the M.A. degree in speech pathology or clinical psychology, and four held the Ph.D. degree at the time they served in this study; thirteen of the seventeen now hold the Ph.D. degree. Special medical examinations were made in three cases by physicians, Drs. Edward Lee Russell, H. F. Shirley, and Mark L. Floyd, respectively.

Every stutterer's home was visited by one or more interviewers. This made it possible to supplement the statements of parents, teachers, physicians, and other informants by the interviewers' own observations of the homes, the speech and other behavior of the stuttering children, the conditions to which they were responding, etc. A detailed interview outline was used; the specific items of information which it covered are indicated in the tables and statements of findings . . .

The forty-six nonstuttering children were investigated by one interviewer, Susan Dwyer. Only one interview was made in each case in this part of the study. All interviews were made in the homes. In every case the mother was the chief informant, supplementary information

16

being obtained in some cases from the father and from the University of Iowa Preschool records. (62, pp. 40–41)

On the basis of experience gained in Study I certain methodological changes were made in Study II; the interviewing procedures employed in that investigation have been described by Darley as follows:

Inasmuch as this study was exploratory in nature, it was felt that the scope of the interview should be large. It seemed desirable to secure a relatively complete history of each case and to assess parental attitudes regarding many areas of life. It was assumed that every realm of life was potentially the locus of distinctive attitudes which might have a bearing directly or indirectly on the development of stuttering. The result was the compilation of a massive questionnaire comprising 846 questions . . .*

The selection of questions was accomplished as follows: The case history outline used in the Iowa Speech Clinic was the initial source [61, 1948 ed., pp. 419–421];† other questions were modeled on parts of the case history outline suggested by Van Riper [113]‡ and the form utilized by Wood in his study of the parents of articulatory defective children [132]. The "Record of Problem Case" form used by the Department of Pupil Adjustment of the Des Moines public schools proved helpful in suggesting approaches to certain areas and indicating how parent responses might be objectified and coded [52]. A similar contribution was made by the study of Kinsey, Pomeroy, and Martin [67]. Other questions were devised by the writer and several Iowa Speech Clinic staff members and graduate assistants. An attempt was made to avoid multiple questions that might elicit ambiguous replies. Wording was made simple and the point of each question was made as obvious as possible.

Kinsey, Pomeroy, and Martin have provided what seem to this writer to be the best available guides to the use of the interview as a research instrument. They emphasize among other things the desirability of recording immediately and expeditiously the data yielded by the interview. They further recommend rapid-fire questioning.

In line with these recommendations, an adaptation was made of Kinsey's device of codifying answers. Whenever possible, questions were framed in such a way that they could be answered rather objectively by the use of a simple scale of responses (for example, "Yes-No," "Often-Seldom-Never," "Much more than average — Somewhat

* See Table 1 for the sections into which the questionnaire was divided for convenience of administration and analysis, and the number of questions in each section in both Study II and Study III.

† This case history outline, a revision and condensation by Spencer F. Brown, M.D., Ph.D., of earlier and more detailed versions by Lee Edward Travis and Wendell Johnson and their associates, is not included in the revised edition, 1956, of *Speech Handicapped School Children* (61), but it is included, together with relevant additional information and discussion, and with an extended treatment of the techniques of interviewing as formulated by Frederic L. Darley, in Johnson, Darley, and Spriestersbach (64, pp. 1–12).

‡ Pp. 443–462 in the second edition (1947), pp. 545–566 in the third edition (1954).

more than average — About average — Somewhat less than average — Much less than average," etc.). Symbols were selected to represent these answers. Even where this simplification was not feasible, possible answers were anticipated and given letter or number codes before any interviewing was done; subsequently elicited answers not previously coded were assigned code letters or numbers during the interviewing. This system made it possible for the interviewer to record an answer quickly by simply jotting down the appropriate symbol, letter, or number representing the answer given, and then to proceed with minimal delay to the next question. It permitted completion of the interview within a period of tolerable length, accurate recording of answers, maximum eye-contact, and ease in tabulation of responses after the interview.

The case-study method, of which this is an example, suffers from the weaknesses inherent in human memory and human bias. To counteract and to check on these sources of error, Kinsey, Pomeroy, and Martin recommend the use of cross-checks on accuracy in the form of overlapping or interlocking questions. In their study they found it advisable, as well, to confine their questions to matters of overt activity and to avoid securing verbalizations of attitudes which in their opinion might have had little relationship to overt behavior. In the present study the former suggestion has been followed but the second has not been, owing to the very nature of the study as an exploration of parental attitudes. Other checks have been utilized, however.

The following are the means used in this study for securing maximum accuracy of reporting and for checking the accuracy of the informants' responses:

1. Inclusion of overlapping and interlocking questions.

2. Appeal to the informants to help their children (in the case of the experimental group) or other children, parents, and the experimenters (in the case of the control group), by careful consideration of the truthfulness of their responses.

3. Rapid questioning, with maximum eye-contact.

4. Assurance that information given would not be divulged to the husband or wife or to unauthorized persons not directly connected with the study or the clinical handling of the children, as well as assurance that family identity would in no case be preserved in the summary of the results of the study.

5. Securing of objective information for comparison with subjective descriptions of attitude. For example, a parent's subjective estimate of his own severity in discipline was obtained, as well as a more objective statement of frequency and manner of punishment used.

6. Estimating a parent's attitude by securing not only his own statement but also a statement from his mate regarding, for example, parental strictness. Thus four statements were obtained: (1) the father's estimate of his own strictness (too strict, too lax, about right); (2) the mother's estimate of her own strictness; (3) the father's estimate of the mother's strictness; (4) the mother's estimate of the father's strictness. Analysis of the four responses gives a basis for comparing the father's and mother's attitudes and also for obtaining an estimate of the home situation.

7. Supplementing case-history data with test data. . . .

All mothers and fathers were interviewed separately. The majority of the parents of the stuttering children were interviewed in a private office in the Iowa Speech Clinic. Most of the rest of the experimental group parents, as well as the bulk of the parents in the even-numbered control group families, were interviewed in their homes in Iowa City or other Iowa towns. [The selecting and interviewing of the fifty control group families were done by Sara Conlon, Robert Higinbotham, and the writer. Miss Conlon selected and interviewed twenty-five families. The interviewing of the other twenty-five families was done by Mr. Higinbotham and the writer.] Miss Conlon selected her twenty-five pairs of control group parents in the vicinity of Washington, D.C., doing all her interviewing in the homes of the families during the summer of 1949. Interviewing of the experimental group parents took place between June 7, 1948, and July 18, 1949. Interviewing of the remaining control group parents was done between January 10, 1950, and September 10, 1952.

In all cases the interview was preceded by a brief explanation of the purpose of the interview, the informants being urged to give the most truthful answers possible. Assurance was also given at that time that the record would be kept confidential within the limitations described above.

The questions were typically presented in the following sequence: sections A to H inclusive, sections N to U inclusive, and, finally, sections I to M inclusive. This sequence provided for an initial gathering of routine information of an innocuous nature, not emotionally colored; a rather prompt attack on the presenting speech problem (in the case of the experimental group this was especially desirable), approached through the birth, developmental, and medical history, and followed by the closely related areas of social adjustment of the child, school history, and family discipline practices; and a final group of questions relative to topics typically more charged emotionally (social adjustment of the parents, home environment, and marital relationship), with a rather neutral terminal section regarding family health. It was found that this sequence was conducive to good rapport and the effective eliciting of information concerning all the areas listed. By the time the final group of questions (sections I to M) was reached, rapport had in almost every case been maximally developed and the interviewing relationship was secure enough to ensure the eliciting of reasonably trustworthy answers from the informants.

Answers were recorded in code on . . . data sheets . . . Each block containing an answer was also numbered by the interviewer during the interview to indicate the section and number of each question.

To help the informants make their answers uniform in pattern, cards indicating the scale of answers appropriate for certain questions were provided and the informants were asked to choose what was to them the best answer. This device materially speeded up the interviewing. On other occasions when the informant seemed at a loss to know how to answer a question, the interviewer would orally suggest a number of possible answers, taking care to avoid any special sequence in the list and to avoid making the last item especially appropriate.

The Onset of Stuttering

Interviews averaged about three hours in length, those of the mothers taking somewhat longer than those of the fathers. This difference is attributable in part to the fact that certain groups of questions pertaining to birth history and physical development were asked only of the mothers. The assumption was here made that the mothers could be considered the more reliable informants in these areas; also there seemed to be no special value in comparing the mothers' answers with those of the fathers on these questions. The range of times required for completion of the interviews of the experimental group parents was roughly from 1.75 hours to 5.0 hours. Interviews of the control group parents were, on the average, somewhat shorter, because many questions related to the speech defect could be omitted.

The phrasing of the questions was kept as constant as possible from case to case, pains having been taken from the outset to make the wording simple and the point of each question plain. However, occasional clarifications were necessary, such as definitions of words or restatements in the vernacular of the informant. (24, pp. 76–82)

Essentially the same interviewing procedure was used in Study III. The writer served as director of both Study II and Study III, as well as Study I, and sought to make the two later studies comparable with each other while at the same time applying in Study III such methodological improvements as seemed indicated by experience with the earlier investigations. The interview itself was re-evaluated and somewhat revised between Study II and Study III, as is indicated in Table 1 and, with respect to the wording of individual items, in the Summary Table in Appendix A. The 600 interviews in Study III were done by seven different interviewers. Of these, one held the Ph.D. degree in speech pathology from the University of Iowa; one had received the M.A. degree and another was a candidate for the M.A. degree in the same field at the same institution; one held the M.A. degree in speech pathology from Brooklyn College; one had received the M.A. degree in speech from Cornell University; one held the M.A. degree in educational counseling and guidance from the University of Iowa; and one was a graduate student in the School of Social Work at the University of Minnesota. The training of these interviewers in the use of the Study III procedures was supervised by Frederic L. Darley, the chief investigator in Study II. As a means of ensuring uniformity of interviewing procedures for both the experimental and control groups, all completed interviews were checked by a designated member of the project staff and frequent staff conferences were held in order to pool experiences and problems in presentation of specific questions and interpretation of particular responses.

The questions asked of the experimental group parents in Study III were asked also of the control group parents, with certain changes in wording in the items referring to stuttering. Item 195 (see the Sum-

Table 1. Sections of the Interview Outline and Number of Questions in
Each Section in Study II and Study III*

Section	Number of Questions Study II	Number of Questions Study III	Section	Number of Questions Study II	Number of Questions Study III
A. Identifying information	6	6	N. Birth history of child	34	38
B. Age	3	3	O. Physical development of child	73	56
C. Race	1	0			
D. Geographical origin	12	2	P. Medical history of child	29	55
E. Rural-urban background	2	1	Q. Development of speech and speech problem	117	193
F. Educational background	21	2			
G. Religious background	6	3	R. Social development of child	155	171
H. Occupational history and economic status	26	42	S. Disciplinary practices and attitudes	50	34
I. Physical home environment	20	7	T. School history of child	51	29
J. Social adjustment of parents	40	20	U. Comparison of children within family	9	11
K. Marital relationship	78	54	V. Impression of interview	5	4
L. Social home environment	44	31	W. Index of status characteristics	5	8
M. Family health (including handedness characteristics and speech problems)	59	44	Total	846	814

* The complete interview outline, as used in Study III, is reproduced in the Summary Table in Appendix A at the end of this volume.

mary Table), for example, was worded for the experimental group parents in this way: "Has the child ever stuttered?" For the control group parents it was worded: "Does the child now show or has he, or she, ever shown any nonfluencies — repetitions, hesitations, etc. — in speech?" Item 196 was put as follows to the experimental group parents: "How old was the child when he first began to stutter?" It was put to the control group parents this way: "How old was the child when you began to notice his speech in these respects?" Throughout the relevant section of the interview this essential distinction was maintained.

The interviews were done between November 1951 and June 1954. As a rule, first the mother was interviewed and then the father. As in Study II, assurance as to confidentiality was given at the time of the interview, and the questions were presented in the sequence which had been found in Study II to be conducive to good rapport and the effective eliciting of the desired information. Answers were recorded by code number during the interview and were subsequently punched on IBM cards by the Statistical Service of the University of Iowa.

The interviews in Study III averaged about three hours in length, ranging from a little less than two hours to a little more than four hours. As in Study II, the interviews of the mothers were somewhat longer than those of the fathers, because a number of questions, mostly pertaining to birth history and physical development of the child, were asked only of the mothers. Also interviews of the control group parents were, on the average, somewhat shorter, because many questions concerning the development of the speech problem and reactions to it were necessarily omitted.

Tests

In addition to the information obtained through interviewing, certain data were gathered by means of tests. The use made of intelligence tests has been indicated. In Study I an attempt was made to administer intelligence tests to both the experimental and control group subjects. In Study II mental tests were given only to the experimental group children. In Study III intelligence tests were not used. Two considerations governed the decisions made in this connection. One concerned need. In general, relevant data have strongly indicated that unselected samples of stutterers and nonstutterers are essentially alike with respect to measures of intelligence (24, 56, 57, 76, 96, 107, 110, 113, 116, 125). Moreover, in both Study II and Study III the question of matching the experimental and control groups was systematically considered, and after a thoroughgoing weighing of the various alternatives it was decided that the most adequate formula would be achieved by matching with reference to chronological age, sex, and socioeconomic status of the family. It is reasonably to be assumed that so far as this matching procedure would have any relevant effect it would tend to increase the similarity between the groups with respect to intelligence. The second consideration was that persuasive practical reasons for dispensing with measures of intelligence outweighed the apparently slight need to employ them. This was particularly true so far as the control groups in Study II and Study III were concerned. The families in these groups were investigated in their own homes under conditions ordinarily removed from clinical facilities and personnel required for mental testing, and, moreover, the demands made on their time were such that it was necessary to eliminate any procedures that were not clearly essential. The pertinent budgetary considerations were also of some importance. In Study II, therefore,

*Brief Handedness Questionnaire**

(Below are 10 questions pertaining to manual acts. You are to indicate with which hand you *almost always* perform them. If you have not done any of them, please indicate the way in which you would be most likely to perform them. R means almost always right; L means almost always left; E means almost always with either hand interchangeably. Draw a circle around the proper one.)

1. Which hand uses the hammer?	R L E
2. Which hand uses the needle in sewing?	R L E
3. Which hand uses the tooth brush?	R L E
4. Which hand holds the knife when you whittle?	R L E
5. Which hand uses the can opener?	R L E
6. Which hand uses the saw?	R L E
7. Which hand uses the screw driver?	R L E
8. Which hand swings the tennis racquet?	R L E
9. Which hand throws the ball?	R L E
10. Which hand uses wrenches?	R L E

mental tests were not administered to the control group children, and such tests were eliminated for both groups in Study III.

In Study I some use was made of certain handedness measures. On the basis of questioning of the parents and observation of the children, a hand usage questionnaire was filled out for each of the nonstutterers and for thirty-six of the stutterers. The questionnaire called for "right," "left," or "either" in response to each of several questions concerning the hand commonly used by the child for each of a number of unimanual activities. In a few cases supplementary information was obtained through observation of the child under various conditions, as indicated in the original report (62, pp. 52–62). The major interview also covered the matter of handedness in this study, as it did, even more thoroughly, in Study II and Study III. Relevant parts of the interview reproduced in the Summary Table are items 94–111 and and 775–778. In addition to information secured through interviewing, data on handedness were obtained for all children (see item 788) and their parents (see item 783) in Study III by means of the Iowa Unimanual Hand Usage Questionnaire.† Scores are summarized in items 783 and 788. In addition each parent was asked to fill out the Brief

* This questionnaire was scored by means of the formula $R + .5E/N$, in which R, E, and N represent, respectively, the number of items answered by circling the R, the number answered by circling the E, and the total number of items answered. Scores can range from 0, indicating that all responses were L, to 1.00, representing all R responses.

† Adapted from the original form developed by Wendell Johnson and Arthur H. Davison, and used by the latter in a study done as an M.A. dissertation at the University of Iowa. See Davison (26). This test is reproduced, with instructions for its administration and scoring, in Johnson, Darley, and Spriestersbach (64, pp. 155–157).

The Onset of Stuttering

Handedness Questionnaire reproduced on page 23; scores obtained by means of this test are summarized in item 775.

In Study II the following tests were used, as indicated in the original report:

Tests for Parents. Each parent was asked to fill out two paper-and-pencil questionnaires. The first of these, the Iowa Scale of Attitude Toward Stuttering, requires one to indicate what he feels a stutterer should do in each of forty-five situations, and yields an estimate of the individual's degree of tolerance or intolerance toward stuttering.* Hence it provides a useful supplement to the answers to more direct questions about attitudes toward stuttering contained in the interview.

The second scale administered was the Inventory of Factors STDCR, devised by J. P. Guilford on the basis of factor analysis studies of items in personality questionnaires. The five factors referred to are S, "social introversion-extraversion"; T, "thinking intro-version-extraversion"; D, "depression"; C, "cycloid disposition"; and R, "rhathymia" (or happy-go-lucky-ness). The S, T, and R factors, according to Guilford, "belong in the area of personality traditionally known as introversion-extraversion . . . Factors C and D are more appropriately designated as emotionality factors" [46]. . . .

The information gained from [this test] is considered supplementary to that obtained in the interviews and of interest as providing a possible check on the impressions of personality gained by means of the interview.

Tests for Children. All the stuttering children were given an intelligence test by a competent psychological examiner in the Iowa Speech Clinic, in the Des Moines public school system, or in one of the field clinics of the Iowa State Services for Crippled Children. The Wechsler-Bellevue Intelligence Scale, Form I, was administered to four of the older stutterers; the Revised Stanford-Binet Scale, Form L, was administered to the remaining forty-six children. It was impossible to secure intelligence test scores for the majority of the children in the control group.

The Rogers Test of Personality Adjustment was also administered individually to the children in both groups who were eight years of age and above. This test, described by Rogers in *Measuring Personality Adjustment in Children Nine to Thirteen Years of Age* [92] and in the test manual [91], "measures roughly the extent to which a child is satisfactorily adjusted toward his fellows, his family and himself . . . The test is largely made up of questions which any psychologist or psychiatrist, skilled in children's behavior, might use in an interview. These questions are put in such form that responses may simply be checked rather than written out . . . Four 'diagnostic scores' are obtained: the Personal Inferiority score, the Social Maladjustment score, the Family Maladjustment score, and the Daydreaming score" [91, pp. 1–2]. (24, pp. 83–84)

---

* See Ammons and Johnson (1). This test is reproduced, with instructions for its administration and scoring and a discussion of its possible uses, in Johnson, Darley, and Spriestersbach (64, pp. 143–146).

The Iowa Scale of Attitude toward Stuttering was also administered to each parent in Study III, and in this study the Minnesota Multiphasic Personality Inventory (MMPI) was administered to the parents instead of the Inventory of Factors STDCR that was used in Study II. The use made of the MMPI in Study III and the findings obtained by means of it are presented in Chapter 7 of this report.

In Study III tape-recorded samples of speech were obtained from eighty-nine matched pairs of children, and the analysis of these is presented in Chapter 8.

Analysis of Data

Analysis of the data obtained in Study I was concerned almost wholly with a delineation of the speech problem of the children who were reported to be stuttering and with a comparison of the two groups of children; in each of the two later studies comparison was also made of the experimental and control group parents and of the mothers and fathers within each group. In a general sense, it may be said that Study I was concerned with allegedly stuttering and non-stuttering children, whereas the two later investigations were concerned with such children viewed within their family constellations. These latter studies particularly, therefore, have yielded considerable normative information of general interest to child psychologists, pediatricians, cultural anthropologists, and others whose interests are directed to parent-child relations, child-rearing practices and problems, and family life in the times and cultural settings covered by these researches.

In Study I the experimental and control group children were matched with regard to age, sex, and intelligence and were compared with respect to conditions of birth; physical development; speech development; medical history; handedness and eyedness; and stuttering and handedness characteristics among parents, siblings, and blood relatives. In addition, relevant data from previously published studies were used in evaluating data for the allegedly stuttering children with regard to birth conditions, diseases and injuries, "nervous habits" (thumb sucking, nail biting, and enuresis), and handedness. The attempt was made to explore in considerable detail the possibility of any relationship between conditions of handedness, particularly changes of handedness, and the onset and early development of stuttering, as well as changes in the severity of the speech problem during its course, and its later disappearance, or marked improvement, or persistence, or increased severity, as the case proved to be, in association with measures recommended and attempted with respect to handedness during therapy. Certain comparisons between the experimental and control groups were involved in this exploration.

In addition to these comparisons between the two groups of children, the problem of stuttering itself was investigated with special reference to age of onset, interval between the beginnings of speech and the onset of stuttering, the nature of the stuttering at the time of onset, and conditions surrounding the onset of stuttering or affecting its subsequent severity. Finally, the parents of the experimental group children were counseled and certain recommendations were made to them, and subsequently the condition of each child's speech was evaluated. A summary of the findings from Study I is presented in Chapter 2.

Darley has described the plan of analysis of the data in Study II as follows:

Analysis of the data secured from both groups includes the following seven main parts:

1. Description and comparison of the two groups of children, based on interview data (child intergroup comparison).

2. Description and comparison of the two groups of parents, based on interview data (parent intergroup comparison).

3. Comparison of mothers with fathers within each group (parent intragroup comparisons).

4. Family-by-family comparison of the two groups of parents (intrafamily intergroup comparison).

5. Analysis of parents' test results (both intergroup and intragroup comparisons).

6. Analysis of children's intelligence and personality test results (intergroup comparison).

7. Analysis of data pertaining to the onset and development of stuttering. . . .

A number of questions in the interview yielded numerical responses (ages and frequencies, for example). Measures of central tendency (mean) and dispersion (standard deviation) were computed in the analysis of these data. Many of the non-numerical response questions have the answers distributed along a two-, three-, four-, or five-category continuum. The most meaningful statistical treatment of the resulting distributions of responses, appropriate for both intergroup and intragroup comparisons, was found to be the chi-square test. . . .

Lewis and Burke list as the two most basic requirements in any correct application of the chi-square test "(a) independence among the separate measures, and (b) theoretical frequencies of reasonable size" [74, p. 436]. A minimal value of ten is strongly recommended: "When the number of degrees of freedom is less than four or five, and especially when df = 1, the use of theoretical frequencies of less than ten should be strictly avoided" [74, p. 460]. In this present analysis of data by the use of the chi-square test both of the above requirements have been satisfied. In every case the single measures used in the tables are independent. Categories have been rationally grouped so as to provide for sufficiently large theoretical frequencies.*

Fisher's table of chi-square, adapted by Guilford [47], has been used to determine the significance of each obtained value of chi-square. The 5 per cent level of confidence was selected as the cutting point for the consideration of values obtained as significant. (24, pp. 84–85)

While the method of analyzing the data in Study III was relatively more detailed in certain respects, it was essentially the same as that used in Study II. The seven parts of the analysis listed by Darley in the quotation immediately above were duplicated in Study III, with the exception of No. 6; the tests involved in this part of the analysis were not used in Study III.

* In instances in which these requirements were not met the Yates correction was applied. See Lewis and Burke (74, pp. 462–463) and also Yates (133, pp. 217–237). This correction provides for the reduction of all differences between observed and theoretical frequencies by 0.5 in order to compensate for errors arising from the use of relatively small theoretical frequencies; the correction was applied in every case involving only one degree of freedom. It was not applied in tables involving more than one degree of freedom. In Study III there were no theoretical frequencies less than five in any contingency table. Only ten tables contained theoretical frequencies less than ten. The numbers of cells with theoretical frequencies less than ten were distributed as follows: one in each of two tables with df = 2; one in each of three tables with df = 3; two in each of three tables with df = 3; one in each of two tables with df = 4. See Appendix B for statistically significant values of chi-square obtained in Study III, with associated degrees of freedom.

PART ONE

The Earlier Studies

CHAPTER 2

Main Findings of Studies I and II

IT SEEMS extraordinary that as late as 1934, when Study I was under-taken, there had not yet been a comprehensive and systematic investi-gation of the onset of stuttering. Case studies and a number of more or less general discussions concerning the matter had been published (10, 56, 68, 76, 77, 99, 110, 123), and Froeschels (34) in 1921 and Bluemel (15) in 1932 had reported that in certain cases they had noted an early or beginning phase during which what was referred to as stuttering appeared to consist mainly of a rather simple repeti-tiousness in speech. In presenting these clinical impressions, however, they seemed to assume, in accordance with prevailing custom, that stuttering begins in the speaker and originally appears, presumably at a definite point in time, in the form of a clinically significant disturb-ance of speech behavior, or failure of speech, or change in the speaker's habitual manner of speaking. In the meantime, there seems to have been no substantial documentation of such disturbance, or failure, or change in speech behavior in any indicated proportion of systemati-cally investigated cases.

In the absence of intensive research, there was nevertheless a con-siderable body of opinion concerning the causes of stuttering. The alleged causes were viewed as the conditions under which stuttering, in the form of impaired speech, was said to begin, and as the sup-posedly distinctive characteristics, physical and emotional, of children said to manifest the speech disturbances regarded as stuttering. It was generally asserted that children classified as stutterers were de-ficient in motor coordination, or in emotional stability, or they were injured at birth or subsequently weakened by illness, or they were lacking in neuromuscular integration, or were deficient in cerebral dominance, or were in a state of biochemical imbalance, or they spoke faster than they thought or thought faster than they spoke, or they were nervous, or they had imitated others who stuttered, or they had inherited stuttering—or some presumably essential but undesignated bodily characteristic—or they had been born with at least a predisposition to, or proneness for, the disorder, as stuttering was usually called. The onset of stuttering was asserted by various writers to occur mainly or usually or often at the beginning of speech, or in early childhood, or between five and eight years of age, or at the time of entering school, or during adolescence, or occasionally, particularly under emotional stress of some sort, in adult years. The onset was said to be associated with, or caused by, illnesses of various kinds, especially those involving high fevers, or injuries, or severe frights, or shock, or emotional insecurity, or conflicts with or rejection by or oversolicitousness of parents, or the birth of a new baby brother or sister with consequent decrease in parental attentiveness and affection, or change of handedness, or various other circumstances (10, 14, 34, 56, 68, 76, 77, 99, 110, 116, 123).

In some such terms one may sketch the backdrop against which the findings of the first phase of the research reported in this book were to be viewed. Against such a backdrop the findings appeared strange. They were decidedly at variance with expectations based on prevailing belief, in the mid-thirties, and they were by no means readily or quickly accepted and assimilated by the writer and his co-workers, or by others. Their acceptance in any significant sense necessitated a theoretical reorientation for which there was no clear precedent, and this, together with the occurrence of World War II, was the more significant part of the reason why the first study in this research program was not followed by the second investigation until roughly ten years had passed. During those ten years a sufficiently extensive theoretical reworking was accomplished to make possible the formulation of the problem and the investigative procedures employed in Study II.

The main findings of both Study I and Study II are presented in this chapter, and these will be followed in the succeeding chapters by a detailed presentation of the findings of Study III, which was a further refinement and extension of the two earlier investigations.

Study I

In Study I, as explained in the preceding chapter, a comparative investigation was made of two groups of children.* The children in the experimental group were thought by their parents to be stutterers, while those in the control group were regarded by their parents as nonstutterers. The experimental group, thirty-two boys and fourteen girls, ranged in age from about two years, three months to nine years,

* See Johnson (62) for the full report of this investigation.

three months, with a median age of four years, two months. The control group, thirty-three boys and thirteen girls, ranged in age from approximately two years, three months to nine years, ten months, with a median age of four years, five months. The two groups of children were relatively matched with respect to intelligence, the allegedly stuttering children ranging in I.Q. from 80 to 159, with a median of 114, and the allegedly nonstuttering children ranging in I.Q. from 95 to 158, with a median of 116. The groups were compared in ways indicated by the following summary of findings.

BIRTH AND EARLY DEVELOPMENT

In general, the two groups of children appeared to be quite similar with respect to conditions of birth, diseases and injuries, and indices of development, including speech development. For four of the forty-six experimental group children and for two of the forty-six control group children something reported as "definite birth injury" was noted, as follows:

For the two nonstutterers "birth injury" meant simply bruises about the head occasioned by the use of forceps. For the four stutterers "birth injury" is to be interpreted as follows: Case 7, slight bruise on the forehead from forceps, birth otherwise normal. Case 15, use of forceps resulted in a mark on the temple which cleared in four weeks, and the affected side of the face appeared paralyzed for one-half day following birth; birth was two weeks premature; there was some difficulty in initiating breathing. Case 28, forceps left apparently insignificant marks on the temples; two weeks postmature; generally normal birth otherwise. Case 34, breech delivery with forceps; some apparent injury to neck, mouth, arm, and shoulder; difficulty initiating breathing; slow pulse; difficulty initiating nursing reactions; later evidence of slight spasticity. This was the one case in whom birth injury was probably serious; by the end of the study this child was no longer stuttering. (62, p. 43)

For the experimental group eighty-eight diseases and injuries, 1.9 per child, were reported up to the date of interview; for the control group the corresponding number was eighty-four, with a mean of 1.8 per child.

In only four cases was any kind of disease condition mentioned among the factors possibly associated in time with onset of stuttering: one case was reported to have had infected tonsils at the time he began to stutter; another case was said to have had a cold and a sore throat; a third was thought to have been weakened by pneumonia shortly before stuttering began; and a fourth child was reported to have had "very mild measles" at about the time of onset of stuttering. In each of these cases, however, there was no clear functional relationship between the indicated condition and the onset of stuttering. (62, p. 49)

The Onset of Stuttering

With respect to toilet training the control group subjects tended to be somewhat more advanced, but there appear to have been no group differences with regard to age of standing alone without support, walking, sitting up, creeping, teething, feeding self, dressing self, and saying first words and first sentences.

The incidence of "nervous habits" — thumb sucking, nail biting, and enuresis — in the experimental group children did not appear to be distinctive.

HANDEDNESS

There were no important differences between the two groups with regard to handedness. Thirty-six in each group were reported as being right-handed, and ten in each group as being either left-handed or ambidextrous. Twelve of the stutterers and fourteen of the nonstutterers were judged to have undergone some degree of change in handedness, two stutterers and one nonstutterer from left- to right-handedness, two in each group from left-handedness to ambidexterity, and eight stutterers and eleven nonstutterers from ambidexterity to right-handedness. Moreover, changes in speech observed during the study did not appear related in any important manner to changes in handedness, or absence of such changes. Although there was a possible indication of more left-handedness among the blood relatives of the experimental group subjects, the handedness data of parents and siblings, for whom such data were relatively more reliable, were essentially similar for the two groups.

STUTTERING IN THE FAMILIES

Each of fifteen stutterers and four nonstutterers was said to have one or more stuttering relatives outside the immediate family. The fathers of one stutterer and two nonstutterers were stutterers, and the fathers of four stutterers were former stutterers. The mothers of two stutterers were stutterers and the mothers of three were former stutterers; the mother of one nonstutterer was also a former stutterer. Data concerning stuttering were obtained for fifty-eight siblings of stutterers and thirty-six siblings of nonstutterers. Of the stutterers' siblings nine were stutterers (these nine included two who were among the forty-six subjects in the experimental group — these two were brothers, and so each is counted as a sibling of the other) and three were former stutterers; a sibling of one nonstutterer was also a stutterer.

ONSET AND DEVELOPMENT OF THE PROBLEM OF STUTTERING

The essential findings concerning the onset of the stuttering problem, the relevant circumstances, and the course of severity of the problem may be indicated in the following paragraphs from the full report of Study I:

Age of onset of the stuttering peaked markedly at three years, 50 per cent of the cases having onset, as reported, between the ages of two years, six months and three years, two months. The interval between first spoken words and onset of stuttering ranged from six months to eight years, the median interval being twenty-three months. During this interval the children presumably spoke normally. The speech phenomena originally diagnosed or labeled as stuttering consisted solely in forty-two cases, and chiefly in all forty-six cases, of effortless, brief repetitions of syllables (that is, parts of words), whole words, or phrases, repetitions of which the child was evidently "unaware." These phenomena would appear, on the basis of data reported by Davis [25], to be normal. This fact is to be related significantly perhaps to the further fact that in nearly all cases these repetitions were originally diagnosed as stuttering by laymen, usually the parents. The generally commonplace and undramatic conditions under which these apparently normal speech reactions were occurring when first regarded by the lay judges as stuttering further suggest that the lay judges were classifying normal speech behavior as stuttering. To the degree that this is to be taken as a fair statement, it is to be inferred that the onset of stuttering took place not only, if at all, in the child's mouth, as it were, but also, and perhaps solely, in the parent's ear. This, then, would indicate that at the moment of "onset" or original diagnosis it was not only the child, if at all, but also the parent — *not only the speaker, if at all, but also the listener* — who was the patient. To the degree that this is taken to be an acceptable statement, it requires that any theory of the onset of stuttering explain not only the behavior of the child, if this should be in question, but also, and perhaps solely, the behavior of the parent — *not simply the behavior of the speaker, if at all, but also that of the listener* — at the moment of onset.

At the close of the study, speech was judged to have improved in 85 per cent of the cases, and to be "normal or nearly normal" in 72 per cent. In general, this result was associated with a type of counseling of the parents designed to get them to regard their children as normal, to give major attention not to the child's speech repetitions and hesitancies, as such, but to the conditions affecting the youngster's speech, and to adjust downward their standards of speech and behavior generally, in order to reduce tensions, both for the child and for themselves, and to make it easier for the child to gain essential feelings of success and approval. (62, pp. 70–71)

Study II

Study II, as indicated in Chapter 1, involved a comparative investigation of fifty children, thirty-nine boys and eleven girls, with ages ranging from two years, two months to fourteen years, four months, who were regarded by their parents as stutterers, the experimental group, and a control group of fifty children of like sex, age, and socio-economic level of family who were regarded as nonstutterers by their parents. The two groups of children were compared, as were their mothers and fathers also, in the respects indicated by the following summary of findings.*

INTERGROUP COMPARISON OF CHILDREN

A total of thirty-eight (18 per cent) of 210 [interview] items yielded intergroup differences significant at the 5 per cent level of confidence. They reveal that the stuttering children reportedly incurred more injuries, had more food dislikes, had more physical energy, had repeated more grades in school, and were more perfectionistic than the non-stuttering children. On twelve out of fifteen personality traits the stuttering children were rated significantly less favorably by their parents than were the nonstuttering children, the reverse being true on the other three traits. Likewise certain types of "undesirable" behavior were reported more commonly by the mothers of the stuttering children.

The nonstuttering children appeared to be slightly advanced over the stuttering children on three measures of speech development, and the stuttering children were judged by their parents to have been slower in speech development and less adequate in current vocabulary. The stuttering children were also reported to have had more talking done for them and to have been interrupted more than the nonstuttering children, although the incidence of quite talkative members of the family was greater in the nonstuttering group and more correction of grammar was done in the nonstuttering families. The stuttering children reportedly were called upon to recite pieces more frequently than the nonstuttering children. . . .

No significant differences were found in comparisons of reports of the mothers' health, appetite, falls, injuries, shocks, and work history during pregnancy, length of pregnancy, length of labor, position of the baby at birth, use of instruments, birth injuries to child and mother, birth weight, birth length, incidence of prematurity as determined by birth weight, or incidence of defects noted at birth. . . .

No significant between-group differences were found with regard to duration of breast feeding, parental ratings of children's muscular coordination in nine different activities (intergroup comparisons having been made of mothers' and fathers' responses separately), early hand preference, parental handling of early hand preference, incidence of change of handedness, present handedness, incidence of restraint of hands, or incidence of writing backwards. . . .

No significant differences were found between the groups of children with regard to incidence of the five most commonly reported infectious childhood diseases; incidence of tonsillectomies, adenoidecto-

---

* The rest of this section is composed wholly of passages written by Dr. Frederic L. Darley and previously published as part of a detailed report of Study II (24, pp. 74–153). The passages presented here have been selected with Dr. Darley's permission and approval.

mies, or total operations; parental ratings (by both mothers and fathers, separately) of the child's physical development status; incidence of physical defect, hearing difficulty, or necessity for glasses; or maternal ratings of appetite, digestion, and soundness of sleep. . . .

No significant intergroup differences were found with regard to the amount of early babbling reported; the amount of verbal output currently, as well as between ages one and five; parental ratings of early need for speech ("Did the child usually get what he wanted without talking?"); use by parents of "baby talk"; incidence in the children of any difficulty with mouth, teeth, throat, or nose; [and] privileges of the children to talk at table . . .

[On 87 out of 111 items dealing with social development the two groups did not differ significantly.] A partial list of the many items on which the two groups appear essentially similar follows: number and kind of friends and relationships with them; twenty-one different personality traits; frequency of occurrence of twenty-nine different kinds of "undesirable" behavior and fears; relationships with siblings; amount of laughing at and teasing to which children are subjected; types and amounts of assigned home responsibilities; freedom of children to select their activities; preference for games; preference for and activity in other pastimes; adequacy of allowance; response to discipline and reprimand; self-evaluation of abilities; perfectionism concerning home tasks and schoolwork; and general preference for one parent over the other. . . .

INTERGROUP COMPARISON OF PARENTS

A total of seventy-seven (32 per cent) of 238 items yielded significant intergroup differences. They show the experimental group parents to be older than the control group parents, somewhat better educated (the mothers tending to be better educated than the fathers), and to have smaller families. Although experimental group parents reported better school achievement and the mothers were more socially active than their control group counterparts, they were less well satisfied with their own abilities and accomplishments and more sensitive of the opinions of others. They were more tense, laughed less, had higher standards of neatness, had studied more about child development, and were less well satisfied with their children's behavior, intelligence, school achievement, and speech, acknowledging more frequent punishment for certain types of behavior, more frequent punishment in anger, and more frequent reprimanding of their children (although they expressed more dissatisfaction with their own strictness and adequacy as disciplinarians).

The experimental group families nevertheless were reportedly more harmonious than the control group families with regard to several common sources of parental friction. Experimental group parents as a whole were better satisfied with the husband's employment than the control group parents, and they worried less about getting sick than did the control group parents. Greater incidence of all types of speech defects was reported in experimental group families, though the relative incidence of stuttering in the families did not differentiate the

two groups. As determined by Warner's Index of Status Characteristics, the fifty families in both groups (matched for socioeconomic
level) were distributed in all five socioeconomic classes (upper
through lower-lower), 80 per cent of the families belonging to the
upper, upper-middle, and lower-middle classes. . . .

No significant intergroup differences were found with regard to
parental ratings of how well-to-do the families were; regularity of income; judgments of the security of the fathers' jobs; judgments of the
suitability of the fathers' employment in terms of their abilities; frequency of change of residence; or ownership of homes. The homes of
the control group were found to be only slightly more crowded than
those of the experimental group, with mean "overcrowdedness ratios"
of 1.44 and 1.49 respectively (the ratio was calculated by dividing the
number of rooms in the home by the number of persons residing in
the home). . . .

No significant differences were found between the two groups of
mothers, the two groups of fathers, or the two groups of parents
(fathers and mothers combined) when a comparison was made of relative numbers falling into three categories: college graduates, high
school graduates plus graduates with some college work, and those
who had attained a level anywhere short of high school graduation. . . .

No significant intergroup differences were found with regard to
parental evaluations of the importance of their education, amount of
participation in extracurricular activities in high school or college, or
incidence of membership in college social fraternities or sororities. . . .

The two groups of families did not differ significantly in terms of
the numbers of families in which the parents had similar or different
church affiliations. . . . Significantly more mothers and fathers in the
experimental group were church members (1 per cent level of confidence). However, no significant intergroup differences were found
among either mothers or fathers with regard to the degree of religious adherence (e.g., frequency of church attendance), or to the
conservatism or liberality of their religious beliefs (among Prot-
estants). . . .

No significant differences were found in intergroup comparisons
(mothers and fathers both separately and combined) of frequency
with which they helped organize new community and social groups;
frequency of holding public office; number of friends claimed; or
judgments of care of appearance and ease in adjustment to new situations or friends . . .

No significant differences were found between the groups with regard to frequency of prior marriages (five parents in each group had
been previously married); expression of enjoyment of evenings spent
at home together; parental ratings (mothers and fathers separately)
of the amount of quarreling, the seriousness of differences arising concerning seven topics (religion, discipline, ambition, employment of
wife, politics, reading interest, and radio listening), and satisfaction
with the existing marital relationship; frequency of maternal participation in decisions concerning finances, purchases of husband's
clothes, and vacations; readiness to confide in mate; self-judgment of

tenseness, irritability, easygoingness, and level of standards of conduct and neatness; judgments of irritability and standards of conduct of mate; frequency of claims that other parent had spoiled child, been too easygoing with child, worried too much, was away from home too much, or was with child too much; or self-judgments concerning frequency of siding with child against mate. . . .

The fifty pairs of experimental group parents had a total of 111 children (mean = 2.22 children), while the fifty pairs of control group parents had a total of 141 children (mean = 2.82). Eleven of the stuttering children were only children, as were five of the nonstuttering children; the difference is not statistically significant.* However, when the families are grouped into those with one or two children and those with three or more, we find a statistically significant difference between experimental and control groups, with the control group families being larger (1 per cent level of confidence). Significantly more control than experimental group parents also stated that they planned to have more children.

No significant intergroup differences were found with regard to whether the children were planned and wanted; the number of families in which both parents were currently (or during the children's infancy) working outside the home; average number of nights per week both parents were home with the children; amount of help the mothers had with housework; who managed the children most; incidence of persons other than immediate family living in the homes; expressions of liking for neighbors; preference [for living] in other neighborhoods; judgments of neighbors' treatment of children concerned; communality of family interests; frequency of family participation in three activities (picnics, auto rides, attending sports events); expressions of favor toward children's friends coming over to their house, of suitability of neighborhood children as companions for their children, and of wish that their children were more popular; amount of time that parents spent playing with children; or expressions of degree to which children interfered with or added to their parents' pleasure. A family-by-family comparison of the parents' estimates of how much they laughed indicates no significant pattern of interfamily dissimilarity in this regard. . . .

No significant intergroup differences were found with reference to present health of the parents or their health during the early years of the children's speech development; attributing by mothers of personal ailments or weaknesses to the circumstances of the birth of the child concerned; number of illnesses of mothers during children's lifetime; self-ratings of amount of worry about self or child getting sick; ratings of appetite, digestion, and sleep of self and other parent; number of food dislikes; type of handedness, change of handedness, or opinions of handedness; twinship; self-ratings of current amount of physical energy; frequency of smoking and use of alcohol; or family incidence of physical handicaps. . . .

Ratings by the interviewers of the quality of speech of the parents

* See, however, the statement on page 72 concerning the statistically significant difference obtained when the subjects investigated in Studies II and III were combined.

did not reveal a significant intergroup difference. . . . In twenty-six of the experimental group families at least one parent knew of at least one other stuttering relative, while the same was true in eighteen of the control group families. . . .

No significant intergroup differences were found on items pertaining to estimates of current frequency of punishment; mother's statements concerning the frequency of punishment for twenty types of misbehavior; parental responsibility for punishment; opinions of the amount or method of school discipline and the strictness of the children's "best" teacher; or ratings of the other parent's strictness. The methods of discipline reportedly used were essentially the same in both groups, spanking, deprivation of privileges, and sending children to their rooms being the three most common methods, in that order, reported by both groups. . . .

PARENT INTRAGROUP COMPARISONS

A total of thirty-two (8 per cent) of 412 computations of chi-square (based on 313 interview items) yielded significant differences between the experimental group mothers and fathers; corresponding differences between the control group mothers and fathers were found on only seven of these thirty-two items. The differences obtained which are distinctive of the experimental group indicate that the experimental group mothers may be characterized as more self-depreciative, more irritable, more annoyed by their children and their children's lack of neatness, and more concerned about their children's speech deviations, while being less easygoing and less satisfied with their husbands' employment than were their husbands. They more readily acknowledged having made mistakes in handling their children's speech problems, rated those speech problems as more severe, considered their children more sensitive about those problems, and considered their children to be more perfectionistic in speech than did their husbands. They also considered their children to be less happy, and evaluated parental differences concerning discipline to be more serious than did their husbands. [These parental differences are to be evaluated with reference to the fact that in over 90 per cent of the comparisons made the mothers and fathers were found to be essentially alike in the attitudes or reactions in question.]

INTRAFAMILY INTERGROUP COMPARISONS

A total of eleven (14 per cent) of seventy-six items analyzed to determine intergroup differences in degree of intrafamily agreement yielded significant differences. A review of the differences shows that the experimental group is distinguished from the control group by greater strictness on the part of the mothers than on the part of their husbands concerning their children's neatness, by higher maternal than paternal ratings of their children's attractiveness, and by lower maternal than paternal ratings of the amount of their children's bragging. At the same time the control group is distinguished from the experimental group by generally more disagreement on nine items (concerning ratings of four of their children's characteristics, the importance of parental differences on four subjects, and the excellence of the children's first school); by higher maternal than paternal ratings of their children's ability to concentrate, self-confidence, and amount of bragging; by less strictness on the part of the mothers than of the fathers concerning their children's neatness; and by lower maternal than paternal ratings of the attractiveness of their children. [The differences listed here are, like those rated in preceding sections, to be evaluated against the background of general similarity between the groups being compared.]

ANALYSIS OF PARENTS' TEST RESULTS

No significant intragroup or intergroup differences were found in the analysis of scores on the Iowa Scale of Attitude toward Stuttering. The results obtained on the Guilford Inventory of Factors STDCR show that there was a tendency for both the experimental and control groups of parents to be more sociable, more extravertive in thinking, more cheerful and optimistic, more even in disposition, and more happy-go-lucky, carefree, and impulsive than Guilford's normative group. Differences between the experimental and control group of parents are statistically significant on none of the five factors.

ANALYSIS OF CHILDREN'S INTELLIGENCE AND
PERSONALITY TEST RESULTS

The I.Q.'s of the experimental group children ranged from 54 to 162, distributed in all ranges of intelligence from "moron" to "very superior" in a manner not statistically significantly different from the manner of distribution of I.Q.'s in the general population.

In none of the five distributions of scores ("Personal Inferiority," "Social Maladjustment," "Family Maladjustment," "Daydreaming," and total score) on the Rogers Test of Personality Adjustment were the two groups of children found to differ significantly. Comparison of group means for the four area scores and the total score reveals only negligible intergroup differences; all these mean scores fell in the "Low" or "Average" classifications (suggesting generally satisfactory adjustment) with the exception of the mean "Social Maladjustment" scores, both of which fell just within the "High" classification (suggesting a rather serious degree of maladjustment). There was a tendency (not statistically significant) for the stuttering children to make higher area and total scores than the nonstuttering children, and more stuttering than nonstuttering children rated "High" in more than one of the five areas.

ANALYSIS OF DATA PERTAINING TO THE ONSET
AND DEVELOPMENT OF STUTTERING

Mothers and fathers varied widely in their estimate of the age of their children at the onset of stuttering, the discrepancies varying from 1 to 108 months, with a median discrepancy of 10.50 months,

41

the mothers as a group reporting onset earlier than the fathers. The median ages of onset of stuttering as given by the mothers and fathers were 3 years, 7.9 months and 4 years, .75 months, respectively. Every child reportedly had a period of "normal" speech between the ages of speaking his first words and onset of "stuttering," the median interval being more than two and a half years. The median interval between ages of speaking sentences and onset of stuttering was more than one year.

The child was in most cases first [thought to be] stuttering by one or both parents, in all other cases by a teacher, relative, or friend. In forty-seven of the fifty cases the diagnosing or labeling of this speech behavior as "stuttering" was done, according to the statement of at least one parent, by a layman not professionally trained in speech pathology, usually by the parents. The speaking situations which at first seemed to be characterized by more stuttering were largely described as situations involving tensions which might well make a person speak with less assurance and greater hesitancy. The sole type of speech reaction initially classified as stuttering by at least one parent of each of forty-one of the children consisted of repetitions of sounds, syllables, words, or phrases. In all but two cases the repetitions as described resemble the normal nonfluencies well known to characterize the speech of young children. Furthermore in about 90 per cent of the cases the parents agreed that the nonfluencies first regarded as stuttering were characterized by no muscular tension. In only three cases did both parents agree that the child from the first was aware of any difference in his speech. In all but two cases (in which cases the parents were interviewed within one month of onset) one or both parents had made numerous comments or suggestions to the children about their speech. There was much disagreement about the recent course of the stuttering. Forty-two children had come, following such home therapy as had been attempted, to show more tension, and thirty-eight had developed grimaces and bodily movements associated with their stuttering, according to at least one parent in each case.

As a group the mothers expressed great concern over the stuttering from onset. Both mothers and fathers rated the present stuttering as significantly more severe than did the speech clinicians who examined the children. In enumerating the suspected causes of stuttering, only 16 per cent of the parents indicated that they considered the role of parents to be of causal importance in the development of stuttering, attributing greater importance to constitutional factors, illnesses and injuries, specific events, the child's personality type, and conflicts arising in other interpersonal relationships.

A general conclusion which may be drawn is that while the two groups of parents were markedly similar on the vast majority of items studied, there are areas which appear to warrant closer investigation to determine their importance with regard to etiology and prognosis in stuttering. These include parental standards and expectations generally, and specifically with regard to speech, the early management of observed nonfluencies in the children's speech, parental sensitivities generally, and specifically with regard to speech deviations, and parental drive and dominance characteristics. (24, pp. 86–112, 147–152)

Implications

Two facts about Study I indicate most sharply the way in which it differed from Study II and the changes in research orientation that were worked out between these two investigations. The one concerns the nature of the investigative procedure employed in Study I: it centered around an interview that was to an important degree open-ended and loosely structured, although major lines of inquiry were outlined. The main reason for this was that in 1934 there was a relatively limited basis for precise decisions concerning the information to be sought. So far as decisions of this kind seemed justified, they were influenced chiefly by current and traditional views. This accounted for the second distinctive fact about Study I: the information sought had to do in the main with the speaker, the person designated as a stutterer, and only in a subordinate and relatively ambiguous fashion with anything else. Moreover, the objectives of the investigation were most clearly defined with regard to the physical facts about the speaker, such as conditions of birth, diseases and injuries, indices of motor and behavioral development, and handedness.

When one considers the preconceptions that were presumably operating and the relatively large mesh of the net, so to speak, that was used in searching for any facts that were not assumed to be central to the problem, it is not immediately clear why so much that was apparently not being looked for in Study I was found nevertheless. The explanation probably lies in one particular aspect of the interview: the informants were asked, with respect to each experimental group child, to specify the person who first decided the child was stuttering, and what exactly this person was responding to in the child's speech, and under what specific circumstances. It was not that some such questions as these had never before been put by anyone to the parents of children regarded as stutterers; this would seem incredible. What does appear to have been true is that such questions had never before been asked so pointedly, with quite as much insistence upon the pinpointing of times and places and upon detailed descriptions of the speech behavior involved. Moreover, it appears that never before had enough such questions been asked of enough informants soon enough after the alleged onset of stuttering to yield in any one investigation a sufficiently large mass of reasonably dependable data to bring into clear focus the sorts of findings obtained in Study I. Nor had anything like this been done previously in such a way as to point up pertinent comparisons between allegedly stuttering children and a relevantly matched group of presumably nonstuttering children.

It oversimplifies and dramatizes the situation somewhat, and yet points up the essential fact, to say that we had not previously discovered the more crucial findings of Study I concerning the origins of the problem of stuttering in specific instances because we had not assumed they existed and so we had not gone hunting for them. As has been true over and over again in the history of scientific research, certain facts were found as soon as someone looked for them, even though to some degree inadvertently.

In this case the most important findings appeared to be that the problem referred to as stuttering concerned certain persons in addition to the speaker, if indeed it involved the speaker personally in any significant sense at all before it involved his listeners; that the problem was one which was originally diagnosed, or judged to have come into being, by laymen; that the speakers judged by these laymen to be stutterers were generally indistinguishable, on the basis of the criteria employed, from appropriately matched persons judged not to be stutterers; and that, so far as could be determined, the childhood speech behavior classified by these laymen as stuttering was not clearly different from speech behavior generally characteristic of children at the approximate age and developmental levels of the allegedly stuttering children.

As the writer and his students became increasingly familiar with these and the related findings, and more and more accustomed to thinking operationally about them, they were influenced to reformulate the problem of stuttering accordingly. They came to view it as a problem involving the learning and the exercise of specific perceptual and evaluative reactions by the listener, and the learning, as an apparent consequence, of corresponding perceptual, evaluative, and overt responses by the speaker, these learnings occurring within the framework provided by demonstrable patterns of interpersonal relationships. The settings defined by family constellations appeared to be of special significance. It became increasingly clear that further relevant information was to be gained by investigating the pertinent behavior of both speaker and listener, in relation not only to parent-child interactions but also to those of parent and parent, child and sibling, and family and community. In academic parlance, the writer "was led by the problem" to the experimental psychology of learning and perception, to cultural anthropology, and to the study of speech and language functions and relevant symbolizing and abstracting processes, particularly as these are to be considered within the frames of reference of general semantics, information theory, and the systematic study of the process of communication.

Meanwhile a considerable amount of relevant scientific work, much of it stimulated at least in part by the findings of Study I, served to clarify the problem of stuttering in some measure during the years between roughly 1935 and the beginning of Study II in 1948. The more pertinent research was that concerned with (1) possible relations between stuttering behavior and various aspects of personality development and adjustment, (2) conditions associated with variations in amount or severity of stuttering, and (3) the search, which yielded a steadily mounting accumulation of negative findings, for possible significant neurophysiological differences between stutterers and nonstutterers.* Other related developments of special importance included the refinements of interviewing technique, particularly by Kinsey and his associates (67), which proved to be effectively adaptable to the requirements of the present research. The problem was further clarified by the fact that, following publication in abstracted form of Study I in 1942 (57), studies were made by LaFollette (71) and Moncur (84) of certain aspects of the relations between stuttering children and their parents. A study by Wood (132) of parental adjustments in relation to functional articulatory speech problems in children also yielded relevant information.

By 1948, then, it was possible to be relatively clear and definite about the specific information to be sought in the further investigation of the origins of stuttering, and so it proved possible to formulate the 846-item interview and to select the related procedures employed by Darley in Study II. The information to be sought was much more comprehensive than that covered in Study I and it concerned not only the physical characteristics of the speaker and the speech behavior originally regarded in each case as stuttering, but also the presumably relevant attitudes and adjustments of the parents and the related circumstances of family life, as well as the various other matters specified in the interview outline used in Study II and reproduced in large part in Appendix A.

Once the data obtained in Study II were assembled and analyzed two general conclusions seemed in order. The first was that the data from Study II not only extended considerably but also confirmed

* Historical and evaluative accounts of these and related lines of research during and before the period indicated may be found in "The Time, the Place, and the Problem," Chapter 1 of *Stuttering in Children and Adults* (62), and in "Stuttering," Chapter 5 of *Speech Handicapped School Children*, revised edition, 1956 (61).

essentially the findings of Study I. The second was that further research, involving a larger sampling of subjects and certain refinements of procedure, would be worthwhile. In his report of the second investigation, Darley made the following statement with regard to further study:

The . . . outcome of the present study suggests areas worthy of further investigation in an attempt to clarify what pattern of circumstances coupled with what constellation of parental characteristics and attitudes may lead to the development of the speech behavior and state of mind which we call stuttering . . . Further study would be more definitive and fruitful if the number of cases were materially increased, if information concerning onset of stuttering and subsequent developments were secured in more meticulous detail through more exhaustive interviewing, if the effect of memory lapse could be minimized by closely limiting the allowed interval of time from onset to date of interview, if data were secured in detail from control as well as from experimental group parents regarding observations and management of speech nonfluencies in their children, and if the data secured through interview were supplemented with data obtained through the administration to all parents of a personality test of wide scope and demonstrated validity. (24, pp. 145–46)

These suggestions were utilized, along with related considerations, in the planning of Study III. The experience gained in Study II and the continual weighing of the ever-growing body of data suggested refinements in the interview approach. Moreover, the trends with respect to theoretical orientation and ways of formulating the problem of stuttering that had developed before 1948 were carried forward after that date, with the gains in both complexity and clarification that generally accompany scientific investigation and the contemplation of its products. The continuing investigation of the speech of stutterers and nonstutterers, including the exploration of the presumably normal range of nonfluency in the speech of both children and adults (60), was instrumental in providing the basic method adopted in Study III for tape recording and analyzing samples of the speech of matched pairs of experimental and control group children. For reasons presented in Chapters 1 and 7, the decision was made to use the Minnesota Multiphasic Personality Inventory in Study III. Other differences in theoretical orientation and procedure between Study III and the two earlier investigations will become apparent in the pages that follow, in which the findings of Study III are presented.

PART TWO

Study III

CHAPTER 3

The Children

STUDY III involved 150 allegedly stuttering children and 150 allegedly nonstuttering children, matched for age, sex, and socioeconomic level of family. The mother and father of each child were interviewed separately. The methods employed in the 600 interviews and related investigative procedures have been described in Chapter 1.

In this investigation the interval between the onset of stuttering, as reported by the mothers, and the interview (813) * ranged from less than 1 month to 39 months, with a mean of 17.5, a median of 17.5, and a 90th percentile of 34 months. The mean interval, based on time of onset as reported by the fathers, was 18.2 months, and the median interval was 17 months. The characteristics of the informants, as reported by the interviewers, varied (this is indicated in 610), but in general they were judged to have responded adequately to the interviews. Only 10 of the 600 parents declined to answer all questions. These 10, as shown in 609, were reluctant to discuss certain of their own or their spouses' ideals, attitudes, and feelings; 2 fathers, 1 in each group, and 1 control group mother "refused," or preferred not, to discuss some aspects of their children's speech. There were no interruptions in 176 of the control group interviews and in 201 of those in the experimental group, and in only 3 cases, all in the control group, were there many or seriously interfering interruptions (612). Each of 292 interviews of control group parents and 275 interviews of parents in the experimental group was completed in one sitting; each of the other 33 interviews required two sessions (611).

Data obtained in both Study II and Study III are set forth in detail in the Summary Table in Appendix A. Significant chi-square values obtained in Study III, with associated degrees of freedom, are listed in Appendix B. In this chapter and the seven following the

* This number refers to item No. 813 in Appendix A, the Summary Table. This method of referring to items in the Summary Table is used throughout the report of Study III. Wherever confusion might arise between these numbers and citations of bibliographic references, "R" will precede the latter.

main findings from Study III are presented, together with a number of statements comparing various aspects of these findings with those from the two previous investigations, and certain interpretive and explanatory comments.

The two groups of children investigated in Study III differed, as indicated earlier, in one crucial respect: those in the experimental group were regarded by their parents as stutterers while those in the control group were not so regarded by their parents. In order to determine as effectively as possible whether this crucial difference was associated with other differences, the factors of sex, age, and socioeconomic status of family were held relatively constant for the two groups, and they were compared with respect to a large number of other kinds of data.

Conditions of Birth

The mean birth weight was 7.4 pounds for both groups of children in Study III (36). In Study II the experimental group mean was 7.3 and the control group mean was 7.2 pounds. It was found that five stuttering and five nonstuttering children in Study III would be considered prematurely born if all children weighing less than 5.5 pounds at birth were so regarded (see references 24, 62). According to the mothers, fifteen in the control group and four in the experimental group were considered premature by their attending physicians (see Table 2 and item 26 in the Summary Table).

The experimental group mothers reported a mean duration of labor of 11.4 hours, with a standard deviation of 3.6 hours, as compared with a control group mean of 9.0 hours, and a standard deviation of 3.3 hours (28). The t test of the difference between these means yielded a value of 5.88 which, with 286 degrees of freedom, was significant at the 1 per cent level. The median values for the experimental and control group mothers were 7.2 and 5.9 hours, respectively. In Study II the difference between the two groups with respect to length of labor was not statistically significant. "It was found that twelve stuttering and thirteen nonstuttering children were born after only four hours or less of labor, while five stuttering and six nonstuttering children were born after thirty or more hours of labor" (R24, p. 86). The findings from Study III are to be evaluated with reference also to the fact that in Study I the median values of duration of labor were seven hours for the experimental group and twelve hours for the control group.

For seventeen of the remaining items in Study III concerning birth

Table 2. Results of Chi-Square Analysis of Responses to Items Concerning Birth History on Which
Mothers of Experimental and Control Group Children Differed Significantly*

Item	Direction of Difference	Level of Confidence	Remarks
What illnesses did the mother have during pregnancy? (19)	Illnesses reported by more experimental than control group mothers	1%	
Was the mother able to eat regularly and retain food during most of the pregnancy? (20)	More control than experimental group mothers reported they were able to eat and retain food	1%	Distribution of fathers' responses unfavorable for computation of chi-square
What was the length of the pregnancy? (25)	More control group mothers reported terms more or less than 9 months; more experimental mothers exactly 9 months	5%	
Was the child considered premature by the doctor? (26)	Premature birth of child reported by more control than experimental mothers	2%	Distribution of fathers' responses unfavorable for computation of chi-square
Was labor induced? (29)	Induced labor reported by more control than experimental group mothers	5%	
Were there any other unusual circumstances or conditions connected with the birth? (50)	Such circumstances or conditions reported by more control than experimental group mothers	5%	Fathers did not differ significantly

* See Darley (R24, p. 86) for a discussion of corresponding data from Study II. In that investigation no statistically significant differences were found with respect to these particular items, except for the last one listed here, with respect to which, contrary to the present finding, more experimental than control group mothers reported one or more unusual conditions associated with the birth of the child (the difference is significant at the 1 per cent level of confidence). Statements concerning the direction of difference reported for specific items in this and subsequent tables are not of statistical significance, but are based only on observation of the theoretical and observed cell frequencies in each instance. A significant value of chi-square indicates that the cell frequencies are not independent; no specific direction of difference between the categories employed is implied. In most cases, however, the direction of difference is clearly indicated by the data, and the reader is urged to evaluate particular statements concerning the direction of difference in this and subsequent tables on the basis of the raw data in the Summary Table in Appendix A. See Appendix B for a complete list of statistically significant chi-square values represented in Tables 2 through 37, with associated degrees of freedom.

histories the distributions of responses proved to be unfavorable for computation of chi-square. These items covered shocks, injuries, and falls experienced by the mother during pregnancy, injuries to the baby, twin births, presence of cyanosis at birth, difficulty initiating breathing, cord around neck, infant unusually quiet, pulse at birth slow or weak, jaundice of baby at birth, and convulsions during delivery. From inspection of the relevant items in the Summary Table, Nos. 18–51, it is apparent that in general the occurrence of these conditions or events was relatively rare in both groups and that there were no marked group differences.

For six of the remaining items chi-square values were statistically significant at or beyond the 5 per cent level, as shown in Table 2. More of the experimental group mothers reported illnesses, and more control group mothers reported that they were able to eat and retain food during pregnancy. The question as to the degree to which these responses constituted descriptive, as contrasted with self-projective or evaluative, reports is to be considered in light of the finding that the control group mothers reported more variation from the expected nine months in the duration of pregnancy, and that more control group mothers also reported premature deliveries, induced labor, and unusual circumstances or conditions connected with childbirth.*

Physical Development

For five items concerning physical development statistically significant chi-square values were obtained, and these are summarized

* Table 2 might lend some degree of plausibility to the tentative conjecture that there was generally more concern, or conflict, over the experience of giving birth on the part of the experimental group mothers, although, with the possible exception of length of labor (for which the group difference was significant in Study III but not in Study II, and for which the group difference in Study I was in a direction opposite to that in Study III), the control group mothers seem to have had more substantial objective reasons for anxiety as indicated by the details on length of pregnancy, induction of labor, and unusual circumstances connected with delivery. Moreover, somewhat more conflict on the part of the experimental group mothers about having children may be inferred from the fact that they had had fewer children, 348 to 412, than the control group mothers (725), and had more only children, 25 to 15 (726). Similar findings were obtained in Study II, in which control group mothers reported 5 only children and a total of 141 children and experimental group mothers 11 only children and a total of 111 children. Among other possibly related considerations is the fact that in both Studies II and III the control group mothers breast fed their babies for longer periods (56 and Table 3). Due caution in elaborating this line of conjecture is to be drawn from the essentially similar responses made by the two groups in both studies to such items as 54, "Was the child planned?" 55, "Was the child wanted by both of you?" 58, "Did you or the other parent hold the child during bottle feeding?" and, in Study III but not in Study II, 727, "Do you expect to have any more children?" It is possible that for certain readers additional data presented in the Summary Table might prove to be relevant to particular hypotheses with respect to this general question.

Table 3. Results of Chi-Square Analysis of Responses to Items Concerning Physical Development on Which the Experimental and Control Group Children Differed Significantly

Item	Direction of Difference	Level of Confidence	Remarks
How long was the baby breast fed? (56)	Control group mothers reported longer periods than experimental group mothers*	5%	
Rate your child's coordination in catching (82)	More experimental than control group mothers rated their children's coordination as inferior	1%	Fathers did not differ significantly
Rate your child's coordination in jumping (85)	More control than experimental group fathers rated their children's coordination as superior	1%	Mothers did not differ significantly
Rate your child's coordination in running (87)	More control than experimental group fathers rated their children's coordination as superior	5%	Mothers did not differ significantly
What was the child's original hand preference for pencil or crayon? (96)	More experimental than control group mothers rated their children's original hand preferences to be very much right	2%	Fathers did not differ significantly

* For the control group the mean was 11.5 and the median 6.4 weeks; for the experimental group the mean was 6.9 and the median 2.8 weeks. In Study II the means were 16.7 and 9.5 weeks for the control and experimental groups, respectively.

53

in Table 3. The control group children had better coordination in catching as rated by their mothers though not by their fathers, and in running and jumping as rated by their fathers though not by their mothers. The control group mothers reported their children were breast fed for longer periods than the experimental group mothers reported for their children. More experimental group youngsters, according to the mothers but not according to the fathers, very much preferred the right hand when starting to use a pencil or crayon.

There were no significant differences between the two groups of children, so far as either the fathers' or the mothers' answers were concerned, with respect to coordination in throwing (81), drawing and coloring (83), writing (84), cutting (86), in manipulating blocks, tinker toys, and beads, and in other tasks requiring manual dexterity (88). There were also no significant differences between the two groups with regard to original hand preference in using a spoon (100); present hand preference in using a pencil, crayon, or spoon (97 and 101); and the number whose hands had ever been restrained (105).

The mean scores of the experimental and control groups of children on the Iowa Unimanual Handedness Questionnaire (788) were 1.4 and 1.3, respectively, and for both groups the median score was 1.6.

There were no significant group differences in the number of children in whom physical defects were noted at or shortly after birth (51), the number of children who were held during bottle feeding (58), the number who experienced feeding problems soon after birth (60), and the amount of crying shortly after birth (61). Nearly all answers by both groups of parents to "Has the child ever written backwards?" were negative; approximately one third of the children in both groups had learned to write (107).

Two items, which concerned methods of bowel and bladder training, could not be categorized for computation of chi-square values (91 and 92). It is to be noted, however, that when the responses listed for 91, which has to do with methods of bowel control training, are divided into those which appear coercive and punitive (responses numbered 4, 6, 7, and 10) and those which seem permissive and rewarding (those numbered 1, 2, 3, 5, 8, 9, 11, and 12), it is seen that eighty-eight experimental and fifty-nine control group mothers reported coercive methods, while eighty control and forty-eight experimental group mothers reported permissive procedures. These group differences were significant at the 1 per cent level ($\chi^2 = 12.81$; df $= 1$). The same group differences, though less marked and not of statistical significance ($\chi^2 = 1.79$; df $= 1$), appear with respect to bladder control training (92): ninety-seven experimental and eighty-two control

Table 4. Mean Ages in Months at Which the Control and Experimental Group Children Accomplished or Began Training on Certain Physical Achievements as Reported by Their Mothers

Item	Control Group			Experimental Group			Diff.	Significance Level of t
	N	Mean Age	S.D.	N	Mean Age	S.D.		
First tooth (63)	143	6.59	1.94	147	6.69	2.57	.10	*
Full set of 20 baby teeth (65)	80	22.49	8.15	92	22.41	6.58	.08	*
Creeping or crawling (67)	140	7.53	2.49	144	7.56	3.03	.03	*
Sitting up unsupported (69)	137	6.41	1.59	137	6.43	1.65	.21	NS†
First steps alone (71)	149	12.04	2.19	149	12.25	2.15	.21	NS
Voluntary control of bowels (73)	134	20.36	7.37	141	20.04	7.99	.32	NS
Voluntary control of bladder, day (75)	142	21.36	6.56	140	21.59	7.34	.23	NS
Voluntary control of bladder, night (77)	124	25.89	10.17	119	26.71	12.07	.18	NS
Using spoon in feeding self (79)	130	15.36	5.19	129	14.81	5.03	.55	NS
Beginning of bladder training (89)	144	15.06	5.57	148	13.52	4.96	1.54	1%
Beginning of bowel training (90)	148	13.02	3.83	144	11.79	4.47	1.23	*
Replacing of bottle feeding by cup feeding (59)	148	11.33	4.28	143	10.30	4.58	1.03	5%

* F test for equal variance was significant at or beyond the 10 per cent level, and t test was not computed.
† Not significant.

55

group mothers indicated coercive methods (responses numbered 3, 4, 6, 7, 8, 10, and 14), while forty-three control and thirty-four experimental group mothers reported permissive approaches (responses numbered 1, 2, 5, 9, 11, 12, and 13). It is to be noted that these figures are exclusive of responses given by fewer than three mothers in either group (see footnotes to 91 and 92).

Twelve developmental items for which t tests were computed are presented in Table 4. The mean ages of accomplishing the specified aspects of physical development were very similar for the experimental and control groups. For the experimental group the beginning of both bladder and bowel training was earlier, and cup feeding replaced bottle feeding sooner. Study II (R24) findings were essentially similar to these.*

Health and Physical Status

For three items concerning health and physical status of the children chi-square values were statistically significant, and information with respect to these items is presented in Table 5. More experimental than control group children had sustained no injuries (153–156). More of the experimental group mothers stated that they felt their children tired more easily than the average child (375). More of the control group parents reported that their children slept very well (170); at the same time, the mean number of hours each group was reported to sleep per night did not differ significantly. The median was 11 hours and the mean was 10.9 hours for both the experimental and control groups, with corresponding standard deviations of 1.16 and 1.02 hours (171). The numbers of children in the experimental and control groups who had undergone surgical operations were not significantly different.

The mean height of the experimental group children was 43.3 inches with a standard deviation of 4.5 inches, while the mean height of the control children was 42.9 inches with a standard deviation of 4.3 (158). The mean weights of the experimental and control children were 43.9 and 42.6 pounds, respectively, with corresponding standard deviations

* See also items 113–115, having to do with ages at which the parents believed a child should have achieved bowel control and daytime and nighttime bladder control; the ages given by the experimental group parents are in general earlier than those stated by the control group parents. These data serve to suggest the question of a possible relation between the tendency for the experimental group parents to move a little faster than the control group parents in attempting to achieve training of their children and the cluster of factors connected with pregnancy, delivery, handling of the baby, and size of family referred to in the footnote on page 52.

Table 5. Results of Chi-Square Analysis of Responses to Items Concerning Health and Physical Status on Which the Experimental and Control Group Children Differed Significantly

Item	Direction of Difference	Level of Confidence	Remarks
What injuries has the child sustained? (153–156)	More experimental than control group mothers reported no injuries	1%	Fathers followed same trend, significant at 2% level
How well does the child sleep? (170)	More control than experimental group mothers rated their children as sleeping very well	1%	Fathers followed same trend, significant at 1% level
As compared with other children, how easily does your child get tired? (375)	More experimental than control group mothers reported their children get tired more easily than average child	5%	Fathers did not differ significantly

of 10 and 9.6 pounds (160). The group differences in height and weight were not statistically significant.

The information obtained in response to items 125 through 148, presented in detail in Appendix A, is summarized in Table 6. In Study

Table 6. Means and Standard Deviations of Total Number of Illnesses, Number of Illnesses Regarded as Serious, and Number of Illnesses Accompanied by Unusually High Fevers (103° and Over) That Occurred More Than One Month before Age of Onset of Stuttering (and Corresponding Age for Matched Subjects in Control Group), within One Month of Onset Age, within One Month after Onset Age, and since That Time, as Reported by Control and Experimental Group Mothers

	Control Group				Experimental Group			
	N	No.	Mean	S.D.	N	No.	Mean	S.D.
Serious illnesses	150	61	.41	.61	149	109	.73	.94
Remote pre-onset . . .	150	38	.25	.50	149	61	.41	.83
Month before onset . .	150	3	.02	.14	149	7	.05	.24
Month after onset . . .	150	3	.02	.14	149	3	.02	.18
Since then	150	17	.11	.40	149	38	.25	.65
Illnesses with high fever .	148	170	1.13	1.31	149	205	1.37	1.32
Remote pre-onset . . .	148	105	.70	1.28	149	115	.77	1.16
Month before onset . .	147	1	.01	.08	149	8	.05	.25
Month after onset . . .	147	4	.03	.16	149	5	.03	.21
Since then	147	60	.40	.84	149	77	.51	1.14
All illnesses	147	397	2.65	.91	149	443	2.95	.27
Remote pre-onset . . .	144	219	1.46	1.57	149	270	1.80	1.65
Month before onset . .	142	10	.07	.28	149	21	.14	.46
Month after onset . . .	142	10	.07	.28	149	13	.09	.36
Since then	147	158	1.05	1.40	149	156	1.04	1.43
Total illnesses, including undated* . . .	150	418	2.79	2.10	149	443	2.95	2.12

* These include the illnesses summarized in 148C, which in turn include the undated illnesses summarized in 148A but not the responses presented in 148B (see the Summary Table). The difference between mean total numbers of illnesses is nonsignificant, even though the distributions are considerably skewed and the value of t is inflated accordingly. Because of the character of the distributions, t tests were not computed for the other mean differences.

III questions 125 through 148 were addressed to both the fathers and the mothers, but it was found that from 5 to 25 per cent of the fathers were unable to give reasonably definite answers, particularly with reference to the time of specific illnesses in relation to the onset of stuttering, and for this reason analysis has been restricted to the apparently more trustworthy responses of the mothers. With respect to these, also, it is to be considered that recall was probably not completely dependable in all instances, and that due allowance is to be made for such indefiniteness as was evidenced in fixing the date of onset of stuttering in given cases (see pp. 117–125).

The illnesses reported by the control and experimental group mothers in Study III have been grouped in four periods according to date: those that occurred (1) more than one month before the onset of stuttering, (2) within one month before or at time of onset, (3) within one month after onset, and (4) since one month after onset. In addition, a classification was made of those illnesses reported by informants who could state the number of illnesses but could not date them (148A). The responses of these informants are listed as "undetermined" in even-numbered items 126–148, and the number of informants contributing these responses is to be found in 148A. Also, those informants who reported that illness had occurred, but could not give the number of illnesses or date them, were noted (148B). Moreover, illnesses that had been evaluated as severe were treated separately, as were also those accompanied by unusually high fever (103° and over). Finally, the total number of illnesses identified or dated was computed (148C).

Quantitative data are presented in Table 6. A few general statements concerning these data seem warranted. When all illnesses are considered, the average child in the experimental group was said to have had 2.95 and the average child in the control group 2.79 illnesses. Even though the distributions were skewed and exhibited heterogeneous variances, the t test indicated that the difference between these two means was nonsignificant. It is a relatively small absolute difference, of course, and such as it is, it is to be accounted for mainly by reference to the illnesses reported for the period that predated the onset of stuttering by more than one month. The experimental group mothers reported 270 illnesses, or an average of 1.80, and the control group mothers reported 219, or an average of 1.46, for that period. Differences in variance and extreme skewness argue against the use of t tests of subgroup mean differences. It is to be noted that for the presumably critical interval that extended from one month before to one month after the onset of stuttering, there were few illnesses, particularly serious ones, reported.

Examination of the odd-numbered items 125–147 in the Summary Table does not suggest that any particular disease was found more often to any noteworthy degree in either group. The essentially negative findings with respect to asthma (125 and 131) are of some interest perhaps in view of a few previously published statements to the effect that asthma and other allergic conditions might be found to be associated with stuttering (R19, R125). (See also 774, in which data concerning allergies in the families of the two groups of children are summarized; these reveal no significant group differences.)

If there is any appreciable difference between the two groups it lies in the reported incidence of illness during the period more than one month before the parental concern over stuttering arose. If there is sufficient fact here to warrant speculation, perhaps the major question to be raised has to do with the degree to which the experimental group mothers were more inclined than the control group mothers to give attention to childhood indispositions and to recall them more readily. This possibility would appear to be suggested more or less by the fact that more control than experimental group mothers, 13 to 2, were unable to date illnesses (148A) or to give either the dates or the numbers of illnesses their children had had (148B), the difference in this case being 11 to 1. Another aspect of this matter to be considered is the reaction of the parents to the child's illness, real or fancied or exaggerated, and some measure of light is thrown on this by the responses to items 163 and 164. Significantly more experimental than control group parents reported that when their children had been ill they had been "spoiled and indulged excessively" and in general a greater degree of solicitousness on the part of the experimental group parents was suggested by the responses to 163. Moreover, significantly more control than experimental group mothers and fathers indicated that, after care for illness, their children needed no readjustment or readjusted immediately (164). These parental reports intimate that the data summarized in Table 6 reflect degrees of parental concern over, attention to, and memory of their children's illnesses as well as objective information concerning the illnesses as such.

The data here being reviewed are to be related to other information which indicates that the two groups of children were quite similar so far as their general health and physical development were concerned.

No significant differences between the two groups of children were found in frequency of colds (157), parental evaluations of height and weight (159 and 161), appetite (169), number of children sleeping alone (172), number having food dislikes (173), amount of energy possessed by the children as rated by parents (174), and the number for whom constipation was reported (442).

History of Speech Development and Speech Status

For three of the items concerning speech development and speech status chi-square values computed were statistically significant, as shown in Table 7. More experimental than control group children were rated by their mothers as "much slower than average" in speech acquisition (182). A peculiar and probably basic importance of this

Table 7. Results of Chi-Square Analysis of Responses to Items Concerning History of Speech Development and Speech Status on Which Experimental and Control Group Children Differed Significantly

Item	Direction of Difference	Level of Confidence	Remarks
Do you consider the child to have been slow in beginning to talk in comparison with other children? (182)	More experimental than control group mothers rated their children much slower than average	1%	Fathers did not differ significantly
How often do you correct your child's grammar each day? (352)	Experimental group children reported by their mothers to have been corrected less often than control group children	5%	Fathers followed similar trend, significant at 2% level
As a child learning to talk, did your child have chances to talk as much as he wanted to? (188)	More control than experimental group fathers rated their children's chances to talk as "more than average"	2%	Mothers did not differ significantly

group difference in parental evaluation is to be inferred from its relation to the relatively objective data obtained concerning speech development: there are no corresponding statistically significant differences between the two groups of children reflected in the mean ages, reported by mothers, at which they spoke their first words and sentences (180–181 and Table 8).* Moreover the median and mean

Table 8. Median and Mean Ages, in Months, with Standard Deviations, at Which the Control and Experimental Group Children First Spoke Words and Sentences (180–181), as Reported by the Mothers, Exclusive of Uncertain and Indefinite Responses

Item	Control Group				Experimental Group			
	N	Median	Mean	S.D.	N	Median	Mean	S.D.
First words*	131	10.7	10.8	3.9	137	11.4	10.9	4.6
First sentences*	131	21.1	21.0	6.3	136	21.7	21.8	7.3

* Differences between group means were not significant at the 5 per cent level.

values for both groups, as shown in Table 8, lie well within normal limits. Nor were any significant differences found between the ratings of the two groups with respect to amount of talking the children did between the ages of one and five years (183), children's vocabularies (355), children's grammar (356), current amount of talking done by the children (309), and amount of talking the children are allowed to do at the dinner table (310) and when guests are present (312). It is also to be noted that the two groups of parents did not differ significantly in response to the question "How frequently did your child get what he wanted without talking, in comparison with other children?" (185).

As indicated in Table 7, the experimental group children had their grammar corrected less often than did those in the control group, according to both the fathers and mothers. More control than experimental group fathers (the difference for the mothers was not significant) rated their children's chances to talk, however, while they were learning to talk, as "more than average."

The experimental and control group parents were asked to state whether their children had had speech defects, including those other

* As shown in Table 18, the experimental group mothers differed significantly from those in the control group in giving earlier mean ages at which they thought a child should speak his first words and sentences. With higher standards as represented by these differing means, the experimental group mothers may have been more inclined to judge the speech development of their own children as relatively slower than it was, objectively gauged.

than stuttering. Their responses are summarized in 194. The problems involved in securing the closest possible approximation to objective data concerning speech impairments and their origins are discussed in considerable detail in Chapter 5. It seems well to point out here, however, certain features of the parents' responses to 194, "Has your child ever had a speech defect? What defect?" All the parents in the experimental group had met the criteria set forth in Chapter 1; nevertheless, 11 of the fathers and 5 of the mothers gave a simple negative response to this question. Allowance must be made, of course, for the ambiguity of "speech defect" and equivalent terms as they are used, especially by laymen, and for the transient confusion that may have been experienced by some respondents in spite of the care exercised in making clear that stuttering was one of the speech problems, but not the only one, in which the investigators were interested in connection with this question. With these and other implied considerations noted, it is to be observed that aside from the 13 fathers and 21 mothers in the experimental group, as against none in the control group, who said their children had "stuttering and articulatory defect," and aside from the responses that referred to "stuttering" or "repetition, not called stuttering," and "hesitation, not called stuttering," there were actually more control group parents, 9 fathers and 11 mothers, than experimental group parents, 6 fathers and 2 mothers, who reported that their children had speech defects other than stuttering, such as "baby talk," "lisping," "other articulatory defect," "speech retardation," "inability to find right word," "articulatory problem and 'speech block' not called stuttering," and "nasal speech." It seems apparent, therefore, that the number of experimental group children who were said to have "speech defects" other than those classified as "stuttering" or as "stuttering and articulatory defect" was not appreciably different from the number of control group children who were said to have such defects. The numbers were absolutely small in both groups. It is to be noted, however, that when those reported as having "stuttering and articulatory defect" are included with those having other designated speech impairments aside from stuttering, the totals, as given by the mothers, are 11 children in the control group and 23 in the experimental group.

Social Development

The items having to do with the children's social development for which significant chi-square values were obtained are indicated in Table 9. Due consideration is to be given to the question of the degree to which these ratings represent objective data concerning the chil-

Table 9. Results of Chi-Square Analysis of Responses to Items Concerning Social Development on Which Experimental and Control Group Children Differed Significantly

Item	Direction of Difference	Level of Confidence	Remarks
How much does your child daydream? (399)	Control group mothers rated children more favorably (less daydreaming)	5%	Fathers followed similar trend, significant at 2% level
How much does your child play alone? (402)	Control group mothers rated children more favorably (less playing alone)	5%	Fathers followed similar trend, significant at 1% level
How often has nervousness occurred during the past month? (406)	Control group mothers rated children more favorably (less nervousness)	1%	Fathers followed similar trend, significant at 1% level
How often has timidity occurred during the past month? (418)	Control group mothers rated children more favorably (less timidity)	1%	Fathers followed similar trend, significant at 1% level
How often has showing off occurred during the past month? (420)	Control group mothers rated children more favorably (less showing off)	1%	Fathers followed similar trend, significant at 1% level
How often has rudeness occurred during the past month? (422)	Control group mothers rated children more favorably (less rudeness)	2%	Fathers followed similar trend, significant at 5% level
How often has thumb sucking occurred during the past month? (438)	Control group mothers rated children more favorably (less thumb sucking)	5%	Fathers did not differ significantly
Of what sex are most of the child's friends? (365)	More control than experimental group mothers reported their children's friends evenly divided between sexes	5%	Fathers did not differ significantly
How often does the child play with companions? (371)	Greater frequency in control group according to mothers	2%	Fathers did not differ significantly
Compared with other children, how well does your child play with other children? (372)	Control group mothers rated children more favorably	1%	Fathers did not differ significantly
How good a sense of humor does your child have? (376)	Control group mothers rated children more favorably	2%	Fathers did not differ significantly

64

Table 9 – *continued*

Item	Direction of Difference	Level of Confidence	Remarks
How cautious is your child about under-taking new things, going into different situations? (388)	Control group mothers rated children more favorably (less cautious)	1%	Fathers did not differ significantly
How readily does your child give up on hard tasks? (472)	Control group mothers rated children more favorably (give up less readily)	5%	Fathers did not differ significantly
Compared with other children, how afraid is your child of strangers? (482)	Control group mothers rated children more favorably (less afraid)	2%	Fathers followed similar trend, significant at 5% level
How afraid is your child of the dark? (483)	Control group mothers rated children more favorably (less afraid)	5%	Fathers followed similar trend, significant at 5% level
How afraid is your child of other children? (484)	Control group mothers rated children more favorably (less afraid)	1%	Fathers followed similar trend, significant at 1% level
How much is the child laughed at by other children? (493)	Control group mothers rated children more favorably (laughed at less)	1%	Fathers followed similar trend, significant at 1% level
Does the child go to Sunday school? (500)	More experimental mothers reported no Sunday school	1%	Fathers followed similar trend, significant at 1% level
Does the child have pets? (503)	More control group mothers indicated their children have pets	1%	Fathers followed similar trend, significant at 2% level
How does your child respond to your corrections and suggestions? (524)	More experimental group mothers gave their children extreme ratings	1%	Fathers followed similar trend, significant at 1% level
How does your child respond to the corrections and suggestions of your husband (wife)? (525)	More experimental group mothers gave children extreme ratings	5%	Fathers followed similar trend, significant at 2% level
How often does your child make bids for attention? (532)	More control group mothers rated children favorably (less often)	2%	Fathers followed similar trend, significant at 2% level
Which parent does the child **prefer**? (533)	More experimental group mothers said children prefer mothers	5%	Fathers followed similar trend, significant at 5% level

Table 9 – *continued*

Item	Direction of Difference	Level of Confidence	Remarks
After care for illness, how quickly did the child readjust? (164)	More control group mothers rated children favorably (needed no readjustment)	2%	Fathers followed similar trend, significant at 1% level
How often does your child go to a friend's house to play? (367)	Greater frequency in control group according to fathers	5%	Mothers did not differ significantly
How shy is your child? (387)	More control group fathers rated children favorably (less shy)	5%	Mothers did not differ significantly
How self-confident is your child? (391)	More control group fathers rated children favorably (more self-confident)	2%	Mothers did not differ significantly
How often has fighting occurred during the past month? (428)	More control group fathers rated children favorably (less fighting)	5%	Mothers did not differ significantly
How often has jealousy occurred during the past month? (430)	More control group fathers rated children favorably (less jealousy)	2%	Mothers did not differ significantly
How often has lying occurred during the past month? (436)	More control group fathers rated children favorably (less lying)	5%	Mothers did not differ significantly
How afraid is your child of dogs? (480)	More control group fathers rated children favorably (less afraid)	5%	Mothers did not differ significantly
How afraid is your child of doctors? (481)	More control group fathers rated children favorably (less afraid)	2%	Mothers did not differ significantly
How much freedom has the child in determining how he shall use his own play time? (502)	More control group fathers rated children favorably (more freedom)	5%	Mothers did not differ significantly
How does the child adjust to new situations and new friends? (513)	More experimental group fathers gave children most favorable rating	1%	Mothers did not differ significantly
Does the child seem to be a perfectionist about home tasks? (527)	More control group fathers rated children favorably (less perfectionistic)	5%	Mothers did not differ significantly
Does the child seem to be a perfectionist about his neatness? (528)	More control group fathers rated children favorably (less perfectionistic)	2%	Mothers did not differ significantly

dren and the degree to which they reflect parental feelings, perceptual sets, and standards of judgment. The basic data are, of course, judgments about, rather than descriptions of, the indicated characteristics and behavior of the children. The responses represented in Table 9 were made by the parents, not the children. In addition, it is to be appreciated that the parents made these evaluations eighteen months on the average after the reported onset of the problem of stuttering; the ratings may have been affected, therefore, by the parents' concern over or dissatisfaction with their children's speech behavior, and the children may also have been affected during the average period of eighteen months by the dissatisfaction and concern of their parents.

These possibilities noted, the findings are to be summarized in the statement that on 35 of the 36 items in Table 9 the control group children were rated more favorably by their mothers or fathers, or both, than were the experimental group children by their parents. On one item, the experimental group fathers rated their children more favorably than the control group fathers rated theirs, and the two groups of mothers did not differ significantly. With respect to the other 35 items, control group responses that were more favorable, or less indicative of concern, discontent, or difficulty, or involved higher ratings were made by both mothers and fathers to 17 items, by the mothers only to 7 items, and by the fathers only to 11 items. On 7 items the two groups of fathers, and on 12 the two groups of mothers, did not differ significantly.

If relevant items represented in Tables 2, 3, 5, and 7 are added to the 36 in Table 9, a comparative analysis of responses to the total of 51 items involved yields the following results:

1. For 45 items the control group responses were the more favorable, or less indicative of concern, discontent, or difficulty, or involved higher ratings
   a. For 13 items this was true for mothers only
   b. For 14 items this was true for fathers only
   c. For 18 items this was true for both mothers and fathers
2. For 6 items the experimental group responses were the more favorable, or less indicative of concern, discontent, or difficulty, or involved higher ratings
   a. For 3 items this was true for mothers only
   b. For 1 item this was true for fathers only
   c. For 2 items this was true for both mothers and fathers
3. On 15 items the two groups of mothers did not differ significantly

4. On 11 items the two groups of fathers did not differ significantly

The z value of the difference between 45 and 6 is significant at the 1 per cent level ($z = 5.43$). The various subgroup totals were too small to warrant computation of significance values.

The two groups of parents did not differ significantly in rating their children with respect to the age of their children's friends (366), mischievousness (373), concentration (384), aggressiveness (385), carelessness (390), being picked on at school (393), popularity (394), fighting (397), laughing (400), respecting rights of others (401), bed wetting (412), playing with sex organs (414), hitting other children (426), crying at home (432), hurting pets (440), nail biting (444), temper tantrums (450), whining (454), teasing (458), bullying (460), disobedience (462), explaining away faults (471), athletic ability (476), reading (479), ease of crying (487), happiness (489), rivalry (491), amount teased (495), what teased about (496), masturbation (511), stealing (456), evaluation of own abilities (526), child's perfectionism about own speech (530), other strong fears (485), organizations to which the children belonged (501), and parents' ambitions for their children (509).

So few parents reported each of the following that distributions were unfavorable for computation of chi-square values: sleepwalking (416), crying at school (434), face twitching (446), fainting (448), running away (452), stealing (512), children not popular (395), and children laughed at more than average (493). Responses to four items did not lend themselves well to grouping in a contingency table; these items were concerned with how the children's siblings treated them (490), what the children did when teased (497), why the children did not have pets (504), and what the parents wanted their children to be when they grew up (509).

School History

Twenty-nine of the control group and thirty-three of the experimental group children had entered the first grade (569), and there were no differences between the groups with respect to the ages at which they entered this grade or with respect to the present grade placement (572). Approximately 20 per cent of the children had learned to read, and the mean age of learning to read was 6.1 years for both groups (584).

Other school items proved to have distributions unfavorable for computation of chi-square tests of independence. The items (573–583 and 585–595) having to do with school attendance, grade retardation and acceleration, adjustment to school, grades or marks, and related matters were appropriate for too few subjects to warrant analysis of the data obtained by means of them.

Stuttering and Other Speech Impairments in the Children's Families

Nine mothers (6 per cent) and eight fathers (5.3 per cent) in the control group and thirty-five mothers and thirty-five fathers (23.3 per cent in each case) in the experimental group gave affirmative responses to the question "Are there other stutterers in your family?" (325). The difference, for the fathers as well as the mothers, was significant at the 1 per cent level, according to chi-square analysis. The numbers of persons in the immediate families or among blood relatives reported as stutterers by the control group fathers and mothers and experimental group fathers and mothers, respectively, were 10, 9, 47, and 50.* As these figures imply, the husband and wife pairs did not agree completely in their independently given reports of stutterers among relatives (see 325 in the Summary Table in Appendix A for an indication of the degree of agreement shown). Of the control group children, three had stuttering parents (all fathers) and according to the father but not the mother one had a stuttering sibling; of the children in the experimental group, nineteen had fathers and five had mothers who stuttered, while seven according to the fathers and nine according to the mothers had stuttering siblings.

Twenty-two mothers and eight fathers in the control group and forty-four mothers and thirty-two fathers in the experimental group indicated that there were other persons with "speech defects" in their immediate families (719), and while the group difference for both fathers and mothers was significant at the 1 per cent level, as indicated by the value of chi-square, it is to be considered that most of the "speech defects" were the cases of stuttering previously reported in response to 325. (See the footnote to 792.)

These findings would seem to suggest two possible hypotheses. According to the one, the problem of stuttering "runs in families," to the extent that it does, because it is biologically or genetically inherited. According to the other hypothesis, it is a problem that is transmitted from one generation to the next, within families, because the problem is primarily a function of certain attitudes, or beliefs,

* In Study II the corresponding totals were 7, 16, 27, and 30. In Study I also more stutterers were reported in the families of the experimental than of the control group children (see Chapter 2). Studies by Wepman (R121, 122) and by West, Nelson, and Berry (R126) have also indicated that persons classified as stutterers tend to have more relatives also so classified than do persons not classified as stutterers.

or evaluative orientations toward the speech of early childhood, and the problem may arise in a given case if the parental orientation toward childhood speech that is essential for the development of the problem is acquired in sufficient degree by the parents — from their parents. In discussing this question elsewhere the writer (R61) has said:

There are two main reasons, of course, why characteristics run in families. One is biological, genetic, hereditary in a physical sense of the word. We take for granted that this is the kind of reason which accounts for family resemblances in respect to hair color and texture, eye color, and other bodily features. The other reason is social — custom, tradition, training. For example, the Mormon religion, or the Methodist, or Buddhist, or any other tends to run in families. We understand, of course, that this is not due to heredity in a biological sense, but that it is rather a matter of family tradition, something taught by parents to their children, and passed along in this way from generation to generation. Thus we have family traditions with respect to food preferences and dislikes, occupations, literary tastes, political leanings, psychological reactions to illness, ethical and moral tendencies, and attitudes, beliefs, and evaluations generally.

The reason why stuttering tends to run in families seems to be rather definitely a matter of tradition rather than genes. Parents who stutter, or have stuttered, or who have grown up with stuttering brothers and sisters, or parents, or uncles and aunts, or cousins — such parents when faced with the normally hesitant early speech of their own children may be expected, in some cases at least, to react somewhat differently from parents to whom stuttering means little more than an unfamiliar word they have seldom heard or used. And the way they react to the speech of their own children seems to have a great deal to do with determining whether or not their children will develop the self-consciousness about speech, the anxiety-tensions, that make for stuttering. What runs in families (in those cases in which something seems to) appears to be a background of experience with stuttering and therefore a kind of concern, a set of attitudes and a tendency to deal in certain ways with children who are just learning to talk, and with the normal imperfections in their speech. It seems a fair conclusion, and a generally useful one, that these attitudes and training policies in turn tend, to a limited extent, to lead to stuttering in the children of the families in which the attitudes and policies have become traditional.*

In some such words the semantogenic hypothesis, as the writer (R-58) has termed it, may be at least roughly indicated. The relative merits of this and the genetic hypothesis may be more effectively weighed after all the data to be presented in this report have been considered.

* For a more fully developed consideration of the possible reasons why the stuttering problem tends to run in families see Johnson (R61, pp. 225–234).

The Number of Children Who Were Twins

The question of a possible relation between stuttering and twinning has been raised by Berry (R6), Luchsinger (R75), Nelson, Hunter, and Walter (R87), Seeman (R100), and Wepman (R121, 122). In general, these investigators have reported data from which they conclude that more twins than non-twins stutter and that there is more stuttering in families in which twinning occurs than in families in which twinning does not occur. Seeman and Nelson, Hunter, and Walter conclude, in addition, that it is more often true of identical than of fraternal twins that both members of a pair stutter rather than one only. Luchsinger, however, did not confirm this, nor did Graf (R44) in a more recent study of 552 pairs of twins. Graf reported: "In one out of seven pairs of presumably identical twins both twins stuttered, while in two out of nine nonidentical pairs both twins stuttered. In two pairs, in each of which only one member stuttered, the information obtained did not permit a clear judgment as to whether they were identical or nonidentical." * Graf found 21 persons, or 1.90 per cent of her total sample of 1,104, who stuttered. This is probably somewhat higher than the percentage of persons in the general population who stutter, but it is markedly below the figure, 20 per cent of 200 twin pairs, reported by Nelson, Hunter, and Walter. The percentage of school-age children who stutter has been reported by Blanton (R10), Milisen and Johnson (R82), Mills and Streit (R83), Root (R93), Wallin (R116), and Schindler (R96) as 0.72, 2.5, 1.5, 1.2, 0.7, and 0.55, respectively. The American Speech and Hearing Association's Committee on the Midcentury White House Conference on Children and Youth (R22) estimated that 0.7 per cent of school children stutter.

In Study III no child in the control group and only one in the experimental group was a twin. In Study II one nonstuttering child and two stuttering children were members of twin pairs. It was stated that one other experimental group child in Study II may have been a twin, and that supposedly a miscarriage at three months resulted in loss of the other member of the pair. Of the 200 stuttering children in both studies, then, three, or 1.5 per cent, were definitely members of twin pairs, and a fourth child may have been, and of the 200 nonstuttering children, one, or 0.5 per cent, was a twin. Graf (R44) found

* In Study II the question of type of twin was not raised; in Study III the one child who was a twin could not be unequivocally classified as belonging to an identical or nonidentical pair because the other member of the pair was lost during pregnancy, although this fact would appear to constitute presumptive evidence that the members of this pair were nonidentical. See 37, in the Summary Table.

1.29 per cent of 85,680 school children surveyed by her to be twins. Hamlett (R48), in a study of United States census reports from 1922 to 1930, found that 1.13 per cent of whites and 1.42 per cent of Negroes were twins.

It is also to be noted that in Study III five parents, two fathers and three mothers, in the control group, and three parents, two fathers and one mother, in the experimental group, were twins.

The informants in Study III were asked whether there were any twins among their relatives; 49 (21 fathers and 28 mothers) in the control group and 40 (19 fathers and 21 mothers) in the experimental group reported relatives who were twins.*

Birth Order

Proportions of Only Children. Twenty-five subjects in the experimental group and 15 in the control group were only children; the difference is not statistically significant at the 5 per cent level of confidence.† It is to be noted, however, that in Study II also there was a corresponding nonsignificant difference in the same direction, 11 of the 50 members of the stuttering group and 5 of the nonstuttering group being only children (see code "1" in 725). When the two samples of Study II and Study III are combined, there are 36 only children out of 200 in the experimental groups and 20 out of 200 in the control groups, and the difference between these figures is statistically significant at the 5 per cent level of confidence. Relevant supporting data have also been reported in a study of 522 stutterers by Rotter (R94).

Position in Family. The order of birth of the children in the experimental and control groups in Study III is shown in 726. The data may be summarized by noting that in the control group of 150 children, 15 were only children as has been indicated, 41 were oldest, 53 youngest, and 41 were middle children (second, third, fourth, fifth, or sixth in order of birth) in their respective families; and for the experimental group the corresponding figures were 25 only children as previously stated, 56 oldest, 45 youngest, and 24 middle children (second, third, or fourth in order of birth). It is to be considered that the oldest child in any family occupied the position of an only child until the arrival of a sibling, and, therefore, by combining the only

* The detailed data from both studies are presented in 790. The data from Study II are not wholly comparable with those from Study III, because more types of relatives were included as indicated by responses 22–26 in 790.

† See 726. Note that one child in the control group was an only child by virtue of the fact that a sibling had died at birth.

and oldest children in each group in Study III it is found that in the control group 56, or 37 per cent, and in the experimental group 81, or 54 per cent, of the children were, or for a time had been, only children. The difference between these two percentages is significant at the 2 per cent level, as indicated in Table 15.

CHAPTER 4

The Parents

In study iii each set of parents in the experimental group was placed in that group by virtue of the fact that a child of theirs had been accepted in the experimental group of children, according to the criteria set forth in Chapter 1. For each such child, another child of like sex, age, and socioeconomic level of family, who was not considered by his or her parents to be a stutterer, was selected for inclusion in the control group of children — and the parents of each such child became, by virtue of that fact, members of the control group of parents. The experimental and control groups of parents were compared with reference to many different dimensions and within each group the mothers were compared with the fathers in a variety of ways; the consequent findings are presented in this chapter.

Basic Data

Table 10 summarizes information concerning the ages of the parents in the experimental and control groups at time of marriage (676), at time of birth of the child participating in the present study (8), and at date of interview (7). The control group mothers were, on the average, approximately nine months younger than the experimental group mothers on the date of interview, but this difference was not statistically significant at the 5 per cent level ($t = 1.80$; df $= 298$). The control group fathers were, on the average, approximately one year and five months younger than the experimental group fathers, and this difference was statistically significant at the 1 per cent level of confidence ($t = 5.26$; df $= 298$).

Table 11 summarizes information concerning the geographical areas of residence of the 600 parents. The two groups were much alike in this respect, and the bulk of the parents in both groups had been long-time residents of the midwestern section of the United States. There was no significant difference with respect to rural-urban background between either the two groups of fathers or the two groups of mothers (11).

Table 10. Mean Ages, in Years and Months, of Experimental and Control Group
Mothers and Fathers at Time of Present Marriage (676), at Birth of Child (8),
and at Date of Interview (7)

Item	Control Group		Experimental Group	
	Fathers (N = 150)	Mothers (N = 150)	Fathers (N = 150)	Mothers (N = 150)
At marriage				
Mean	24:2	22:0	26:0	23:4
S.D.	3:9	2:10	4:6	3:5
At birth of child				
Mean	29:6	27:4	30:10	28:1
S.D.	5:2	4:9	5:7	4:11
At interview				
Mean*	34:5	32:3	35:10	33:0
S.D.	5:2	4:9	5:10	5:1

* The difference between group means was significant at the 1 per cent level for
fathers; nonsignificant for mothers. Other differences between control and experimental
group means were not significant, according to t test, at the 5 per cent level.

Table 11. Geographical Areas of Residence of Experimental and
Control Group Mothers and Fathers (10)

Section of United States	Experimental Group		Control Group		Total
	Mothers	Fathers	Mothers	Fathers	
Midwestern	137	139	134	140	550
Northeastern	6	4	6	5	21
Southeastern	0	0	3	0	3
Southern	2	2	2	2	8
Southwestern	0	0	0	1	1
Western	3	2	3	0	8
Other areas	2	3	2	2	9
Total	150	150	150	150	600

Socioeconomic Status and Education

The numbers of experimental and control group families falling
within each of five socioeconomic classes, as defined by Warner,
Meeker, and Eels (R117), are shown in 623, and for each group the
range, mean, median, and 90th percentile of the index of status characteristics are presented in 622. The two groups were matched for
socioeconomic status, and an attempt was made to match families
not only with respect to socioeconomic class, as such, but also within
the class with regard to index. The mean socioeconomic indexes were
45.5 and 45.3 for the experimental and control groups, respectively,
with corresponding standard deviations of 10.7 and 10.4. Neither the
variances nor the means differed significantly. Approximately 70 per

cent of the families in both groups were in the middle and upper classes, although only seven families were classified in the upper class, while 45 per cent were in the lower-middle class (623). In Study II 80 per cent of the families investigated were in the middle and upper classes.

Warner does not indicate the proportion of families in the general population falling in each of his classes, but on the basis of such information as was available Darley expressed the opinion that his distribution of families in Study II was "markedly different from that of the general population, with a greater than normal sample from the upper-middle and lower-middle classes, and a smaller than normal sample from the lower classes" (R24, p. 97). Since the two groups of families were matched in both studies, the status of the experimental group families was the base of reference. It is to be kept in mind that in Study II most of the experimental group families were in some measure selected by virtue of the fact that they availed themselves of the clinical services of the University of Iowa. It is possible that the apparently somewhat lower mean socioeconomic status of the experimental group families in Study III was due to the fact that while all of them were served in or by the authority of university speech clinics, and were responsive to the appeals used or implied and the services made available to them in this investigation, relatively more of them than of the families in Study II may have been included because of the cooperation of professional workers, agencies, and organizations, and so may have been selected on a somewhat less restricted, or more nearly random, basis. Even so, in Study III, too, the distribution of the families in Warner's social classes appears definitely skewed, with relatively more of them in the middle and upper classes than is probably true for the general population. To the extent that this indication validly suggests that stuttering is a part of the price paid for civilization, it is of obvious theoretical and practical significance and invites further investigation.

For four additional items regarding the socioeconomic status and education of the parents there were statistically significant group differences, for either the mothers or fathers, or both, and these are summarized in Table 12. In general, compared with the experimental group, the control group parents had completed more formal education, rated more highly the degree to which the father's employment demonstrated and used his abilities, and rated their economic status more highly. More of the experimental group fathers gave living conditions as the main reason for moving whenever the family moved, and more of the control group fathers gave business reasons. The con-

Table 12. Results of Chi-Square Analysis of Responses to Items Pertaining to Socioeconomic Status and Education of Parents on Which the Experimental and Control Groups Differed Significantly

Item	Direction of Difference	Level of Confidence	Remarks
Level of education (13)	Control group mothers had completed more formal education than experimental group mothers	2%	Fathers followed similar trend, significant at 5% level
How well-to-do do you consider yourself to be now? (625)	Control group mothers rated themselves higher than experimental group mothers	5%	Fathers did not differ significantly
How well do you think your husband's present employment uses and demonstrates his abilities? (630)	Control group mothers rated the employment of their husbands higher than experimental group mothers	1%	Fathers followed similar trend when rating own employment (1% level) and when estimating wives' rating of their (fathers') employment (1% level)
What was the main reason for moving whenever the family moved? (633)	More experimental group fathers gave living conditions as the main reason, whereas control group fathers tended to give business reasons	1%	Mothers did not differ significantly

77

trol group parents had attended school more years on the average than had the experimental group parents (13). The difference was significant at the 1 per cent level ($t = 2.71$; df $= 298$) for the experimental and control group mothers, whose means were 12.6 and 13.4 years, respectively. Corresponding values for the fathers were 13.3 and 14.6 years, and the difference between these means was also significant at the 1 per cent level ($t = 3.33$; df $= 298$).

The two groups did not differ with respect to regularity of employment (624), security of job (627), membership in college social societies (14), degree to which mothers liked their husbands' employment (629), frequency of change in residence (632), degree of pride in spouses' accomplishments and abilities (635), socioeconomic ratings of fathers (642), number of magazines subscribed to (648), number having adequate play space for children inside and outside, regardless of whether the house was owned or rented (649 and 650), and socioeconomic rating of the fathers of the parents during the parents' preschool years (805) and youth, 12–18 years of age (812).

Religion

Significantly more control than experimental group fathers and mothers were of the Protestant faith (15). There was no significant difference between the control and experimental group parents in reported amount of church attendance (17).

Social Adjustment and Attitudes

Fourteen items concerning social adjustments and attitudes of the parents were analyzed. For eight of them chi-square tests indicated statistically significant group differences, and these are presented in Table 13. The control group mothers and fathers were evaluated by the interviewers as having more social interests than the experimental group mothers and fathers. The control group mothers belonged to more organizations, gave higher ratings to the value of friendships, and participated more frequently in musical activities than did the experimental group mothers. The control group parents held more offices in organizations than did the experimental group parents. The experimental group parents claimed to feel, however, that they could adjust to new situations and friends better than the control group parents thought they could.

The two groups did not differ in frequency of attendance at movies (654), frequency of dancing (655), playing cards (656), vacations (660), or parties (661), or degree of concern over impressions made on others (668).

Table 13. Results of Chi-Square Analysis of Responses to Items Concerning Social Attitudes and
Adjustments on Which the Experimental and Control Group Parents Differed Significantly

Item	Direction of Difference	Level of Confidence	Remarks
How many community organizations do you belong to? (652)	Control group mothers belonged to more organizations than experimental group mothers	1%	Fathers did not differ significantly
In how many organizations do you hold an office? (653)	Control group mothers held more offices in organizations than experimental group mothers	1%	Fathers followed similar trend, significant at 1% level
How frequently do you take part in musical activities? (657)	Control group mothers more frequently than experimental group mothers	1%	Fathers did not differ significantly
Interviewer's evaluation of informant's social interests (662)	Control group mothers rated as having more social interests than experimental group mothers	1%	Fathers followed similar trend, significant at 1% level
How important are your friendships to you? (664)	More important to control group mothers than to experimental group mothers	1%	Fathers did not differ significantly
How important are friendships to your husband (wife)? (665)	More important to control group fathers (according to mothers) than to experimental group fathers	5%	Fathers did not differ significantly in rating their wives
How easily do you adjust to new situations and new friends? (669)	More experimental than control group mothers said they have unusual poise and ability	1%	Fathers followed similar trend, significant at 2% level
How easily does your wife (husband) adjust to new situations and new friends? (670)	More experimental than control group mothers said their spouses have unusual poise and ability	2%	Fathers followed similar trend, significant at 2% level

Table 14. Results of Chi-Square Analysis of Responses to Items Concerning Marital Relationships on
Which the Experimental and Control Group Parents Differed Significantly

Item	Direction of Difference	Level of Confidence	Remarks
How well satisfied are you with your present marital relationship? (696)	More control than experimental group mothers were completely satisfied	1%	Fathers did not differ significantly
As a general rule, how tense are you? (699)	Experimental group mothers rated themselves as comparatively more tense	5%	Fathers did not differ significantly
Do you consider the other parent to be too demanding of the child? (711)	More experimental than control group mothers answered "yes"	5%	Fathers did not differ significantly
How do you think your married life compares in happiness with that of your married friends? (719)	Control group mothers rated themselves more favorably than did experimental group mothers	1%	Fathers did not differ significantly
Do you consider the other parent to have spoiled the child? (709)	More experimental than control group mothers answered "yes"	2%	Fathers did not differ significantly
How much do you quarrel, as compared with your married friends? (679)	Experimental group fathers reported more quarreling than control group fathers	5%	Mothers did not differ significantly
How readily do you confide in others? (698)	Control group fathers confided more often than experimental group fathers	5%	Mothers did not differ significantly
How tense is your wife (husband)? (704)	Experimental group fathers rated their wives as more tense than control group fathers rated their wives	2%	Mothers did not differ significantly in rating their husbands
Do you consider the other parent to be too easygoing concerning the child? (710)	More experimental than control group fathers answered "yes"	5%	Mothers did not differ significantly
Do you believe that the other parent worries too much? (712)	More experimental than control group fathers answered "yes"	5%	Mothers did not differ significantly

80

Additional data concerning the adjustment patterns of the two groups of parents are to be found in Chapter 7, in which the analysis of responses to the Minnesota Multiphasic Personality Inventory is presented.

Marital Relationships

Too few parents in either group had been previously married (671), or separated from their present spouses (678), and too few were dissatisfied with the way their spouses were rearing their children (694), to warrant statistical evaluation of responses to these items. Moreover, the usual moods of the parents as rated by their spouses could not be categorized into a contingency table suitable for chi-square analysis (724).

Ten items for which chi-square values indicated statistically significant group differences for either the mothers or fathers, or both, are summarized in Table 14. The differences for all these items indicated better marital status and relationship in the control than in the experimental group families. The experimental group respondents seemed to be more dissatisfied with the behavior of their spouses, including their behavior toward the child in question in each case, and they also reported more behavior which would be likely to create tense, undesirably emotional, and generally unfavorable home environments.

No significant group differences were found for the remaining similar items, which covered the degree to which the husbands and wives said they enjoyed being with each other (677); the degree of differences over religion (680), use of money (681), discipline of the children (682), amount of social life desired (683), kind of entertainment preferred (684), types of friends preferred (685), amount of ambition (686), attitudes toward husband's employment (687), attitudes toward wife's employment (688), feelings about in-laws (689), notions about how to spend vacations (690), preferred recreation (691), politics (692), and radio and television listening (693); how well satisfied each parent was with the other parent's participation in the rearing of the child in each case (694); degree to which they confided in each other (697); extent to which they were easygoing (701); standards of neatness (703 and 708); amount of time spent with child (518); degree to which each feels the other is inconsistent in handling the child (715); frequency with which one of the parents sides with the child against other parent (716 and 717); and desire to be single (718).

Social Home Environment

Of the items concerning social home environment, there were three, dealing with the nature of the fathers' prolonged absences from home, that yielded distributions unfavorable for computation of chi-square values. Military service was the main reason for prolonged absence in both groups (750 and 751). Three items were evaluated by means of t tests. For five items, as responded to by the mothers, there were statistically significant chi-square values. The fathers differed on two additional items. Table 15 presents a summary of these seven items. As has already been observed, more of the experimental than control group children were oldest or only children. More of the experimental than control group mothers enjoyed the oldest child the most. Control group families more frequently went on picnics, according to the mothers but not the fathers. According to the fathers but not the mothers more of the experimental group families never played games together. The control group parents rated their neighbors as more friendly than did the experimental group, although the experimental group mothers reported that their neighbors treated their children more favorably than did the control group mothers. More experimental than control group fathers had been absent from home for six months or more, according to the fathers but not according to the mothers.

The two groups were essentially similar with respect to the mean total amount of time the mothers and fathers, respectively, had been separated from their children (754 and 755). The median value was one month for all four subgroups; the means were greater than the medians, but the group means were not significantly different for either the fathers or mothers.

The mean numbers of children of the present marriages of the control and experimental group parents were 2.75 and 2.32, respectively, with standard deviations of 1.18 and 1.05 (725). The F test of variance was not significant, and the difference between the means was statistically significant at the 1 per cent level ($t = 4.85$; df $= 298$). Consideration is to be given, however, to the non-normal character of the two distributions.

The two groups of parents did not differ significantly in their answers to questions concerning intention to have more children (727), number of wives having outside employment (730), number of families in which both parents worked during the infancy or early years of the child's life (731), frequency with which both parents were home evenings (732), number of persons other than members of the immediate family who had lived in the home at any one time (735);

Table 15. Results of Chi-Square Analysis of Responses to Items Concerning Social Home Environment on Which the Responses of the Experimental and Control Group Parents Differed Significantly

Item	Direction of Difference	Level of Confidence	Remarks
What is the birth order of the child? (726)	More experimental than control group children were oldest or only children according to mothers	2%	Question not asked of fathers
How friendly are your neighbors? (741)	Control group mothers rated their neighbors as more friendly than experimental group mothers rated theirs	5%	Fathers followed similar trend, significant at 1% level
How do your neighbors usually treat your child? (742)	Experimental group mothers rated their neighbors more favorably than control group mothers rated theirs	2%	Fathers did not differ significantly
How often do you and your family go all together on picnics? (748)	More experimental than control group mothers answered "once a year or less"	1%	Fathers did not differ significantly
What is the age of the child you enjoy most? (599)	More experimental than control mothers answered "oldest child"	5%	Fathers did not differ significantly
How often do you and your family play parlor or card games together? (747)	More experimental than control group fathers answered "never"	1%	Mothers did not differ significantly
Has the father been absent from home for any extended period of time (six months or more)? (750)	More experimental than control group fathers answered "yes"	5%	Mothers did not differ significantly

83

length of time this maximum number had lived in the home (736); frequency with which the child met visitors in the home (737); degree of belief in having "child seen and not heard" (738 and 739); degree to which the parents liked their neighbors (740); how often the family had taken part in auto trips (744) and movies (745); amount of wholehearted laughing done by the parents (748 and 749); sex of the child enjoyed most (600); whether or not the child in question was enjoyed most (598); and whether the child in question was said by his or her parents to be the brightest (606), slowest (607), or the one of whom they demanded the most (608).

Family Health

For three items concerning family health the distributions were unfavorable for computation of chi-square values: nearly all children of both groups had good appetites (169), not very many children had many food dislikes (173), and only two fathers and three mothers in the control group and two fathers and four mothers in the experimental group reported persons with epilepsy in their families (772). Only one item yielded a significant chi-square value. The experimental group fathers rated themselves more highly than did the control group fathers with regard to the amount of energy they felt themselves to have (793); the difference was statistically significant at the 2 per cent level of confidence. The mothers did not differ on this item.

The two groups did not differ significantly with respect to the number of twins in the family (790), present health of the parents (756 and 758), number of times members of the family had been ill (759), total time covered by illnesses in the family (760), the places where ill persons in the family were taken care of (761), the persons who cared for them (762), what was done with the child during family illnesses (763), how much the parents worried about getting sick (764 and 765), the parents' appetites (766 and 768), how well the parents slept (767 and 769), the parents' food dislikes (770 and 771), diabetes (773) and allergies (774) in the families, and frequency with which the parents used alcohol (795 and 796).

Handedness

There were no group differences with regard to the number of parents who had had their own handedness changed (776). The mean scores of the four parental subgroups on the Brief Handedness Questionnaire (775) were 93, 93, 91, and 95 for the control group fathers and mothers and experimental group fathers and mothers, respectively. On the Iowa Unimanual Hand Usage Questionnaire (783) a mean score of 1.3 was made by both groups of fathers, and both groups of mothers scored a mean of 1.5. The median value for both groups of fathers was 1.5; the median of the control group mothers was 1.6 and that of the experimental group mothers 1.7. As has been stated in Chapter 3, the mean scores of the two groups of children on this questionnaire (788) were 1.3 and 1.4 for the control and experimental group children, respectively; for both groups the median was 1.6.

The numbers of persons per family (the child's parents, siblings, uncles, aunts, and grandparents — blood relatives only) who were right-handed, left-handed, mixed as to handedness, or undetermined (784–787) are indicative of no appreciable group differences. The handedness of the informants' siblings and parents appeared to be very similar; 94 per cent of the siblings of the experimental group mothers and 92 per cent of those of the control group mothers, and 95 per cent of the siblings of both groups of fathers, were right-handed (777–779). Of the maternal grandmothers of the experimental group children, 97 per cent were right-handed, and of the maternal grandmothers of the control group children 92 per cent were right-handed; corresponding percentages for the paternal grandmothers were 93 and 96 (780). Of the maternal grandfathers of the experimental group children 93 per cent were right-handed, and of the maternal grandfathers of the control group children 93 per cent, the same proportion, were right-handed; corresponding percentages for the paternal grandfathers were 97 and 92 (781). The differences between the experimental and control groups were not significant for either the mothers or fathers for any of these items (777–781).

Speech Attitudes and Characteristics

The parents' answers to thirty-one questions were involved in this section of the analysis. Two of these items yielded distributions unfavorable for computation of chi-square values: too few parents tried to prevent their children from coming in contact with stutterers (334), or compared them with stutterers (337).

The statistically significant chi-square values are summarized in Table 16. These items reflect the experimental group parents' greater concern, worry, and sensitivity about their children's speech. It is to be duly considered that the responses in question represent the attitudes of the two groups of parents, not before the problem of stuttering arose, but at the time of the interview, eighteen months on the average after the reported onset of the problem. The greater concern of the experimental group parents may well have been in some degree

Table 16. Results of Chi-Square Analysis of Responses to Items Pertaining to Speech Attitudes and Characteristics of Parents on Which the Experimental and Control Groups Differed Significantly

Item	Direction of Difference	Level of Confidence	Remarks
Have you ever been concerned about the child's speech? (190)	More experimental than control group mothers answered "yes"	1%	Fathers followed similar trend, significant at 1% level
Has your husband (wife) ever been concerned about the child's speech? (191)	More experimental than control group mothers answered "yes"	1%	Fathers followed similar trend, significant at 1% level
Has any other relative ever been concerned about the child's speech? (192)	More experimental than control group mothers answered "yes"	1%	Fathers followed similar trend, significant at 1% level
How concerned are you now about the child's stuttering (nonfluency)? (321)	Experimental group mothers more concerned than control group	1%	Fathers followed similar trend, significant at 1% level
How concerned is your husband (wife) now? (322)	Experimental group mothers rated husbands as more concerned	1%	Fathers followed similar trend, significant at 1% level
How ashamed are you of the child's speech now? (323)	More experimental than control group mothers were ashamed	1%	Fathers did not differ significantly
How ashamed is your wife (husband) of the child's speech now? (324)	More experimental than control group mothers said spouses were ashamed	5%	Fathers followed similar trend, significant at 5% level
Describe your impression of what normal speech is like (364)	More control than experimental group fathers accepted nonfluencies as part of normal speech	1%	Mothers followed similar trend, significant at 1% level

Table 17. Results of Chi-Square Analysis of Responses to Items Concerning Parental Attitudes and Standards Concerning Child Development on Which the Experimental and Control Group Parents Differed Significantly

Item	Direction of Difference	Level of Confidence	Remarks
Do you believe there is any relationship between the child's handedness and his developing stuttering? (110)	More control than experimental group mothers answered "yes"	1%	Fathers followed similar trend, significant at 1% level
Does your wife (husband) believe in such a relationship? (111)	More control than experimental group mothers answered "yes"	1%	Fathers answering for their wives followed similar trend, significant at 1% level
How helpful were developmental norms to you in rearing the child? (122)	More experimental than control group mothers said norms were disturbing or not helpful	1%	More experimental than control group fathers were not aware of norms, significant at 5% level
At times when the child has been ill, how much attention did he or she get? (163)	More experimental than control group mothers said children were "waited on constantly" or were "spoiled and indulged excessively" when ill	1%	Fathers followed similar trend, significant at 1% level
Do you wish the child were more or less alert? (378)	More experimental than control group mothers wished the child were more alert	5%	Fathers did not differ significantly
Do you wish the child were more or less cautious? (389)	More experimental than control group mothers wished their children were different, either more or less cautious	5%	Fathers did not differ significantly

a function of the problem, or an integral part of it. With this understood, then, it is to be noted that more experimental than control group parents indicated that they felt, and that they believed their spouses felt, some degree of shame over their children's speech. In describing "normal speech" more control than experimental group parents indicated that they accepted nonfluencies as part of normal speech (364).

The interviewers judged more experimental than control group fathers, twenty-six and four, respectively, to have some kind of defective speech; it is to be noted that except for ten of the experimental group fathers for whom some degree of stuttering was reported, twelve of the twenty-six were said to have made minor articulation errors and four were reported to have spoken with a foreign dialect (797).

No significant group differences were found with respect to the amount of speech the parents used during the interviews, as rated by the interviewers (798), the parents' reactions to stutterers they had known (330), the degree of importance attached by the parents to contact of the child with a stutterer (333), the amounts of reading the parents had done about stuttering (over 95 per cent in both groups of parents had read in material on stuttering only slightly or not at all; 75 per cent of the experimental group parents and 70 per cent of the control group parents had done no reading about the problem; 338), the degree of concern the parents had felt over whether their own children might develop stuttering (340 and 341), the degree to which the parents had corrected each other's pronunciation (354), the amount of talking done by the parents or someone else for their children (186), the number of family members reported to be talkative (187), and the number of children who had had physical trouble with some part of the peripheral speech mechanism (193).

Attitudes and Standards Concerning Children's Development

The few items in this category for which chi-square values were statistically significant are summarized in Table 17. More control than experimental group parents stated a belief in a relationship between handedness or change of handedness and the development of stuttering. The experimental group mothers had found developmental norms more disturbing and less helpful than control group mothers had; more experimental than control group fathers were unaware of these norms. More experimental than control group parents indicated that their children were "waited on constantly" or "spoiled and indulged excessively" when ill. More experimental than control group mothers wished their children were more alert and either more or less cautious.

Nonsignificant differences were obtained with respect to the proportions expressing a desire to have their children be more or less mischievous (374), cooperative (380), aggressive (386), self-confident (392), popular (396), and well-mannered (405).

Chi-square treatment did not reveal a significant difference between the two groups of parents with respect to the degree of satisfaction with the intelligence of their children (596), or with regard to their ways of comparing their own with neighborhood children in intelligence (597). With regard to encouraging or discouraging their children to play alone (508), and to desiring to have their children's friends come to their homes (369–370), the two groups were similar.

The following characteristics or problems were reported for insufficient numbers of children to warrant chi-square analyses: parents' concern over their children's sleeplessness (409), nightmares (411), bed wetting (413), hitting other children (427), fighting (429), jealousy (431), crying at school (435), lying (437), hurting pets (441), constipation (443), nail biting (445), face twitching (447), fainting (449), bullying (460), and disobedience (463). Other distributions were unfavorable for chi-square analysis because too few parents wanted their children to be more attractive (475), too few children showed left-handed preferences (96 and 100), too few parents had changed their children's handedness (102 and 103), too few children were reported to have written backwards (107), and too few parents had discouraged left-handedness (108 and 109). Another item that did not prove amenable to chi-square treatment was 58; the responses to this question may be summarized by saying that fourteen of the experimental group and nine of the control group did not hold the child during bottle feeding, according to the fathers, but the answers of the two groups of mothers differed only by one, and so far as the other coded responses to this item were concerned the two groups of parents were essentially alike.

The number of items pertaining to parents' attitudes and standards concerning the development of their children to which the responses of the experimental and control group informants were generally similar was so large that reference is to be made to the Summary Table for further and detailed negative findings.

Responses to eight items (112–119) pertaining to the parents' standards of child development are summarized in Table 18. The experimental group mothers indicated that they had consistently higher standards than the control group mothers, although the differences are not statistically significant for all eight items. The experimental group fathers followed a similar but somewhat less pronounced trend.

Table 18. Means and Standard Deviations, in Months, of the Ages at Which the Experimental and Control Group Parents Believed a Child Should Achieve Various Abilities (112–119)

Item	Control Group			Experimental Group			Diff.	Significance Level of t
	N	Mean	S.D.	N	Mean	S.D.		
According to Mothers								
Walk alone	150	18.04	3.71	150	17.45	3.53	.59	5%
Have bowel control	149	28.60	8.96	148	25.92	9.44	2.68	5%
Have bladder control (day)	149	30.15	8.36	148	27.31	6.20	2.84	*
Have bladder control (night)	148	43.19	19.05	146	37.61	17.18	5.58	*
Speak words	149	22.81	7.93	150	18.72	6.74	4.09	1%
Speak sentences	148	30.18	7.96	150	28.19	7.88	1.99	1%
Speak intelligibly	149	40.50	12.19	150	38.77	13.38	1.73	NS
Speak fluently	148	52.17	15.66	188	48.90	16.39	3.27	NS
According to Fathers								
Walk alone	148	18.39	6.14	148	17.17	4.57	1.22	*
Have bowel control	141	28.13	9.64	142	25.37	9.91	2.76	1%
Have bladder control (day)	143	29.43	7.30	144	25.66	10.48	3.77	*
Have bladder control (night)	140	43.44	23.41	144	37.70	17.84	5.74	*
Speak words	147	22.20	9.19	146	20.29	7.09	.09	*
Speak sentences	147	30.78	10.56	145	30.66	9.13	.12	NS
Speak intelligibly	149	38.26	12.46	146	41.36	12.28	3.10	1%
Speak fluently	142	53.12	18.92	149	54.92	18.60	1.80	NS

* F test for equal variance was statistically significant and t test was not computed.

Table 19. Results of Chi-Square Analysis of Responses to Items Pertaining to the Parents' Disciplinary Practices and Attitudes on Which the Experimental and Control Groups Differed Significantly

Item	Direction of Difference	Level of Confidence	Remarks
How frequently is the child punished? (536)	Experimental group mothers reported a higher frequency than control group mothers	5%	Fathers did not differ significantly
Is the child punished regularly for quarreling with other children? (554)	More experimental than control group mothers answered "no"	1%	Fathers followed similar trend, significant at 5% level
Do you feel your wife (husband) is too strict, too lax, or about right? (564)	More control than experimental group mothers answered "about right"	5%	Fathers did not differ significantly
How much does it bother you when your child makes a mess around the house? (568)	More experimental than control group mothers were bothered a great deal	2%	Fathers did not differ significantly
How well behaved is your child? (535)	More control than experimental group mothers rated child favorably	2%	Fathers did not differ significantly
Is the child punished for talking back? (543)	More control than experimental group fathers answered "yes"	5%	Mothers did not differ significantly

91

Disciplinary Practices and Attitudes

Significant chi-square values for items concerning disciplinary practices and attitudes of the two groups of parents are presented in Table 19. In general, the experimental group parents seemed a bit less satisfied with their disciplinary relations with their children. More control than experimental group mothers felt that their children were well behaved. More control group mothers felt that their husbands were "about right" rather than too strict or too lax in dealing with the children. More experimental than control group mothers were bothered "a great deal" when the child "made a mess around the house."

The experimental group parents, especially the mothers, seemed not to have their attitudes toward punishment well integrated with their punishment practices. When asked how frequently their children were punished (536), the experimental group mothers reported higher frequencies than did the control group mothers, and yet for the only two specific questions in this connection for which differences were significant, it was the control group parents who more often reported giving punishment; more control group parents said their children were "punished regularly for quarreling with other children" (554), and more control group fathers said their children were punished for "talking back" (543). Moreover, the parents were asked whether or not their children were punished for each of eighteen activities (541–558), and their answers, summarized in 559 and in Table 20, indicate that the control group children were punished for a greater mean number of activities, three of the four mean differences shown in Table 20 being significant at the 5 or 1 per cent level.

Table 20. Means and Standard Deviations of Number of Activities (N = 18) for
Which Children Were Punished, According to Mothers and Fathers
of the Control and Experimental Groups (541–558)

Parent	Control Group			Experimental Group			Significance Level of t
	N	Mean	S.D.	N	Mean	S.D.	
Mothers							
All	150	3.77	2.66	150	3.27	2.00	5%
Punish group* . . .	137	4.13	2.51	124	3.95	2.35	NS
Fathers							
All	150	4.04	2.75	150	3.24	3.04	1%
Punish group* . . .	135	4.49	2.52	122	3.98	2.90	5%

* Exclusive of parents who reportedly punished their children for none of the 18 activities.

In any attempt to interpret this apparent discrepancy between feeling and performance on the part of the experimental group parents, as compared with the control group, due attention is to be given to the related finding of no significant differences between the groups as to the amount of punishment the parents gave their own children compared with what the parents believed to be the amount of punishment the average child receives (537); the frequency with which the children were reportedly punished between the ages of one and four years (538); the number of children punished for messing up their own rooms, for spilling, disobedience, interrupting conversations, lying, swearing, fighting with other children, being rude, destroying things, and getting dirty (541–558); the parents' ratings of their own strictness (561 and 563); how much fathers worry about spoiling their children (566 and 567); and the method of punishment reported as being most effective (540).

Comparative Analysis of Evaluative Responses

A comparative analysis of the responses of the two groups of parents to 45 items in Tables 12–17 and 19 yielded the following results:

1. For 40 items the control group responses were the more favorable, or less indicative of concern, discontent, or difficulty, or involved higher ratings
    a. For 18 items this was true for mothers only
    b. For 8 items this was true for fathers only
    c. For 14 items this was true for both mothers and fathers
2. For 5 items the experimental group responses were the more favorable, or less indicative of concern, discontent, or difficulty, or involved higher ratings
    a. For 1 item this was true for mothers only
    b. For 1 item this was true for fathers only
    c. For 3 items this was true for both mothers and fathers
3. On 8 items the two groups of mothers did not differ significantly
4. On 18 items the two groups of fathers did not differ significantly

The difference between 40 and 5 was significant at the 1 per cent level ($z = 5.23$). The subgroup totals were too small to warrant computation of significance values.

Intragroup Comparisons of Mothers and Fathers

The general hypothesis that stuttering in children reflects tension in the home is probably widely held, at least — and perhaps nearly always — in the form of a vague hunch. It would seem that one of the meaningful ways to test the validity of this notion lies in the sort of analysis that is now to be presented. This consisted of an investigation of the differences between the responses made independently by the mothers and fathers within the experimental and control groups, respectively. The analysis involved simple intragroup, as well as intergroup intragroup, comparisons, and the nature of these can be made clear most readily by presenting the results of the analysis.

Intragroup comparisons were made in order to determine the degree to which mothers and fathers agreed on various items. In Table 21 a breakdown is presented of the number of items selected for analysis, of chi-square tables examined, and of chi-square values computed. The discrepancy between the number of chi-square tables examined and chi-square values computed is due to small theoretical frequencies and patterns of categorization of responses to various items. More chi-square tables than items were examined because cross-comparisons were made on some items, including (1) comparison of mothers' and fathers' self-ratings, (2) comparison of mothers' and fathers' ratings of each other, (3) comparison of mother's rating of self and father's rating of mother, and (4) comparison of father's rating of self and mother's rating of father. A total of 987 chi-square values were computed in comparing fathers with mothers. Of these, 135 were statistically significant at or beyond the 5 per cent level. The statistically significant differences are summarized in Tables 22–37.

ITEMS ON WHICH BOTH GROUPS OF PARENTS DISAGREED

The statistically significant differences between husbands and wives were about equally divided between the experimental and control groups, and on many items both groups differed in the same direction. For example, both groups of fathers had had more education than the mothers; fathers rated their own employment as being more challenging than it was rated by the mothers; fathers belonged to more organizations than the mothers; fathers rated their wives' appearance as better than it was rated by the wives themselves; more fathers than mothers were more dissatisfied with the way fathers participated in the home training and discipline of the children than the fathers were with the way the mothers were rearing the children; mothers confided in the fathers more than the fathers confided in the mothers; mothers were more tense than their husbands (self-ratings); fathers were more easygoing than their wives (self-ratings); fathers rated their wives as more irritable than the mothers rated their husbands; mothers rated their own standards of conduct higher than they were

Table 21. Intragroup Comparisons Involving Evaluation of Differences between Fathers and Mothers within the Experimental and Control Groups

Item	Items Examined	Chi-Square Tables Examined	Chi-Square Values Computed		Chi-Square Values Significant at 5% Level	
			Experimental	Control	Experimental	Control
Birth history and early development of the child	29	29	27	25	0	4
Health and physical status	2	2	1	1	0	0
Speech development of the child	19	19	18	18	0	0
Social development of the child	96	98	89	91	6	4
School history of the child	4	4	2	2	0	0
Basic data on parents	2	2	1	1	0	0
Socioeconomic status, education, and physical home environment . .	24	26	26	24	8	3
Religion	3	3	2	2	0	1
Parents' social attitudes and adjustments . . .	17	20	20	20	3	5
Marital relationship .	53	61	53	54	16	18
Social home environment	27	32	31	29	1	1
Family health	19	31	30	28	6	5
Parents' attitudes toward the child's development	94	104	70	65	12	15
Parents' speech attitudes and characteristics . .	37	46	45	20	6	2
Parents' disciplinary attitudes and practices	34	38	32	32	3	1
Parents' attitudes toward the child's intelligence and school record	8	9	7	4	1	2
Interview reactions . .	3	3	1	1	2	1
Handedness of family .	2	2	1	1	0	0
Age, circumstance, and nature of stuttering/ nonfluency at onset . .	28	29	25	11	1	1
Subsequent development of stuttering/nonfluency .	17	17	18	6	2	0
Parents' attitudes toward stuttering/non- fluency	36	39	38	15	5	0
Total	554	654	537	450	72	63

Table 22. Results of Chi-Square Analysis of Responses to Items Concerning History of Birth and Early Development on Which the Mothers and Fathers Differed Significantly

Items	Direction of Difference	Level of Confidence	Remarks
Occurrence of falls during pregnancy (22)	More control group mothers than fathers reported mother had had falls	2%	Experimental group parents did not differ significantly
Were there any other unusual circumstances connected with the birth? (50)	More control group mothers than fathers answered "yes"	1%	Experimental group parents did not differ significantly
How much did the child cry during the first few weeks or months of its life? (61)	Control group mothers rated more children at extremes than did control group fathers	1%	Experimental group parents did not differ significantly
Rate the child's coordination in catching ball (82)	Control group fathers rated children more favorably than did control group mothers	5%	Experimental group parents did not differ significantly
Rate the child's coordination in running (87)	Control group fathers rated children more favorably than did control group mothers	5%	Experimental group parents did not differ significantly

Table 23. Results of Chi-Square Analysis of Responses to Items Pertaining to Social Development of Child on Which the Mothers and Fathers Differed Significantly

Item	Direction of Difference	Level of Confidence	Remarks
How well does your child play with other children? (372)	Experimental group fathers rated children more favorably than did experimental group mothers	5%	Control group parents did not differ significantly
How often has jealousy occurred during the past month? (430)	Less jealousy in children reported by experimental group mothers than by the fathers	2%	Control group parents did not differ significantly
How readily does your child give up on hard tasks as a rule? (472)	More experimental group fathers than mothers rated children favorably	5%	Control group parents did not differ significantly
Do you think the child feels generally picked on? (498)	More experimental group fathers than mothers answered "no"	1%	Control group parents did not differ significantly
How does your child respond to your corrections and suggestions? (524)	Experimental group mothers did not rate children as favorably as their husbands thought they would	5%	Control group parents did not differ significantly
How shy is your child? (387)	More control group fathers than mothers rated children favorably	5%	Experimental group parents did not differ significantly
How self-confident is your child? (391)	More control group fathers than mothers rated children favorably	5%	Experimental group parents did not differ significantly
How much does your child laugh? (400)	More control group fathers than mothers rated children favorably	5%	Experimental group parents did not differ significantly
What strong fears does the child have other than those concerned with speech? (485)	More experimental group mothers than fathers reported additional fears	1%	Control group parents did not differ significantly

Table 24. Results of Chi-Square Analysis of Responses to Items Concerning Socioeconomic Status, Physical Home Environment, Education, and Religion on Which the Mothers and Fathers Differed Significantly

Item	Direction of Difference	Level of Confidence	Remarks
Level of education (13)	Experimental group fathers had more education than experimental group mothers	1%	Control group parents followed similar trend, significant at 1% level
How well do you like present employment (your husband's employment)? (629)	More experimental group mothers than fathers were dissatisfied with fathers' employment	1%	Control group parents did not differ significantly
How well do you think your present employment uses and demonstrates your abilities (husband's abilities)? (630)	The fathers' jobs were rated as challenging by more fathers than mothers in the experimental group	1%	Control group parents followed similar trend, significant at 1% level
Mothers' evaluation of fathers' rating of employment vs. fathers' evaluation of mothers' rating (630, 631)	More experimental group fathers thought their wives would evaluate their (the fathers') employment as challenging than proved to be the case	5%	Control group parents followed similar trend, significant at 5% level
How proud are you of your abilities and accomplishments? (634)	More experimental group mothers than fathers rated themselves unfavorably	2%	Control group parents did not differ significantly
Mother's evaluation of own pride vs. father's evaluation of mother's pride (634, 635)	Experimental group fathers thought the mothers felt more pride than the mothers said they felt	1%	Control group parents did not differ significantly
Father's evaluation of own pride vs. mother's evaluation of father's pride (634, 635)	Mothers thought the fathers felt more pride than the fathers said they felt	1%	Control group parents did not differ significantly
Father's socioeconomic class vs. his father's (the grandfather's) present class (623, 642)	More experimental group fathers than grandfathers in upper class	1%	Control group parents did not differ significantly
How often do you attend church? (17)	Control group mothers attended church more frequently than control group fathers did	2%	Experimental group parents did not differ significantly

Table 25. Results of Chi-Square Analysis of Responses to Items Pertaining to Social Attitudes and Adjustments of Parents on Which Fathers and Mothers Differed Significantly

Item	Direction of Difference	Level of Confidence	Remarks
Number of organizations to which you belong (652)	Experimental group fathers belonged to more than experimental group mothers did	2%	Control group parents followed similar trend, statistically significant at 1% level
Frequency of participation in musical activities (657)	Control group mothers participated more frequently than control group fathers did	5%	Experimental group parents did not differ significantly
How important are your friendships to you? (664)	More important to control group mothers than fathers	1%	Experimental group parents did not differ significantly
How careful are you of your general appearance in social situations? (666)	More control group fathers than mothers rated themselves at extremes (high or low)	2%	Experimental group parents did not differ significantly
Mother's rating of own appearance vs. father's rating of mother's appearance (666, 667)	Experimental group fathers rated their wives more favorably than the wives rated themselves	1%	Control group parents followed similar trend, significant at 1% level
How much do you care about the impressions you make on others? (668)	Experimental group mothers more sensitive than their husbands	1%	Control group parents did not differ significantly

Table 26. Results of Chi-Square Analysis of Responses to Items Pertaining to Marital Relationship on Which Mothers and Fathers Differed Significantly

Item	Direction of Difference	Level of Confidence	Remarks
How serious are your differences over amount of social life? (683)	More experimental group mothers than fathers reported no differences	5%	Control group parents followed similar trend, significant at 5% level
How serious are your differences over kinds of entertainment preferred? (684)	More control group mothers than fathers reported no differences	1%	Experimental group parents did not differ significantly
How serious are your differences over ambition? (686)	More control group mothers than fathers reported no differences	1%	Experimental group parents did not differ significantly
How well satisfied are you with the way your mate is rearing the child (participates in home training and discipline of the child)? (694)	More experimental group mothers than fathers expressed dissatisfaction with mate	1%	Control group parents followed similar trend, significant at 1% level
How readily do you confide in your wife (husband)? (697)	Experimental group mothers confided more than fathers	1%	Control group parents followed similar trend, significant at 1% level
As a general rule, how tense are you? (699)	Experimental group mothers were more tense than fathers	1%	Control group parents followed similar trend, significant at 1% level
As a rule, how irritable are you? (700)	Control group mothers were more irritable than fathers	2%	Experimental group parents did not differ significantly
How easygoing are you? (701)	Experimental group fathers were more easygoing than mothers	2%	Control group parents followed similar trend, significant at 2% level
Informant's rating of mate's tenseness (704)	Experimental group fathers rated their wives as more tense than their wives rated them	1%	Control group parents did not differ significantly
Informant's rating of mate's irritability (705)	Experimental group fathers rated their wives as more irritable than their wives rated them	1%	Control group parents followed similar trend, significant at 2% level

Table 26 — continued

Item	Direction of Difference	Level of Confidence	Remarks
Informant's rating of mate's easygoingness (706)	Control group fathers rated their wives as less easygoing than their wives rated them	5%	Experimental group parents did not differ significantly
Informant's rating of mate's standards of conduct (707)	Experimental group fathers rated standards of their wives higher than their wives rated their (the fathers') standards	1%	Control group parents did not differ significantly
Mother's rating of own tenseness vs. father's rating of her tenseness (699, 704)	Experimental group mothers rated themselves as more tense than their husbands rated them	2%	Control group parents did not differ significantly
Father's rating of own irritability vs. mother's rating of his irritability (700, 705)	Control group fathers rated themselves as more irritable than their wives rated them	1%	Experimental group parents did not differ significantly
Father's rating of own easygoingness vs. mother's rating of his easygoingness (701, 706)	Control group mothers rated fathers as more easygoing than fathers rated themselves	5%	Experimental group parents did not differ significantly
Mother's rating of own standards of conduct vs. father's rating of mother's standards of conduct (702, 707)	Experimental group mothers rated themselves higher than their husbands rated them	1%	Control group parents followed similar trend, significant at 2% level
Father's rating of own neatness vs. mother's rating of his neatness (703, 708)	Control group fathers rated themselves as less neat than they were rated by their wives	1%	Experimental group parents did not differ significantly
Mother's rating of own neatness vs. father's rating of her neatness (703, 708)	Experimental group mothers rated themselves as more neat than their husbands rated them	1%	Control group parents followed similar trend, significant at 1% level

Table 26 — *continued*

Item	Direction of Difference	Level of Confidence	Remarks
Do you consider the other parent to be too demanding of the child? (711)	More experimental group fathers than mothers answered "no"	1%	Control group parents did not differ significantly
Do you think the other parent worries too much? (712)	More experimental group fathers than mothers answered "yes"	1%	Control group parents did not differ significantly
Do you think the other parent is away from home too much? (713)	More experimental group mothers than fathers answered "yes"	1%	Control group parents followed similar trend, significant at 1% level
Do you consider the other parent to be with the child too much? (714)	More experimental group fathers than mothers answered "yes"	1%	Control group parents followed similar trend, significant at 5% level
How often do you side with the child against the other parent in the presence of the child? (716)	Experimental group mothers did so more frequently than the fathers	1%	Control group parents did not differ significantly
How often do you wish you were single? (718)	Control group fathers wished this more often than the mothers did	5%	Experimental group parents did not differ significantly

Table 27. Results of Chi-Square Analysis of Responses to Items Concerning Social Home Environment on Which Mothers and Fathers Differed Significantly

Item	Direction of Difference	Level of Confidence	Remarks
Father's answer to "As a general rule, do you feel a child should be seen and not heard?" vs. mother's guess as to what his answer would be (738, 739)	More experimental fathers said "no" than the mothers predicted	2%	Control group parents did not differ significantly
Mother's answer to "As a general rule, do you feel a child should be seen and not heard?" vs. father's guess as to what her answer would be (738, 739)	More control mothers said "no" than the fathers predicted	5%	Experimental group parents did not differ significantly

Table 28. Results of Chi-Square Analysis of Responses to Items Pertaining to Family Health on Which Mothers and Fathers Differed Significantly

Item	Direction of Difference	Level of Confidence	Remarks
How was your own health at the onset of the child's stuttering/nonfluency? (757)	More experimental group fathers than mothers were in good health	2%	Control group parents did not differ significantly
How much do you worry about getting sick? (764)	Experimental group mothers worried more than fathers	1%	Control group parents did not differ significantly
Mother's rating of own appetite vs. father's rating of her appetite (766, 768)	Control group mothers gave their appetites better ratings than their husbands gave them	2%	Experimental group parents did not differ significantly
Father's rating of own sleep vs. mother's rating of his sleep (767, 769)	Control group fathers rated their own sleep more favorably than their wives rated it	1%	Experimental group parents did not differ significantly
Do you have many food dislikes? (770)	More experimental group fathers than mothers answered "yes"	1%	Control group parents did not differ significantly
How much physical energy do you believe you have? (793)	Experimental group fathers rated their own energy higher than the mothers rated theirs	1%	Control group parents followed similar trend, significant at 1% level
How much physical energy do you believe your mate has? (794)	Experimental group fathers have more energy than the mothers, according to their mate's rating	5%	Control group parents followed similar trend, significant at 1% level
How often do you use alcohol? (795)	More experimental group mothers than fathers indicated no use of alcohol	5%	Control group parents followed similar trend, significant at 5% level

Table 29. Results of Chi-Square Analysis of Responses to Items Pertaining to Parents' Attitudes toward Child's Development on Which Mothers and Fathers Differed Significantly

Item	Direction of Difference	Level of Confidence	Remarks
Mother's opinion of left-handedness vs. father's estimate of mother's opinion (108–109)	More experimental group fathers said their wives would discourage left-handedness than proved to be the case, according to the wives' responses	5%	Control group parents did not differ significantly
How carefully have you studied the age norms for children? (120)	More experimental group fathers than mothers answered "never"	1%	Control group parents followed similar trend, significant at 1% level
How helpful were these norms to you? (122)	More experimental group fathers than mothers had never thought of norms	1%	Control group parents followed similar trend, significant at 1% level
How consistently did you compare your child's development with these norms? (123)	Experimental group mothers did so more frequently than the fathers did	1%	Control group parents followed similar trend, significant at 1% level
How did the child usually compare with the norms? (124)	Experimental group fathers rated children more favorably than the mothers did	2%	Control group parents did not differ significantly
How do you feel about the child's showing off? (421)	More control group mothers than fathers were disturbed by this	1%	Experimental group parents not compared; distribution unsuitable for chi-square analysis
How do you feel about the child's quarreling? (425)	More experimental group mothers than fathers were disturbed by this	1%	Control group parents did not differ significantly
Father's rating of how well child meets ideal standards vs. mother's guess as to father's rating (467, 469)	Experimental group fathers rated children more favorably than mothers thought they would	5%	Control group parents did not differ significantly
How attractive do you feel your child is? (473)	Control group fathers rated child more favorably than mothers did	5%	Experimental group parents did not differ significantly
Mother's rating of child's appearance vs. father's guess as to mother's rating (473, 474)	Control group mothers rated children less favorably than their husbands thought they would	1%	Experimental group parents did not differ significantly

Table 29 — *continued*

Item	Direction of Difference	Level of Confidence	Remarks
Do you wish your child were a better or less good athlete? (478)	More control group fathers than mothers answered "better"	5%	Experimental group parents did not differ significantly
Do you wish the child would play more or less quietly? (506)	More control group fathers answered "more"	5%	Experimental group parents did not differ significantly
Do you encourage or discourage or say nothing about your child's playing alone? (508)	More experimental group mothers than fathers encouraged the child's playing alone	1%	Control group followed similar trend, significant at 1% level
How much does the child irritate and annoy you? (514)	Experimental group fathers less annoyed than mothers	1%	Control group parents followed similar trend, significant at 1% level
Father's rating of how much child irritates and annoys him vs. mother's guess as to father's rating (514, 515)	Control group fathers less annoyed than their wives thought they were	5%	Experimental group parents did not differ significantly
How often do you take time out to play with your child? (518)	Experimental group mothers took more time out than the fathers did	1%	Control group parents did not differ significantly
How often does your husband (wife) play with the child? (520)	Experimental group fathers credited mothers with more time than the mothers credited the fathers with	1%	Control group parents followed similar trend, significant at 1% level
Mother's rating of time out to play with child vs. father's guess as to mother's rating (518, 520)	Control group mothers' estimates of time taken out were lower than their husbands thought they would be	5%	Experimental group parents did not differ significantly
Father's answer to "How well do you like the child's companions to come to the home?" vs. mother's guess as to his answer (369, 370)	Experimental group fathers enjoyed this more than their wives thought they did	1%	Control group parents did not differ significantly
Mother's answer to "How well do you like the child's companions to come to the home?" vs. father's guess as to mother's answer (369, 370)	Control group mothers enjoyed this more than their husbands thought they did	5%	Experimental group parents did not differ significantly

Table 30. Results of Chi-Square Analysis of Responses to Items Pertaining to Speech Attitudes and Characteristics of Parents on Which Fathers and Mothers Differed Significantly

Item	Direction of Difference	Level of Confidence	Remarks
Interviewer's rating of parent's speech (797)	More experimental group fathers than mothers were rated as defective in speech	5%	Control group parents did not differ significantly
Interviewer's rating of amount of speech (798)	Experimental group mothers were more verbal than fathers	1%	Control group parents followed similar trend, significant at 2% level
Do you think about your child's stuttering/speech when you go to bed? (357)	More experimental group mothers than fathers gave positive answers	1%	Too few control group parents gave positive answers for chi-square computation
Do you talk anxiously to neighbors about your child's speech? (360)	More experimental group mothers than fathers gave positive answers	1%	Too few control group parents gave positive answers for chi-square computation
Do you talk anxiously to family and relatives about your child's speech? (361)	More experimental group mothers than fathers gave positive answers	1%	Too few control group parents gave positive answers for chi-square computation
Are there any cases of speech defects in your immediate family? (791)	More control group fathers than mothers answered "none"	2%	Experimental group parents did not differ significantly
What other stutterers do you know by direct contact outside the immediate family? (328)	Experimental group fathers knew more than mothers did	1%	Control group parents followed similar trend, significant at 1% level

106

Table 31. Results of Chi-Square Analysis of Responses to Items Pertaining to Disciplinary
Attitudes and Practices of Parents on Which Mothers and Fathers Differed Significantly

Item	Direction of Difference	Level of Confidence	Remarks
Is the child punished for talking back? (543)	More experimental group mothers than fathers answered "yes"	1%	Control group parents did not differ significantly
Is the child punished for not doing his chores? (555)	More control group fathers than mothers answered "yes"	1%	Experimental group parents did not differ significantly
Do you feel your husband (wife) is too strict, lax, or about right? (564)	More experimental group mothers than fathers rated mate as too strict	2%	Control group parents did not differ significantly
How well behaved do you think your child is? (585)	Experimental group fathers rated children more favorably than the mothers did	1%	Control group parents did not differ significantly

Table 32. Results of Chi-Square Analysis of Responses to Items Pertaining to Parents' Attitudes Regarding
Child's Intelligence and School Record on Which Mothers and Fathers Differed Significantly

Item	Direction of Difference	Level of Confidence	Remarks
How well satisfied are you with your child's intelligence? (596)	Control group mothers rated children more favorably than fathers did	2%	Experimental group parents did not differ significantly
How does your child's intelligence compare with that of the neighbor children? (597)	Experimental group fathers rated children more favorably than mothers did	5%	Control group parents did not differ significantly

Table 33. Results of Chi-Square Analysis of Data Concerning Interview Reactions and
Procedures with Respect to Which Mothers and Fathers Differed Significantly

Item	Direction of Difference	Level of Confidence	Remarks
Number of sessions necessary to complete the interview (611)	More experimental group mothers than fathers required more than one session to complete the interview	1%	Six control group mothers and two fathers required more than one session; chi-square value not computed
Number of interruptions during the interview (612)	Interviews of experimental group mothers had more interruptions than those of fathers	1%	Control group parents followed similar trend, significant at 1% level

Table 34. Results of Chi-Square Analysis of Data Pertaining to Age, Circumstances, and Nature of Stuttering/Nonfluency at Onset

Item	Direction of Difference	Level of Confidence	Remarks
Did you accept the diagnosis of stuttering? (215)	More experimental group fathers than mothers answered "no"	1%	Control group parents not asked
Did the child have trouble on words scattered throughout sentences? (231)	More control group mothers than fathers answered "yes"	1%	Experimental group parents did not differ significantly

Table 35. Results of Chi-Square Analysis of Data Pertaining to Development of Stuttering/Nonfluency Following Onset with Respect to Which Mothers and Fathers Differed Significantly

Item	Direction of Difference	Level of Confidence	Remarks
How soon after you noticed that he was stuttering did the child begin to avoid speech situations? (256)	More experimental group fathers than mothers answered "never"	1%	Control group parents not asked
Does the child have especially difficult periods? (297)	More experimental group mothers than fathers answered "yes"	2%	Control group parents not asked

Table 36. Results of Chi-Square Analysis of Responses to Items Pertaining to Parental Attitudes Regarding Stuttering/Nonfluency on Which Mothers and Fathers Differed Significantly

Item	Direction of Difference	Level of Confidence	Remarks
How concerned were you about the child's stuttering/nonfluency when you were first aware of it? (262)	Experimental group mothers more concerned than fathers	1%	Control group parents did not differ significantly
Did anyone react to the child's stuttering/nonfluency? (276)	More experimental group mothers than fathers answered "yes"	2%	Too few control group parents answered "yes" for chi-square computation
Did you avert your gaze when the child was having "trouble"? (277)	More experimental group mothers than fathers answered "yes"	5%	Too few control group parents answered "yes" for chi-square computation
Did you look worried when the child was having "trouble"? (283)	More experimental group mothers than fathers answered "yes"	5%	Too few control group parents answered "yes" for chi-square computation
Who first said something to the child about the stuttering/nonfluency? (253)	Both experimental group parents designated themselves more often than either was designated by the spouse	1%	Control group parents did not differ significantly

109

Table 37. Results of Chi-Square Analysis of Responses to Items with Respect to Which Intergroup Intragroup Comparisons Were Made and on Which the Experimental and Control Groups Differed Significantly

Item	Direction of Difference	Chi-Square (df $= 2$)	Level of Confidence
How much did the child cry during the first few weeks of life? (61)	More control than experimental group parents agreed; experimental group mothers said children did more crying than fathers said they did; control group mothers said children did less crying than fathers said they did	16.94	5%
How is your child's coordination in running? (87)	More experimental than control group parents agreed; in control group fathers gave children better ratings than mothers did	11.87	1%
How easily does your child get tired? (375)	More control than experimental group parents agreed; in experimental group mothers rated children as getting tired more easily than did fathers; in control group mothers rated children as getting tired less easily than did fathers	9.65	1%
How frequently did the child get what he wanted without talking? (185)	More experimental than control group parents agreed; in control group fathers said this occurred more often than mothers said it did	8.27	2%
How much does your child explain away his faults and mistakes? (471)	More experimental than control group parents agreed; in control group mothers said children did this more frequently than fathers said they did	9.76	1%
How much does your child read compared with other children? (479)	More experimental than control group parents agreed; in control group mothers said children read more than fathers said they did	6.02	5%

Table 37 — *continued*

Item	Direction of Difference	Chi-Square (df = 2)	Level of Confidence
How much is the child afraid of other children? (484)	More experimental than control group parents agreed; in control group fathers rated children as more afraid than mothers rated them	6.55	5%
How much is the child laughed at by other children? (493)	More experimental than control group parents agreed; in control group fathers said children were laughed at more often than mothers said they were	10.72	1%
How much freedom has the child in determining how he shall use his own play time? (502)	More experimental than control group parents agreed; in control group mothers said their children had more freedom than the fathers said they had	92.10	1%
How serious are your differences over the use of money? (681)	More experimental than control group parents agreed; in control group fathers rated differences as more serious than mothers rated them	6.02	5%
How serious are your differences over kind of entertainment? (684)	More experimental than control group parents agreed; in control group fathers rated differences as more serious than mothers rated them	7.48	5%
How serious are your differences over recreation? (691)	More experimental than control group parents agreed; in both groups mothers rated differences as more serious than fathers rated them	14.32	1%

111

rated by their husbands; mothers rated their own neatness higher than it was rated by their husbands; mothers considered fathers to be away from home more than the fathers considered the mothers were away from home; fathers more often considered the mothers to be with the children too much than the mothers considered fathers to be with the children too much; fathers appeared to have more physical energy than the mothers, according to both self-ratings and spouse ratings; more mothers than fathers used no alcohol; more fathers than mothers said they never studied child development norms, and more fathers than mothers said they had never thought of such norms; mothers compared their children with the norms more frequently than fathers did; more mothers than fathers encouraged their children to play alone; mothers were more annoyed or irritated by their children than fathers were; fathers thought the mothers took more time out to play with the children than the mothers thought the fathers did; mothers talked more than fathers during the interviews; the interviews with the mothers were interrupted more than were those with the fathers; and the fathers had known more stutterers outside the immediate family than the mothers had.

ITEMS ON WHICH THE PARENTS IN ONLY ONE GROUP DIFFERED SIGNIFICANTLY

Significant Experimental Group Differences. Experimental group fathers said the children played with other children better than the mothers said they did; more mothers than fathers said children were not jealous; more mothers than fathers said children gave up easily on hard tasks; more mothers than fathers said children felt picked on; mothers did not say children responded to suggestions or corrections as well as fathers thought the mothers would; mothers were not as proud of their own accomplishments and abilities as fathers thought they were; more mothers than fathers reported the children had strong fears other than those concerned with speech; more mothers than fathers were dissatisfied with the father's employment; more mothers than fathers rated themselves unfavorably with respect to pride in own accomplishments; fathers thought mothers felt more pride in their own accomplishments than the mothers said they felt; mothers were more sensitive than their husbands about the impressions they made; fathers rated their wives as more tense than their wives rated them; fathers rated their wives' standards of conduct higher than mothers rated their husbands' standards of conduct; mothers rated themselves as more tense than their husbands rated them.

More fathers than mothers thought spouse was too demanding of the child; more fathers than mothers thought spouse worried too much; more mothers than fathers sided with the child against spouse in child's presence; more fathers said "No" than mothers predicted would say "No" in response to "As a general rule, do you feel a child should be seen and not heard?"; more fathers than mothers were in good health at the time of onset of the child's stuttering; the mothers worried about their health more than the fathers did; more fathers than mothers said they had food dislikes; more fathers said their wives would discourage left-handedness than proved to be the case, according to the wives' responses; fathers rated children more favorably than mothers did in indicating how they felt their children usually compared with "the norms"; more mothers than fathers were disturbed about the child's quarreling; fathers rated their children more favorably than their wives thought they would with respect to "how well the child meets ideal standards"; mothers took more time out than fathers did to play with the child; fathers enjoyed having the child's friends come to the home more than their wives thought they did. More fathers than mothers had speech defects, according to the interviewers, but, as has been noted, these did not amount to a very notable total proportion and, aside from stuttering and "minor articulatory defects," the speech "defects" were for the most part classifiable as foreign dialect, and there were only four cases of this.

More mothers than fathers said they thought about their child's speech while lying in bed, and talked to neighbors and relatives about the child's speech; more mothers than fathers said the child was punished for "talking back"; more mothers than fathers rated spouse as too strict; fathers rated the children's intelligence more favorably, in comparison with that of the neighbor children, than did the mothers, and more of them said the children were well behaved; more fathers than mothers said they did not accept the diagnosis of stuttering at first; more fathers than mothers said the child never avoided speaking situations; more mothers than fathers said the child did have especially difficult periods; more mothers than fathers were concerned about the child's speech when it was first thought that there was anything wrong with it; and more mothers than fathers reacted to what they took to be the child's stuttering.

Significant Control Group Differences. More mothers than fathers reported that the mother had had falls during pregnancy and that there had been unusual circumstances about the child's birth; more mothers than fathers made extreme ratings of the amount of crying done by the child during the first weeks of life; fathers rated children's coordination in catching and running more favorably than the mothers did; more fathers than mothers rated their children favorably with respect to shyness, self-confidence, and tendency to laugh; mothers said they attended church more often and took part in more musical activities than the fathers did; friendships were more important to the mothers than the fathers; more fathers than mothers gave themselves extremely high or low ratings on carefulness about their appearance in social situations; more mothers than fathers said they had no differences with their spouses over preferred kinds of entertainment or degree of ambition; mothers were more irritable than fathers, according to self-ratings; fathers rated their wives as more easygoing, however, than their wives rated them, and yet their wives rated them as more easygoing than the fathers rated themselves, and the fathers rated themselves as more irritable and less neat than they were rated by their wives.

Fathers wished they were single more frequently than mothers did; mothers answered "No" more often than fathers did to "As a general rule do you feel a child should be seen and not heard?"; mothers said their appetites were better than their husbands thought they were, and fathers said they slept better than their wives said they did; more mothers than fathers were disturbed by the child's showing off, but more fathers than mothers said they wished the children would play more quietly; fathers rated children's attractiveness more favorably than mothers did, and the mothers' ratings of their children's attractiveness were less favorable than the fathers thought they would be; more fathers than mothers wished their children were better athletes; the fathers were less annoyed by the children than the mothers thought they were; mothers enjoyed having their children's friends come to their homes more than the fathers thought they did; mothers said they took less time out to play with their children than the fathers said the mothers did; more fathers than mothers said there were no cases of defective speech in their families; more fathers than mothers said the children were punished for not doing their chores; mothers rated the children's intelligence more favorably than did the fathers; and more mothers than fathers said the children who were said to speak nonfluently "had trouble" on words scattered throughout the sentence.

Intergroup Intragroup Comparisons

In order to compare the groups more fully with regard to intragroup differences, ninety-two items were further analyzed. The responses to each of these items involved a rating quantitatively expressed in such a way that the responses of the two parents could be classified in one of three ways: (1) both parents gave the same rating, (2) the mother's rating was higher than the father's, and (3) the father's rating was higher than the mother's. The distributions of the responses into these three categories for the two groups were compared. One of the ninety-two items had a distribution unfavorable for the computation of a chi-square value: too few of the parents in both groups disagreed on how much the children were picked on. Chi-square values were significant for twelve of the other items, all of which are summarized in Table 37. There was greater agreement in the experimental than in the control group on ten of these twelve items, but the direction of the disagreement that was present in each case was of special interest. In Table 37 disagreement is indicated with respect to three items for the experimental group parents and in all three instances the mothers expressed less favorable evaluations of their children or more distress over designated differences with their spouses. By contrast, disagreement is indicated with respect to all twelve items for the control group parents, and in nine of the twelve instances the fathers expressed less favorable evaluations of the children or more distress over disagreements with their spouses.

A comparative analysis of the relevant items in Tables 22–37 yielded the following results:

1. Responses by the control group parents to 102 items were appropriate for analysis

    a. On 33 items the mothers and fathers did not differ significantly

    b. For 34 items the fathers' responses were the more favorable, or less indicative of concern, discontent, or difficulty, or involved higher ratings

    c. For 35 items the mothers' responses were the more favorable, or less indicative of concern, discontent, or difficulty, or involved higher ratings

2. Responses by the experimental group parents to 110 items were appropriate for analysis

    a. On 43 items the mothers and fathers did not differ significantly

    b. For 52 items the fathers' responses were the more favorable, or less indicative of concern, discontent, or difficulty, or involved higher ratings

    c. For 15 items the mothers' responses were the more favorable, or less indicative of concern, discontent, or difficulty, or involved higher ratings

The difference between the values, 33 and 34, for the control group fathers and mothers was not statistically significant, while the difference between the values for the experimental group fathers and mothers, 52 and 15, respectively, was significant at the 1 per cent level $(z = 4.58)$.

The over-all picture of disagreement within the experimental group was one of greater dissatisfaction on the part of the mothers than the fathers, while within the control group discontent appeared to be more or less equally shared by the fathers and mothers. If the sharing was not wholly equal, it was probably the fathers who were less serene. Comparatively speaking, whenever the tension of disagreement between parents was found, it tended in half — or even slightly more than half — of the instances, in the control group, to be representative of a conflict between a relatively contented mother and a discontented father, whereas in the experimental group it involved as a rule a conflict between a relatively contented father and a discontented mother.

CHAPTER 5

The Problem

A T W H A T time in the child's life and under what circumstances did someone, in each experimental group case, arrive at the judgment that the child was stuttering? And who was the person that first arrived at this judgment? Data relevant to these questions are presented in this chapter.

Time of Onset of the Problem of Stuttering

The five criteria, set forth in Chapter 2, that were used in accepting subjects for Study III were applied in each case in advance of the interview. During the interview each mother and father in the experimental group was asked, "Has the child ever had a speech defect? What defect?" (194) and, "Has the child ever stuttered?" (195). The ways in which the parents responded to these and related questions are of special interest in relation to basic theoretical considerations concerning the problem of stuttering.

While no control group parent indicated that his or her child stuttered, 5 mothers and 11 fathers in the experimental group, as has been indicated previously, gave a "No" response to 194, "Has the child ever had a speech defect?"; 3 mothers and 6 fathers gave the response "Repetition, not called stuttering"; 1 mother and 2 fathers identified the speech condition as "Inability to find the right word"; 2 fathers gave responses coded as "Hesitation, not called stuttering; child not called stutterer"; 1 father gave the response "Articulatory problem; 'speech block,' not called stuttering"; 139 mothers said their children stuttered, and 21 of these said they also had articulatory defects; 122 fathers stated that their children stuttered, and 13 of these also said they had articulatory defects.

The next question they were asked was (195) "Has the child ever stuttered?" and 144 of the experimental group mothers gave a "Yes" response, 2 said, "Yes, but not at present time," and 4 said, "No"; 136 fathers gave an unqualified "Yes," 2 said, "Yes, but not at present time," 3 gave a response coded as "?" (uncertain, indefinite), and 9

117

said "No." And when, next in the interview, they were asked (196), "How old was the child when he first began to stutter?" responses were given by all 150 of the experimental group mothers and by 141 of the fathers; only 3 of the 9 fathers who had given the "No" response to 195 failed, however, to state an age at which the child began to stutter, and three even gave a description, in response to 197, of "the situation in which the child stuttered the very first time." Indeed, in response to 217, in which the informants were asked to imitate what the child was doing in his speech when he first stuttered, only 1 of these 9 fathers gave a response coded "?" (can't recall, uncertain), and this father gave definite answers to all of items 198 through 212, which concern specific reactions which the child may have exhibited in the first situation, or the first one the informant could remember, in which the child stuttered. Moreover, this particular father, when asked (215) whether he accepted "the decision or diagnosis" that the child was stuttering when it was first made by someone, answered, "Yes." A check of the responses made to all items concerning the child's stuttering (196–349) by the 9 fathers who gave a "No" response to 195 revealed that each answered nearly all these questions one way or another. It seems clear that even these 9 fathers felt or assumed that in some way their children's speech was not satisfactory, but, together with some of the other parents, they were uncertain and inconsistent in their attempts to give verbal expression to their feelings and assumptions.

Reference is to be made again, in view of these figures, to criterion No. 3 on page 13, according to which a child was accepted into the experimental group, provided the other four criteria were met, if the child "was considered to be a stutterer by at least one parent." Stated positively, the application of this criterion meant that every child in the experimental group was included by virtue of the fact that either the child's mother or father, or, as was nearly always true, both, unequivocally wanted to have the child included, knowing that the basic reason for doing so was to investigate something that at least one of them — and, as it turned out, both of them in varying degrees — regarded as stuttering, and having been informed of the considerable amount of time and effort to be required of them.

The investigators were aware at the same time of conceivable extraneous motivations that might have prompted certain parents to attempt to have their children included in the experimental group. Of these, there are three that seem noteworthy. First, the parents may have been unusually conscientious and, upon learning about the investigation, may have regarded a speech examination for their child as one of the stones not to leave unturned in providing him with "the best of care"; due vigilance was exercised, and it seems quite impossible that any parents with only such motivation were included. It is practically certain beyond question that one or both — and in all or very nearly all cases both — of the parents of every child included in the experimental group had felt before learning of this investigation that the child was stuttering.

Second, certain parents may have wanted to be extremely cooperative and when, in a PTA meeting, for example, it was announced that this study was being carried on, they may have volunteered simply to be helpful. Again, due vigilance was exercised, and it is unquestionably certain that no parents were included in the experimental group for such a reason as this. An appeal to cooperativeness, as such, was made, of course, in seeking subjects for the control group.

Third, the parents may have been, in some degree consciously or unconsciously, seeking clinical help for themselves rather more than for their child; an aspect of this possibility is discussed in Chapter 7. There would seem to be significant implications of such a possibility, so far as the parental motivations in question may be demonstrated, with respect to the fundamental formulation of the problem of stuttering and with respect to the question of the person or persons whose problem it is in each case, particularly at moment of origin.

It is to be considered that in some cases the relevant evaluative reactions of the parents may have varied or wavered sufficiently, between the time when they were given an appointment and the day when they appeared for the interview, to account for some degree of the apparent inconsistency of their responses to 194–196. Finally, due consideration is to be given to differences among individual respondents with respect to their evaluational, or interpretive, or, in a more or less deep and comprehensive sense, their semantic reactions to the specific phrasings and intonations of the questions asked during the interview, as these were presented by the different interviewers, and as they were affected by the particular situations in which the questioning was carried on. Moreover, the complex self-reflexive effects on each respondent of his own reactions to the questions as they were successively presented are to be given appropriate weight in interpreting the apparent degree of consistency of the informants from any given part of the interview to any other. These various effects, so far as they were operative in individual cases, were presumably compounded by the ambiguity characteristic of the terms "stuttering" and "stutterer," and their equivalents, in common usages. Considerable light would seem to be thrown on this aspect of the matter by the variability of response to items 217, 218–232, 236, and 293, which were concerned in each instance with the speech behavior of the child to which the designation "stuttering" was applied (see Tables 38–47 and accompanying text).

Before examining the data with regard to time of onset of the problem of stuttering, it is also to be recalled that each mother and father in the control group was asked whether the child had a speech defect (194) and, as has been stated, in no instance did either parent of any control group child indicate that he was a stutterer. Each control group parent was also asked (195), "Does the child now show or has he, or she, ever shown any nonfluencies — repetitions, hesitations, etc. — in speech?" Sixty-six mothers and sixty-three fathers gave an unqualified "Yes" response to this question; nineteen mothers and eleven fathers gave the response "Yes, but not at present time"; two mothers and four fathers gave a response coded as "?" (uncertain, indefinite); and sixty-three mothers and seventy-two fathers gave "No" as an answer. When they were next asked (196), "How old was the child when you began to notice his speech in these respects?" definite responses were obtained from sixty-one mothers and fifty-six fathers. Examination of items 197 through 260 in the Summary Table in Appendix A shows, however, that approximately eighty-five mothers and seventy-five fathers answered these questions, thus indicating that they thought of their children as showing, or as having shown, nonfluencies in speech.

What has been said above concerning the variability of response tendencies characteristic of the experimental group parents, and the factors that might be related to this variability, is also to be said, in essence, with reference to the control group respondents. The additional comment is to be made, of course, that since it has been well established that all children "show nonfluencies in speech" (R18, 25, 30, 62, 78), the responses of the parents in the control group who gave a simple "No" answer to 195, and those who consistently declined to consider the succeeding questions through 260, are to be evaluated accordingly. The difference between the numbers of control group parents responding to 195 (and 196) and to succeeding questions may reasonably be assumed to be attributable, in some measure, to the ambiguity and the varied degree of functional significance of the term "nonfluencies in speech" for these respondents.

In 196 there is a summary of information given by both groups of parents in Study III with regard to the age of the child in each case at the time of "onset of stuttering" or, in the control group, the age of the child when the parents "began to notice the nonfluencies" in his or her speech. The mean and median values, in months, for the responses of the mothers and fathers, respectively, in the experimental group were as follows: means, 42.4 and 41.2, medians, 40 and 37. Corresponding values, in months, for the mothers and fathers, respectively, in the control group were: means, 39.2 and 34.4, medians, 36 and 36. The difference between the group means for the fathers was significant at the 1 per cent level ($t = 3.11$; df $= 194$), and the difference between the means of the control group mothers and fathers was significant at the 5 per cent level ($t = 1.99$; df $= 125$). The differences in means for the two groups of mothers and for the mothers and fathers in the experimental group were not statistically significant. In evaluating the difference between the means of the experimental and control group fathers it should be kept in mind that there was a difference of only one month between the medians of the two groups. In general, it seems conservative to say that both groups of parents were reporting their reactions to something their children had done in speaking at an age period that was roughly the same for the two groups of children, this age period extending in the main from two to five years, with the crucial age being three to three and a half years for the majority of the cases.

In evaluating the means of the responses to 196, due consideration is to be given to the average discrepancy between the mothers' and fathers' reports of age of onset or, for the control group, age of the child when attention was first given to nonfluency aspects of the child's speech (814). Although the means of the mothers' and fathers' responses to 196 differed by only 1.3 months for the experimental group and 4.8 months for the control group, the mean discrepancy, pair by pair of parents (814), was 5.5 months for the experimental group and 10.7 months for the control group. This is to say that the mean discrepancies between the dates or ages given by the mothers and fathers, considered as spouse pairs, were greater, for both the experimental and control groups, than were the differences in means between the experimental and control group mothers and fathers, respectively.*

This order of discrepancy is, in itself, of very considerable interest.

* The greater mean discrepancy for the control group parents might be explained in considerable measure by reference to the probability that they were less concerned about what they thought of as *nonfluencies* (or the equivalent) in their children's speech than were the experimental group parents about what they regarded as *stuttering* (or the equivalent) in the speech of their children. Being less concerned, they may well have been less decisive in their reactions and so less definite in their recollections of those reactions. Essentially the same explanation may well be made of the larger standard deviations of the age designations made by the control group parents in response to 196.

The Onset of Stuttering

It is to be noted that in Study II, in which the children investigated were older as a group than those in Study III, the mean ages of the experimental group children in the two studies being 8 years, 8 months, and 5 years, respectively, the mean discrepancy between the experimental group mothers' and fathers' reports of age of onset of stuttering was 15.3 months, even greater than the mean in Study III. Due consideration is to be given to the possibility, or probability, that the major factor operating to produce these discrepancies was memory, or the failures and vagaries of memory. The importance of this, so far as it is a valid interpretation, lies in the intimation that what was being remembered by these parents was difficult to place in time. Why might this have been so? Possibly for the reason that "the onset of stuttering" is an arrangement of words that seldom if ever is used to refer to a clear-cut event, or an unmistakable and marked change in the speech of a child. The data now being reviewed represent occurrences in the awarenesses, evaluative experiences, and memories of the informants as well as, or possibly instead of, occurrences in the neuromuscular activities of their children. This is to say that the data represent events in the receiving, sorting, and storing mechanisms of the listeners as well as, or instead of, occurrences in the coding and sending mechanisms of the speakers.

This view of what the data represent is further suggested by another comparison. In Study II the interval between the onset of stuttering, as reported, and the interview was longer than it was in Study III. The relevant means were, for the mothers, 56.6 and 17.5 months, and for the fathers 50.1 and 18.2 months (813). It is also to be recalled that in Study I the median interval between the reported age of onset of stuttering and the first interview was 5 months and 18 days. Thus, it might be expected that recall of the onset would have been in general more difficult in Study II than in Study III or Study I. The probability that this was the case is indicated by two facts. The first is that the discrepancy between the reports of the age of onset given by pairs of mothers and fathers was, as already noted, greater in Study II than in Study III, the experimental group means and medians being, respectively, 15.3 and 10.5 months for Study II and 5.5 and 3.0 months for Study III. The second is that the onset was reported to have occurred later in Study II than in either Study I or Study III. The median age of onset reported in Study I was three years, or 36 months, and the means for Study III and Study II, respectively, were 42.4 and 46.2 months, as reported by the mothers, and 41.1 and 53 months, as reported by the fathers.

These figures indicate that the question of the age at which stuttering begins was answered differently by mothers and fathers, and the answers given to it depended also in some measure on the length of the interval between the time when the event, whatever it may have been, occurred, and the time when the question was asked.

Moreover, the answer depended on the question that was asked. In 196 the informant was asked, "How old was the child (in months) when he first began to stutter?" The redundancy, in "first began," emphasizes that special care was being used to get the informant to recall the very beginnings of the problem. Even so, when, in the next question (197), the parent was asked to "describe the situation in which the child stuttered the very first time," * only 26 mothers and 18 fathers claimed to recall "the very first time," or said they could recall but could not describe such a situation, and 30 fathers and 24 mothers responded simply by saying that they were not able to recall "the very first" situation. The remaining 100 mothers and 102 fathers offered descriptions of what were presumably the first situations in which they could remember observing their children stutter, but these were not the first situations in which stuttering allegedly occurred.

Even those whose answers were unqualified by expressions of uncertainty gave responses that were for the most part ambiguous rather than descriptive of specific situations at designated times and places; most of them described "the situation in which the child stuttered the very first time" by saying, for example, "When he came in to tell something," or "Telling parent something," or "Asking parent something" (see footnote to 197). In a series of sixteen questions following 197 (198–213), the informants were asked to say whether in this "very first situation" the child was in a condition of frustration and bewilderment (200), or had just received punishment or scolding (202), and the like, and only 20 to 22 fathers and 26 to 31 mothers were able to give responses with reference to "the very first situation."

In 217, the same informants who had answered 196 in the ways indicated were asked to "imitate what the child was doing in his speech when he first stuttered — the very first time you noticed the child stuttering, or during the period when the stuttering still was the same as it had been the very first time it was noticed by anyone." Only four mothers and seven fathers gave responses that were coded "?" (uncertain, indefinite). There followed, then, a series of questions that were assumed to have the same temporal reference, each one beginning with the words "When you first noticed that the child was stut-

* The interviewer was instructed as follows: "If 'can't recall' is the response, ask for a description of the first situation the parent can recall in which he or she observed the child stuttering."

tering . . ." and these were consistently answered by all the experimental group parents, with from five to ten giving responses that were coded "?" to each of these items. When, however, in 233, the informants were asked, "Had anyone, before the time stated in 196 ('How old was the child when he first began to stutter?'), thought that the child was stuttering?" six mothers and fourteen fathers gave a "Yes" answer, and one mother and three fathers gave responses that were coded "?".

Then, in 235, each of the experimental group parents was asked to "describe the first situation in which your child did something which you felt at that time indicated he had a speech problem (you may or may not have called it stuttering)," and in 237 the question was asked "How old was the child at that time (in months)?" The mean age in months was, according to the mothers, 47.3 and, according to the fathers, 44.3. These means are to be compared with those based on the responses to 196, "How old was the child when he first began to stutter?" These means were, for the mothers, 42.4 and, for the fathers, 41.2 months. The differences between the group means were 4.9 months for the mothers and 2.2 months for the fathers. When the discrepancies for the individual informants were tabulated, the mean individual discrepancy was 5.2 months for the mothers and 4.8 months for the fathers (815). The same response was given to both questions, 196 and 237, by forty-nine fathers and fifty-three mothers, roughly one third of the informants; in thirty-three cases both parents gave exactly the same response to 196 while in thirty-one cases both parents gave, to the month, the same response to 237.

Allowing, then, for the indicated margin of ambiguity and indecisiveness, it would seem that whatever these parents were referring to in saying that their children were beginning to stutter, they did not consider it a "problem" until about five months later. Presumably, whatever the children were doing that the parents called "stuttering," it was not sufficiently grave or different from what children commonly do, or from what the parents assumed they should be doing, to be regarded, at first, as a "problem" in most cases. The responses to such questions as 243, "When stuttering was first noticed was it accompanied by any grimaces or bodily contortions?" or 247, "Did the very first stoppages seem to be unpleasant to the child?" are to be evaluated, of course, with due consideration of these various facts and implications, and of the demonstrated ambiguity of "the time of onset of stuttering," or "when stuttering was first noticed," or "when the child first began to stutter," or the equivalents of such expressions.

At what age, then, was the problem of stuttering found to have

begun? That is, in the average case how old was the child when someone first regarded something that he was presumably doing as stuttering? The answer to this question varied, as has been seen, according
to the way in which it was worded, the person to whom it was addressed, and the time at which it was asked. With what would seem
to be reasonable allowances for these sources of variation and for
probable degrees of ambiguity, an appropriate answer appears to be
that however or wherever, and in whatever form and for whom, the
problem of stuttering had begun, it arose as a rule when the child involved was in the fourth year, probably nearer to the third than to the
fourth birthday in most cases.

The Persons for Whom the Problem of Stuttering Arose

In view of the considerable degree to which information about the
origin of the problem of stuttering is influenced by the processes of
perception, evaluation, memory, and recall of the persons who are, of
necessity, the sources of this information, it is of basic importance
that these persons be identified, so far as this can be done.

In Study III each informant was asked (214), "Who first decided
that the child was stuttering (or the equivalent, for example, stammering, hesitating in his speech, impediment, 'something wrong,'
etc.)?" Twelve experimental group fathers and eight mothers gave
responses coded "?" (uncertain, can't recall). The responses of the
remaining informants indicated that in only four cases was the original judgment, or "suspicion," or diagnosis made by some kind of professionally trained person—in two cases by a teacher, in one by a
physician, and in one by a school nurse. In no case was the original
judgment or diagnosis made by a specialist in speech disorders. In
134 cases, according to the fathers, and in 131, according to the mothers, the parents themselves, acting separately or together, were the
first to decide that the child was stuttering. The original judgment was
formed much more often by the mother than by the father, 92 to 12
according to the mothers and 79 to 17 as reported by the fathers. In
the remaining cases other members of the family, particularly grandparents, made the original evaluation. These findings agree very
closely with corresponding data from Studies I and II. In the control
group in Study III 30 fathers and 17 mothers who answered 214 said
they didn't know or couldn't recall who first gave attention to the
child's speech nonfluencies, and all the others who answered indicated
that the nonfluencies were first noticed by the parents, usually the
mother, or some other member of the family.

When asked (215) "Did you accept this decision or diagnosis

then?" 130 fathers and 140 mothers in the experimental group said
"Yes," and, in response to 216, 135 fathers said their wives had accepted the decision and 129 mothers said their husbands had.

In general, then, it is to be said that the beginning of the problem
of stuttering was reported in nearly all cases to have been a judgment
made of the child's speech, as perceived and evaluated by a member
of the child's family, nearly always one or both of the parents, usually
the mother, and in most cases without apparent disagreement between the parents concerning this judgment.

The Circumstances under Which the Problem of Stuttering Arose

In light of the findings just presented, there is special interest in the
information obtainable concerning the nature of the situations in
which those who first decided that the child was stuttering made that
crucial decision. For all practical purposes such information can only
be obtained at first hand from persons who were present in the situations. In Study III each experimental group mother and father was
asked, as indicated in 197, to describe the situation in which the child
stuttered the very first time. Previous research and clinical experience
had indicated abundantly the difficulty most parents have in recalling
"the very first time" their children stuttered, or were thought to have
stuttered. The interviewers were instructed, therefore, to ask any
parent who could not recall "the very first time" to describe "the first
situation the parent can recall in which he or she observed the child
stuttering." The responses are presented in detail in 197 and in the
footnote to 197.

It is to be noted particularly that only eighteen fathers and twenty-
six mothers claimed to be able to recall "the situation in which the
child stuttered the very first time." It is quite impossible to say how
many of the relatively few who made this claim did, in fact, recall
and describe the situation in which they first felt that their child was
stuttering. As is indicated in the footnote to 197, as well as in the
tabulation in 197 itself, the presumed "first situations" were not identified clearly in most cases. They were not described in the sort of
detailed way in which specific situations, clearly recalled as such,
might as a rule be described. The phrases used were such as "telling
parent something," "when he came in to tell something," "asking for
something at the table," "explaining something to parent," etc. More
definite wordings were "reciting a piece at home," "talking about what
had happened while riding in car after slight accident and while competing with others for the privilege of speaking," "after a scolding,"
and "upon meeting father at station after father's two-week absence

and with mother present," this being one of the most clearly designated of the allegedly "first" situations. It is not certain, however,
that even the less vague descriptions are to be accepted as referring
to "first" situations.

It would seem to be particularly significant in this connection that
in only fourteen cases did the mother and father — and it is to be
recalled that they were interviewed independently — agree exactly in
their responses to 197. The most striking of the discrepancies involved
relatively descriptive accounts by one or both parents, showing that
even those situations which were apparently more or less well recalled either were not "first" situations, or else, in such instances, the
"first" situation in which the mother thought the child was stuttering
was not the same as the one in which the father believed the problem
first occurred. It is assumed that, in any case in which the informants
claimed to be able to recall "the situation in which the child stuttered
the very first time" (see the exact wording of 197 in the Summary
Table), both informants would have given accounts of the same inci-
dent or situation had they been in agreement about the first occurrence of whatever they meant by "stuttering." It is not clear that
this can be assumed if the informant, unable to recall the "first"
situation, gave a description of a situation which was said to be the
first one recalled in which the informant "observed the child stuttering" (see the wording of instructions to the interviewer, 197). Even
in some such cases, however, it might be expected that the mother and
father would have known they were in disagreement, if they were,
concerning the "first" situation, and that they might have made some
mention of the fact.

Additional light is thrown on the problems involved in securing
valid evidence with respect to "the very first" occurrence of stuttering
by a comparison of the responses discussed above and those made to
235, "Describe the first situation in which your child did something
which you felt at that time indicated he had a speech problem (you
may or may not have called it stuttering)." The purpose of this question was to explore the possibility that the parents felt, vaguely perhaps, that the child had a speech problem for some period of time
before they arrived at the judgment that the child was stuttering —
or, on the contrary, that some period of time passed after the parents
decided the child was stuttering before they evaluated whatever they
regarded as stuttering as a problem. As it turned out, the findings
indicated, as has been stated, that whatever the parents were referring to in saying that their children were beginning to stutter, they
did not consider it a "problem" until about five months later, on the

average. Over two thirds of the parents, 107 fathers and 104 mothers, could not recall or describe "the first situation" asked for in this question, or any "early" situation either, largely, it appears, because the feeling that their child "had a problem" was not associated for them with any specific situation, but was rather experienced as a gradually growing conviction associated with the feeling that the child "should be getting over it," or with the realization that he would soon be starting to school, or with the belief that his speech was "getting worse," etc., or the parent was told by a teacher or doctor that the child had a speech problem. As in the case of 197, the respondents who could not recall "the first" situation—only fourteen claimed they could —were asked to describe the first situation they could recall in which they felt their child had a speech problem, and the few situations reported were for the most part vaguely indicated. In only six cases did both parents agree exactly in their descriptions.

Finally, although the situations described in response to 197 and 235 were, on the average, about five months apart, twenty-seven fathers and twenty-five mothers gave the same descriptions, as coded, in both cases. In view of the mean temporal discrepancy, these numbers appear to imply that the descriptions given were vague rather than specific in situational reference, and were indicative of the relative incapacity of the informants to recall precisely the beginning of the stuttering problem as they and their children were concerned with it.

The responses to 197 obtained in Study II were essentially like those in Study III. Similar data were also obtained in Study I. The control group parents in Study III, with only fifteen exceptions, said simply that they could not recall any situation of the sort called for.

In items 198 through 213 the parents were asked whether various specific conditions were present in the first situation in which the child was thought to stutter, and again those respondents who could not recall the "first" situation were asked to answer with reference to the first situation they could recall. Roughly 15 to 20 per cent of the informants claimed to be able to respond with reference to the "first" situation, and about the same percentage were unable to recall anything in particular about any specific situation. The items were concerned with the following conditions, and the number of fathers and of mothers who said that each was present in the "first" situation in which the child stuttered is indicated in each case:

1. Competing with someone else for the privilege of speaking; 5 fathers, 11 mothers.

2. Difficulty in thinking of the right words; 10 fathers, 14 mothers.

128

3. Frustration or bewilderment; 8 fathers, 7 mothers.

4. Speaking to someone who was not listening; 5 fathers, 6 mothers.

5. Child had just received punishment or scolding; 1 father, 3 mothers.

6. Severe fright; 3 fathers, 4 mothers.

7. Arrival of new baby (within preceding week, month, or two to three months); 3 fathers, 8 mothers.

8. Child's realization of the mother's pregnancy (within preceding week); 2 fathers, no mothers.

9. Child had been asking to do something not ordinarily allowed; 1 father, no mothers.

10. There had been changes in the child's physical environment (moving of furniture or actual changing of houses); 2 fathers, 10 mothers.

11. Child was trying unsuccessfully to say something before someone else took over the conversation; 5 fathers, 10 mothers.

12. Child in state of excitement; 9 fathers, 10 mothers.

13. Child was failing to make himself understood; 8 fathers, 9 mothers.

14. Child was ill or fatigued; 4 fathers, 4 mothers.

15. Child was in a hurry to tell something; 12 fathers, 17 mothers.

16. Parent had just caught the child doing something of which he was made to feel ashamed; no fathers, 2 mothers.

The number giving "Yes" answers that referred to early but not the "first" situations ranged from no fathers and two mothers (severe fright) to seventy fathers and seventy-five mothers (hurry in speaking); the next highest numbers were thirty-four fathers and twenty-five mothers who reported excitement. The conditions most often said to be present in the situations recalled were hurry in speaking, excitement, difficulty in finding the right word, competing for the privilege of speaking, trying to "hold the floor" (208), and speaking to an unresponsive listener (201). All of these would seem to be rather commonplace conditions. The more unusual and presumably more serious conditions, such as severe fright, shame, punishment, conflict involving disobedience (206), and changes in environment were seldom reported. Frustration or bewilderment, illness or fatigue, and difficulty in making themselves understood, each reported by slightly less than 10 per cent of the respondents, were presumably intermediate between these two general classes of circumstances.

The great majority of the responses to all these items, except for 212 (hurry in speaking) as noted, were negative. And in presenting these items, it is to be recognized, the interviewer was in some measure unavoidably "putting words in the respondent's mouth"; as the tabulations in the Summary Table indicate, there was much overlapping of responses, and this can probably best be interpreted as indicating that the respondents were answering these questions with reference not primarily to any specific situation in each instance, but to the child's speaking in general, as though the response had been initiated in each case with some such words as these: "Well, yes (or no), now that you ask *that*, it seems to me I do remember that sometimes (or never) . . . " In any event, there are differences between the informants' responses to these specific questions and their responses to 197 and 235, which called for their own unaided recall to be expressed in their own words.

One further observation is of interest, in view of the more or less popular notion that one of the causes of stuttering is imitation. Items 331–337 are generally relevant to this matter. The responses to these items indicate that, according to the informants, about one third of the children were in intimate or frequent contact with one or more stutterers (331); that between 15 and 20 per cent of the parents felt their children's stuttering resembled in detail that of some other stutterer with whom he was in frequent contact (332), but that only 10 per cent of the children were said to "know about" the stuttering of these other stutterers whose speech their own presumably resembled (335), and of these less than half, only seven, had found out about the stuttering of these other stutterers by actually hearing them talk (336); that only ten fathers and seven mothers compared their children with other stutterers even occasionally (337); and that while about one third of the parents said they suspected or believed the contact of the child with other stutterers might be important (333), only two fathers and six mothers said they had tried, even seldom or occasionally, to prevent contact of their child with other stutterers. Finally, although when asked, in 344, "What do you think caused your child's stuttering?" eight fathers and three mothers gave "imitation" as an answer, in their responses to 197 and 235 no mother or father included the child's imitation of a stutterer among the conditions or circumstances associated with the beginning of the problem. Without raising the basic question of what precisely might have been meant, or was in fact meant, by "imitation" in this general context as the various respondents used the term, it seems conservative to conclude that probably imitation, however defined in particular instances, was of very slight, if any, importance in relation to the onset of stuttering in the cases investigated in Study III.

In general, the data reviewed indicate that in the large majority of cases the problem of stuttering arose under conditions that the parents were able to remember only vaguely, if at all. Seldom was the onset of stuttering reported to have occurred under dramatic or memorable circumstances. On the contrary, in those few cases in which recall seemed comparatively clear, the situations which were said to have been the first in which the children were thought to stutter were essentially commonplace and uneventful or undisturbing, so far as could be determined. Such circumstances as those involving hurried speech and excitement were reported more often than any others, and they might be expected to occasion nonfluent speech in most, if not all, young children, as was indicated, in fact, by the responses of the control group parents to such items as 209 (excitement) and 212 (hurry). Indeed, the distributions of the control group responses to the items here reviewed were for the most part quite similar to those of the responses of the experimental group informants. This is to say that the conditions reportedly associated with the "first" stutterings of the experimental group children were, in general, the same as those associated with the "first" nonfluencies which the control group parents said they observed in the speech of their children. The major conclusion would seem to be that, generally speaking, the problem of stuttering was found to develop under quite ordinary circumstances.

CHAPTER 6

The Earlier and Later Stutterings

THE data so far reviewed indicate that, in general, the beginning of the problem of stuttering was reported as a judgment or feeling concerning the child's speech, made or experienced by one or both parents when the child was speaking under essentially ordinary circumstances, which were approximately located in time during the child's fourth year of life, probably nearer the third birthday than the fourth. The next question to be investigated, then, has to do with the child's speech. What sort of speaking was the child doing sometime around his third birthday or perhaps a bit later, in some more or less commonplace situation, when one or both of his parents decided he was stuttering?

Descriptions of First Stutterings

In the interview employed in Study III the first approach to a description of the first speech phenomena to be classified as stuttering was the request made of the informant, in 217, to "imitate and describe what the child was doing in his speech when he first stuttered — the very first time you noticed the child stuttering, or during the period when the stuttering still was the same as it had been the very first time it was noticed by anyone." This request was addressed also to the control group parents, with the understanding that they were to answer with respect to what they referred to as the first nonfluencies they had observed in the speech of their children. The imitations performed by the informants were recorded descriptively by the interviewers, and the informants' verbal responses were recorded as given. All responses are presented in detail in 217 in Appendix A, and they are summarized and analyzed in Tables 38–43.

Before scrutinizing these responses, it is well to recall, from previous sections of this report, that the burden of evidence is persuasive of the conclusion that very few parents were able to remember the first

132

instances of whatever they had regarded as their children's stuttering. It would seem to be a conservative assumption that in response to 217 all, or nearly all, informants gave accounts, varying in clarity and validity, of something they asserted their children had done while speaking over a period of time. The periods covered by these accounts extended from a few days to a year or more, during which, either more or less continuously or from time to time, and in most cases with gradually increasing strength of conviction, the informants had entertained the feeling, or judgment, or suspicion that their children were stuttering, or beginning to stutter. So far as this view may seem acceptable on the basis of the data so far reviewed, it provides perspective for the examination of the responses that are presented in 217 and in Tables 38–43.

Two overshadowing facts emerge from examination of the various individual responses listed under 217. Doubtless the more important of these is that there is overlapping of the data for the experimental and control group children, in general the same kinds of nonfluency being reported for both groups. The extent of this overlapping would seem to be less significant than the fact that there was overlapping; the extent is indicated in Tables 38 and 39. The overlapping means, of course, that types of speech behavior referred to by the same presumably descriptive terms were classified as "stuttering" by some listeners but not by other listeners. The other, and of course related, fact is that the great majority of the experimental group children were repeating sounds or syllables, words, or phrases when they were first looked upon as stutterers.

As shown in Table 38, according to the 143 fathers who gave definite answers, 121, or 85 per cent, of the children were performing such repetitions; according to the 146 mothers who answered unequivocally, the figure was 132, or 90 per cent. Moreover, 72 per cent of the fathers and 77 per cent of the mothers did not indicate that their children were doing anything else that they regarded as stuttering, with the exception of 6 children, as reported by the fathers, and 8, according to the mothers, who were also saying "uh uh" or "well uh" or the equivalent.

It is of basic theoretical interest to compare these responses with those of the control group parents who described what they called the "first" nonfluencies they noticed in their presumably normal-speaking, nonstuttering children. Of the 69 control group fathers who gave unequivocal responses, 79 per cent, and of the 80 mothers who answered definitely, 61 per cent said their children's "first" nonfluencies consisted of repetitions of sounds or syllables, words, or phrases. Forty-two per cent of the fathers and 35 per cent of the mothers did not re-

Table 38. Percentages of Control and Experimental Group Fathers and Mothers Who Reported That the Child Was Performing Each of the Indicated Speech Reactions (A) When They First Thought the Child Was Stuttering (217), (B) When They First Thought the Child Had a Speech Problem (236), and (C) at the Time of Interview (293) (Control Group Parents Answered with Reference to the First Time They Thought the Child's Speech Was Nonfluent).

Group and Item*	Repetition					Other Nonfluency			
	Combined†	Only‡	Syllable	Word	Phrase	Sound Prolongations	Silent Intervals, Pauses	Interjections	"Complete Blocks"
A (217)									
Control									
Fathers (N69)	79	42	4	59	23	3	36	30	0
Mothers (N80)	61	35	10	41	24	4	41	21	0
Experimental									
Fathers (N143)	85	72	57	48	8	15	7	8	3
Mothers (N146)	90	77	59	50	8	12	3	9	3
B (236)									
Experimental fathers (N124)	80	57	64	45	9	23	7	16	6
Experimental mothers (N134)	83	63	66	50	8	15	4	18	8
C (293)									
Experimental fathers (N146)	93	64	75	57	10	25	4	12	6
Experimental mothers (N146)	91	62	75	62	8	25	4	15	7

* In computing percentages the value of N in each subgroup represented the number of respondents giving unequivocal responses, "uncertain" and "can't recall" responses being excluded. See the accompanying text for a fuller explanation of column headings and for a discussion of the data. See Tables 39–47 for additional related data, including significance levels of measures of group differences.

† Children for whom repetitions of any kind were reported, alone or in combination with one or more other types of reaction.

‡ Children for whom the only reactions reported were repetitions (and interjections such as "uh uh," which are also usually repeated, provided they were combined with one or more of the categories of repetition — sound or syllable, word or phrase).

Table 39. Significance Levels of Values of z* for Differences between Indicated Pairs of Percentages Shown in Table 38

Differences	Repetition					Other Nonfluency			
	Combined	Only	Syllable	Word	Phrase	Sound Prolongations	Silent Intervals, Pauses	Interjections	"Complete Blocks"
217 vs. 236†									
Experimental fathers . .	NS‡	5% (217)§	NS	NS	NS	NS	5% (236)	5% (236)	NS
Experimental mothers . .	NS	5% (217)	NS	NS	NS	NS	1% (236)	1% (236)	NS
217 vs. 293									
Experimental fathers . .	5% (293)	NS	1% (293)	NS	NS	5% (293)	NS	NS	NS
Experimental mothers . .	NS	1% (217)	1% (293)	5% (293)	NS	1% (293)	1% (293)	NS	NS
Group means for 217									
Experimental fathers vs. control fathers . .	NS	1% (E)	1% (E)	NS	1% (C)	1% (E)	1% (C)	1% (C)	NS
Experimental mothers vs. control mothers . .	1% (E)	1% (E)	1% (E)	NS	1% (C)	5% (E)	1% (C)	1% (C)	NS

* The formula used, as presented by Walker (R115, pp. 77–79), is

$$z = \frac{p_1 - p_2}{\sqrt{(pqN)/(N_1 N_2)}}$$

in which p_1 = sample 1 proportion; p_2 = sample 2 proportion; N_1 = number in sample 1; N_2 = number in sample 2; $N = N_1 + N_2$; $p = (N_1 p_1 + N_2 p_2)/(N_1 + N_2)$; and $q = 1 - p$.

† 217, 236, and 293 refer to items so numbered in the Summary Table and represented in Table 38. See Table 38 for the data involved in this analysis.

‡ NS = nonsignificant.

§ The number of the item, or the designating symbol of the group, for which the percentage value was higher is shown in parentheses.

port that their children were doing anything except repeating, plus interjecting extraneous sounds such as "uh uh" or "well uh" which was indicated by 21 fathers and 11 mothers. While the group differences with respect to these two categories of response were statistically significant, as indicated in Table 39 (with the exception of the proportions of fathers reporting combined repetitions), due attention is to be given to the extent of overlap between the two groups and to the fact that repetitions constituted the major category of the nonfluencies of the control group children, as reported by their parents. With respect to types of repetition, as shown in Table 39, syllable repetitions were reported for significantly more experimental group children, phrase repetitions were reported for significantly more control group children, and there was not a significant group difference with respect to word repetitions.

As indicated in Table 39, there was one additional type of nonfluency, prolongations of sounds, reported for significantly more experimental group children. Twenty-two fathers and eighteen mothers in the experimental group included prolongations in their descriptive accounts; for only eight children, however, did both the mother and father agree in reporting this kind of nonfluency. Significantly more control than experimental group children were reported by their parents to have exhibited silent intervals, or pauses, and interjections. Nonfluencies described as "silent intervals or pauses" were reported as having occurred in the speech of their children by 36 per cent of the fathers and 41 per cent of the mothers in the control group, and by only 7 per cent of the fathers and 3 per cent of the mothers in the experimental group. The interjection of extraneous sounds, such as "well" or "and uh" or "uh, uh, uh," was indicated by 30 per cent of the fathers and 21 per cent of the mothers in the control group, and by only 8 and 9 per cent of the fathers and mothers, respectively, in the experimental group. The values of z for all these group differences were significant at the 1 per cent level.*

Table 38 indicates that there was generally high over-all agreement between the mothers and fathers within the two groups. In view of this fact, the disagreements between spouses in the experimental group were particularly striking with regard to such evaluations as "complete

* Pauses, or silent intervals, were not included among the categories of nonfluency used in the analysis of tape-recorded speech samples of the control and experimental group children (see Chapter 8), but interjections were, and it is to be noted that by objective count the mean numbers of interjections per 100 spoken words were not significantly different for the two groups (see Tables 73 and 74, Chapter 8). The major statistically significant group differences observed in the tape-recorded speech samples lay in the greater frequency of syllable and word repetitions and prolongations of

blocks on first sound of word," "blocks on initial sound," "block before word (guttural sounds emitted)," and "repeated gasps." These were the closest and, with two ambiguous exceptions to be noted presently, the only definite approximations to an account of anything that could be referred to as a "breakdown in speech," or a "sudden failure of speech function," or a "neuromuscular disintegration," or a "spasm" (a term used by some writers even today to refer more or less indiscriminately to the reactions commonly called "stuttering"). No respondents in the control group and only 3 per cent of either the mothers or fathers in the experimental group reported "complete blocks," and the difference, as indicated in Table 39, was not statistically significant for either the fathers or the mothers. What seems more important than this, however, is the fact that only four fathers and five mothers, all in the experimental group, offered the indicated descriptions (see responses numbered 5, 28, 30, 33, 34, 36, 37, 51, and 67 in 217), and that, even though the terms employed would appear to signify some sort of conspicuous, dramatic, and distressing difficulty, it was, in every one of the nine cases, reported only by either the mother or the father, never by both. Since the words used, if employed seriously and thoughtfully, might ordinarily be taken to indicate grave deviations from ordinary speech behavior, deviations likely to disturb any parent confronted by them, the failure of one of the parents in each case to have observed or to have remembered being told by the other parent about them might be regarded as grounds for doubt about the descriptive care exercised by the informants who used these words. The word "block" as commonly used in this particular context, not only by laymen but often by professional workers as well, would appear to have no clearly distinctive meaning; it is not certain what the informants referred to in using it.

Moreover, the same sorts of comment are to be made concerning the two "ambiguous exceptions" referred to a few lines back, which were the responses numbered 11 and 35 in 217. The one, 11, was "Couldn't finish sentence — said 'ah, ah, ah,'" and the other, 35, was a bit more extensive: "Couldn't finish sentence; said, 'ah, ah, ah'; repetition of word, first syllable and initial sound." Except for the words "couldn't finish sentence," these descriptions seem to refer to nothing outside the

sounds in the speech of the experimental group children. The degree to which the distributions of the various measures of nonfluency for the two groups overlapped is of theoretical as well as practical interest (see Chapter 8). It is to be duly noted, of course, that the speech samples analyzed were tape recorded at the time of interview, about eighteen months, on the average, after the reported onset of stuttering (and at the corresponding time for the control group children), while the responses to 217 referred to the child's speech at time of onset.

range of common occurrence in childhood speech, and it would seem questionable that the words "couldn't finish sentence" are to be taken literally, since what they might or could mean descriptively, or extensionally, is not clear. "Couldn't," as distinguished from "didn't," is a judgmental rather than a descriptive term, and if the judgment which it expressed in these instances was derived from observation of the other speech behavior that was described, the judgment would ap-

Table 40. Percentages of Control and Experimental Group Fathers and Mothers Who Reported, in Response to Specific Questions, That When They "First Noticed That the Child Was Stuttering" He or She Was Repeating Whole Words (218), Repeating Syllables (221), and "Making Extraneous Sounds Such as 'Ah,' 'Er,' 'Well,' 'And' " (227), as Compared With Corresponding Percentages Who Reported, as Shown in Table 38, in Response to a General Question (217), That the Child Had Performed These Same Types of Reactions (Control Group Parents Answered with Reference to the First Time They Thought the Child's Speech Was Nonfluent)

	Control Group				Experimental Group			
	Fathers		Mothers		Fathers		Mothers	
Type of Nonfluency and Item	%	N	%	N	%	N	%	N
Combined repetitions, 217	79	69	61	80	85	143	90	146
Yes responses, 218 or 221 or 227	76	75	80	84	93	150	95	150
Yes responses, 218 or 221	54	75	52	85	87	150	89	150
Syllable repetitions, 217	4	69	10	80	57	143	59	146
Yes responses, 221	5	75	8	85	65	150	69	150
Word repetitions, 217	59	69	41	80	48	143	50	146
Yes responses, 218	57	75	47	84	59	150	63	150
Interjections, 217	30	69	31	80	8	143	9	146
Yes responses, 227	55	76	48	85	38	150	42	150

Table 41. Significance Levels of Values of z* for Intragroup Differences between Indicated Pairs of Percentages Shown in Tables 38 and 40

Differences	Control Group		Experimental Group	
	F	M	F	M
A, combined repetitions, 217† vs. B, yes responses, 218 or 221 or 227	NS	1% (B)‡	5% (B)	NS
A, combined repetitions, 217 vs. B, yes responses, 218 or 221	1% (A)	NS	NS	NS
Syllable repetitions (217 vs. 221)	NS	NS	NS	NS
Word repetitions (217 vs. 218)	NS	NS	NS	5% (227)
Interjections (217 vs. 227)	1% (227)	5% (227)	1% (227)	1% (227)

* See the formula in the footnote to Table 39.

† Numbers refer to items so numbered in the Summary Table and represented in Tables 38 and 40.

‡ The number of the item, or the designating symbol of the combination of items, for which the percentage value was higher is shown in parentheses.

pear to have been suspect, if not clearly invalid. However the responses may be interpreted, it is again to be noted that in neither of these two cases did both parents agree in reporting the behavior referred to. If in each case the child had been in any serious sense of the term, neuromuscularly unable to continue speaking, it would seem likely that this presumably alarming development would have been observed by the other parent also, or that it would have been made known to the other parent by the one who did observe it. What seems most probable in the light of general clinical experience is that such wordings as "the child just couldn't go on," or "couldn't say a word," or "had a complete block," are used loosely by parents and are seldom, if ever, employed by them in a spirit of scientific rigor.

Immediately following 217, items 218–232 required responses of "yes," "no," or "?" (uncertain, can't recall) with respect to whether or not the child was doing various specific things when he was first thought to be stuttering. Whereas in responding to 217 the informants were left to their own processes of association, recall, and verbal expression, as well as their capacities for imitation, in responding to 218–232 the informants had words put in their mouths, as it were, and they were asked which of these words felt right and which did not. Since the fact of repetition loomed relatively very large in the responses to 217, it is of special interest to note the responses to 218, 221, and 227, in which each parent was asked whether the child, when first thought to be stuttering, was repeating words, repeating syllables, or "making extraneous sounds such as 'ah,' 'er,' 'well,' 'and.'" In the experimental group, as indicated in Table 40, 93 per cent of the fathers and 95 per cent of the mothers gave "yes" responses to one or more of items 218, 221, and 227; slightly under nine out of ten indicated either word or syllable repetition, or both.

There was a tendency, as shown in Table 40, for more informants, especially in the experimental group, to report the indicated types of nonfluency in response to the specific questions asked in items 218, 221, and 227 than in response to the general sort of question asked in 217. Most of the differences, however, as shown in Table 41, were not significant at or beyond the 5 per cent level. Approximately two thirds of the experimental group parents reported syllable repetitions (221) and about three out of five said their children were repeating whole words (218). Although there was a tendency for more respondents to report these two types of repetition when asked about them specifically in 218 and 221 than when asked, in 217, a general question about what the child had been doing, the differences, as shown in Table 41, were not significant, except for the larger proportion of mothers, 63 per cent, giving "yes" as the response to 218 as compared with 50 per cent who volunteered the report of word repetitions in response to 217.

Interjections were reported by significantly more control than experimental group fathers in response to both 217 and 227, and there was a significant group difference for the mothers also for 217 (Tables 39 and 42). In all four subgroups significantly more respondents reported interjections when asked about them specifically in 227 than when left to their own wordings in 217 (Tables 40 and 41). Whether in response to the open-ended question or the specific questions, significantly more experimental than control group parents reported repetitions of all sorts combined and more syllable repetitions. The experimental group mothers reported significantly more word repetitions in response to the specific question, 218, but not in response to the general question, 217; the fathers did not differ appreciably in response to either question, somewhat more than half in both groups reporting word repetitions (see Tables 39, 40, and 42). As has been stated, however, the fact that the specified group differences were or were not significant, with reference to a designated level of confidence, is not as crucial as the fact that the data for the two groups overlap. What is of major theoretical importance is the finding that essentially the same kinds of behavior were classified differently by different observers.

Although the findings that have just been presented add up to a rather large part of the answer to the question of what it was in the speech behavior of their children that the experimental group parents

Table 42. Significance Values of z* for Intergroup Differences between Indicated Pairs of Percentages Shown in Tables 38 and 40

Item	Fathers				Mothers			
	Number		z Level	Higher %	Number		z Level	Higher %
	Control	Experimental			Control	Experimental		
Combined repetitions (yes responses, 218 or 221 or 227) †	75	150	1%	E	84	150	1%	E
Word and syllable repetitions (yes responses, 218 or 221)	75	100	1%	E	85	150	1%	E
Syllable repetitions, 217	69	143	1%	E	80	146	1%	E
Syllable repetitions, 221	75	150	1%	E	85	150	1%	E
Word repetitions, 217	69	143	NS		80	146	NS	
Word repetitions, 218	75	150	NS		84	150	5%	E
Interjections, 217	69	143	1%	C	80	146	1%	C
Interjections, 227	76	150	5%	C	85	150	NS	

* See the formula in the footnote to Table 39.

† Numbers refer to items so numbered in the Summary Table and represented in Tables 38 and 40.

Table 43. Results of Chi-Square Analysis of Responses to Items Concerning Speech Reactions Associated with Onset of Stuttering, or Nonfluencies, on Which the Experimental and Control Group Parents Differed Significantly

Item	Direction of Difference	Level of Confidence	Remarks
When the stuttering/nonfluencies were first noticed was the child repeating a whole word? (218)	More experimental than control group mothers answered "yes"	2%	Fathers did not differ significantly
When the stuttering/nonfluencies were first noticed was the child repeating a syllable? (221)	More experimental than control group mothers answered "yes"	1%	Fathers followed similar trend, significant at 1% level
When the stuttering/nonfluencies were first noticed was the child prolonging a sound? (224)	More experimental than control group mothers answered "yes"	1%	Fathers followed similar trend, significant at 1% level
When the stuttering/nonfluencies were first noticed were there conspicuous silent periods within the child's speech? (228)	More control than experimental group mothers answered "yes"	1%	Fathers followed similar trend, significant at 1% level
When the stuttering/nonfluencies were first noticed was the child doing what you describe on the first word of a sentence? (229)	More experimental than control group mothers answered "yes"	1%	Fathers followed similar trend, significant at 5% level
Have you ever noticed other children doing such things as your child was doing? (234)	More control than experimental group mothers answered "yes"	1%	Fathers followed similar trend, significant at 1% level
At the time when stuttering/nonfluencies were first noticed, was the child using force or more effort than usual "to get his words out"? (250)	More experimental than control group mothers reported force or effort	1%	Fathers followed similar trend, significant at 1% level
When you first noticed that the child was stuttering/having nonfluencies was he or she making extraneous sounds such as "ah," "er," "well," "and"? (227)	More control than experimental group fathers answered "yes"	1%	Mothers did not differ significantly

took to be stuttering, it is important to be particularly thorough in determining the degree to which the reports of these parents referred to tense or "blocked" speech, or to reactions by the child to his own speech that seemed indicative of emotional disturbance, or at least slight concern or uneasiness. The data obtained in response to 217 and presented in Table 38 point toward the general conclusion that for the most part there was no unusual tension in the speech behavior originally judged to be stuttering. In addition to 217, however, there were eight items in the interview designed to be especially serviceable in this connection. Two of these were relatively general. The first of this pair was 250: "At the time when stuttering was first noticed, was the child using force or more effort than usual 'to get his words out'? Was there more than usual muscular tension?" The other, 305, called for essentially the same kind of information, but with reference to the speech of the child at the time of interview: "When the child stutters does he make any grimaces or odd bodily movements, or does he seem to do anything else out of the ordinary?" Responses to these two items are summarized in Table 47 and group differences with respect to 250 are indicated in Table 43. The other six items dealt with specific types of reaction: 243, "When stuttering was first noticed was it accompanied by any grimaces or bodily contortions?" 244, "Did the child seem indifferent to his very first stoppages?" 245, "When the stuttering was first noticed, did the child seem to be aware of the fact that he was speaking in a different manner or doing something wrong?" 246, "Did the child show surprise or bewilderment after having had trouble on a word?" 247, "Did the very first stoppages seem to be unpleasant to the child?" 248, "Do you think the child felt irritated when the very first stoppages occurred?"

A "yes" response to 244 and "no" responses to the other five questions may be classified as indicating "no tension or concern" reactions on the part of the child, and the responses to these items shown in the Summary Table are mostly of this type. The 1,800 responses made to these six questions by the experimental group parents and the 795 given by the control group parents who regarded the questions, with the exception of 243, as applying to their children are summarized in Tables 44 and 45.

These tables constitute one of the most impressive single arrays of evidence yielded by this investigation of the essential similarity of the speech of the control and experimental group children at the time, in each case, when the parents first felt that the child was stuttering or, in the control group, speaking nonfluently. On the basis of the data summarized in Tables 44 and 45, it may be stated that whatever it was in their children's speech that the experimental group parents had judged to be stuttering, it apparently involved essentially no less and no more tension and emotionality than that which somewhat more than half of the control group parents had regarded as repetitions and other sorts of nonfluencies, but not as stuttering or something abnormal, in the speech of their children.

The rest of the control group parents, about half of the fathers and somewhat over one third of the mothers, said they had not noticed any

Table 44. Percentages of Responses by Control and Experimental Group Fathers and Mothers to Items 243–248 That Were Indicative and Not Indicative of Unusual Muscular Tension or of Some Degree of Irritation, Perplexity, or Awareness of Speaking in Any Way "Different" or "Wrong" on the Part of the Child When the Child Was First Judged to be Stuttering (Experimental Group) or Was First Thought to Be Speaking Nonfluently (Control Group) *

| | Control Group | | Experimental Group | |
Item	Fathers (N = 75)	Mothers (N = 84)	Fathers (N = 150)	Mothers (N = 150)
Percentage of responses indicative of tension and affective sensitivity	6.9	10.7	7.2	11.3
Percentage of responses not so indicative	92.5	87.6	89.0	87.7
Percentage of "?" responses (uncertain, can't recall)	0.6	1.7	3.8	0.9

* Item 243, "When stuttering was first noticed was it accompanied by any grimaces or bodily contortions?" was not addressed to the control group parents.

Table 45. Percentages of Control and Experimental Group Mothers and Fathers Who Gave Designated Numbers of Responses to Items 243–248 That Were Indicative of Unusual Muscular Tension or of Some Degree of Concern, Irritation, Perplexity, or Awareness of Speaking in Any Way "Different" or "Wrong" on the Part of the Child When the Child Was First Judged to Be Stuttering (Experimental Group) or Was First Thought to Be Speaking Nonfluently (Control Group)

| | Control Group | | Experimental Group | |
Number of Reponses Indicative of Child's Tension or Concern	Fathers (N = 75)	Mothers (N = 84)	Fathers (N = 150)	Mothers (N = 150)
6*			1.3	1.3
5	0.0	1.2	1.3	1.3
4	0.0	3.6	1.3	4.7
3	1.3	0.0	1.3	3.3
2	5.3	10.7	2.0	6.0
1	20.0	11.9	11.3	8.0
0	73.3	72.6	82.7	77.3

* Computed only for experimental subgroups, since 243 was not addressed to the control group; all the remaining percentages involve only items 244–248.

nonfluencies in their children's speech. Yet, the control group parents who did report nonfluencies were evidently referring to the ordinary repetitions and hesitations generally characteristic in varying measure of the speech of young children, and so of the speech of the rest of the control group children, too. If these deductions are accepted, it follows that the control group parents who reported no nonfluencies had disregarded, or had not noticed, the common varieties of nonfluency in their children's speech that they might have observed and evaluated somehow. This means, then, that they were providing information, not about their children's speech, but about their own perception.

It would appear, then, that the 600 parents interviewed in Study III distributed themselves, with respect to perceptual set and evaluative orientation, into three groups: (1) those who did not notice, or did observe but disregarded, their children's nonfluencies; (2) those who noticed the repetitions and hesitations in their children's speech, but did not evaluate them as "stuttering," or as "abnormal," or as a "problem"; and (3) those who noticed the repetitions and hesitations in the speech of their children, and did evaluate them as "stuttering," or as "abnormal," or as a "problem."

The fundamental importance of the practical and theoretical implications of the findings summarized in Tables 44 and 45 argued in favor of checking the reliability of the responses to 243–248. It was possible to do this in a simple but relatively adequate way by examining the degree of agreement between the responses made to each of these items and those made to 250 and 305. This was done by noting

Table 46. Percentages of Control and Experimental Group Fathers and Mothers Whose Responses to 243–248 (Concerned with Whether the Child Reacted in Specified Ways When Doing What Parents Regarded as His First Stuttering) Agreed with Their Self-Formulated Statements That "When Stuttering Was First Noticed" (250) and When Stuttering "Now," i.e., at and Recently prior to the Time of Interview (305), the Child was Exhibiting "No Force or Tension"

Item	Control Group				Experimental Group			
	Fathers		Mothers		Fathers		Mothers	
	250 (N = 63)	305 (N = 62)	250 (N = 69)	305 (N = 79)	250 (N = 94)	305 (N = 95)	250 (N = 96)	305 (N = 90)
243					95	88	93	86
244	100	97	94	90	97	92	94	91
245	91	87	84	84	98	91	94	93
246	97	97	99	96	97	96	97	94
247	95	97	96	94	99	93	96	89
248	94	95	93	87	95	90	96	88
Average	95	95	93	90	97	92	95	90

Table 47. Percentages of Control and Experimental Group Parents Reporting That the Child Was Manifesting "No Tension" When They First "Noticed Stuttering" (250) and/or When Child "Stutters Now," i.e., at or Recently prior to the Time of Interview (305) (Control Group Parents Answered with Reference to What They Reported as the Nonfluencies of Their Children)

	Control Group				Experimental Group			
Item and Response	Fathers N = 75		Mothers N = 84		Fathers N = 150		Mothers N = 150	
	N	%	N	%	N	%	N	%
No tension at onset (250) . . .	63	84	59	70	94	63	95	63
No tension at interview (305) . . .	62	83	79	94	96	64	90	60
No tension at onset and none at interview . .	55	87	58	99	63	67	65	68
No tension at interview and none at onset . .	55	89	68	86	62	64	60	67
No tension at interview or none at onset . . .	70	93	80	95	127	85	120	80
Tension at onset . .	10	13	14	17	51	34	54	36
Slight	7	9	9	11	30	20	33	22
Moderate	3	4	4	5	14	9	11	7
Excessive	0	0	1	1	7	5	10	7
Tension at interview	11	14	5	6	54	36	60	40
Tension at both onset and interview	3	4	3	3	28	19	29	19

the number of informants in each subgroup who had stated in response to 250 and to 305 that the child had exhibited "no force or tension" "when stuttering was first noticed" (250) and "now," at the time of interview (305), respectively, and then computing the percentage of that number who had given a "no tension or concern" response to each of 243–248. The resulting percentages, which may be interpreted essentially as measures of reliability of the parental reports of "no tension or concern," are shown in Table 46. For the control group they ranged from 84 to 100 per cent, with 16 out of 20 values being 90 or higher; for the experimental group the values ranged from 86 to 99, with 20 out of 24 being 90 or above. The average percentages of agreement were 90 or higher for all subgroups, the range extending from 90 to 97.

Items 243–248 and 250 referred to the time when the parents first thought the child was beginning to stutter, and the average percentages of agreement for these items ranged from 93 to 99 for the experimental group parents. Item 305 referred to the time of interview, eighteen months later on the average, and so the percentages in Table

46 which pertain to that item may be interpreted as showing that 86 to 96 per cent of the experimental group children who were said to exhibit no tensions or concern in speaking at the time of the interview had also shown none when their parents had first regarded them as stutterers eighteen months before.

Tables 46 and 47 indicate that the respondents did not clearly differentiate between "time of onset" and "now" in answering questions 243–248, and so far as this was the case it would seem to be further evidence of the general unclearness of the parents' memories for the period of time covered by the questions concerning onset and early development of the speech problem. In Table 47 the parents' responses to 250 and 305 are compared.

Roughly two thirds of the experimental group parents who reported "no tension" in their children's speech at "onset" also reported "no tension" at the time of interview, and vice versa. In the meantime, while slightly less than two thirds of these parents reported "no tension" at "onset," and about the same proportion reported "no tension" at the time of interview, 85 per cent of the fathers and 80 per cent of the mothers reported "no tension" *either* at "onset" *or* at the time of interview. Likewise, although over one third of the experimental group parents reported tension in their children's speech at onset of the problem, and slightly more than that reported tension at the time of interview eighteen months later, only 19 per cent indicated tension both at onset and at the time of interview. Meanwhile, in the control group roughly one out of six informants reported that there was tension in what they referred to as the first nonfluencies in the speech of their children, and 14 per cent of the fathers and 6 per cent of the mothers reported tension at the time of interview; 3 to 4 per cent of the control group children were reported by their parents to have shown tension when they were first thought to be nonfluent *and* at the time of interview.

Responses to item 250 were coded to indicate degrees of tension as judged, and the resulting distributions of these responses are shown in Table 47. The proportion of control group parents, 13 per cent of the fathers and 17 per cent of the mothers, who asserted that their children were exhibiting tension in their "first" nonfluencies would seem to imply that the experimental group parents who reported tension in their children's "first" stuttering may have been referring to something more or less like certain of the nonfluencies of the control group children. This implication appears to be reinforced by the breakdown of the control and experimental group responses into those referring to slight, moderate, and excessive degrees of tension, as judged.

146

Only 5 per cent of the fathers and 7 per cent of the mothers in the experimental group reported "excessive tension" in their children's "first" stuttering, and roughly two thirds of those in both the experimental and control groups who reported tension stated that the tension was of slight degree.

These data would seem to reinforce the inference that the speech reactions under investigation were essentially commonplace, and this is further suggested by still another observation. In item 234 the parents were asked: "Have you noticed other children doing such things in their speech — that is, doing the sorts of things you have described and imitated as the things your child was doing when you first noticed he was stuttering?" (For the control group parents: "when you first noticed that he was speaking nonfluently?") Most of the control group parents to whom the question applied, 85 per cent of the fathers and 89 per cent of the mothers, gave affirmative replies. This might suggest a basis for the evident inclination of the control group parents to regard the nonfluencies in their own children's speech as normal. At the same time, only about half of the experimental group mothers and fathers said they had noticed other children "doing such things." In view of the descriptions they gave of what they had regarded as "stuttering" in their children's speech, this would appear to indicate that they were operating with conceptions of statistical normalcy which they had not checked closely against the realities of childhood speech. In several studies of nonfluency in the speech of representative and presumably normal two- to five-year-old children, the writer and his students have found the mean incidence of syllable, word, and phrase repetitions to be 49 instances per 1,000 words in free-play situations and 36 instances per 1,000 words in speech-testing situations (R62, pp. 157–180). The normal range of incidence is from about 15 to more than 100 instances per 1,000 running words. Moreover, the general character of these repetitions, with respect to degrees of tension and apparent concern — or, as is usually the case, evident freedom from tension and concern — associated with them, would appear to be essentially the same, with the possibility of a few exceptions, as the nature of the nonfluencies reported by both the control and experimental group parents in this study.

The fact that half of the experimental group parents said they had never noticed other children "doing such things" in their speech could have meant, therefore, that they did not have a very clear sense of norms. This might have been one of the important reasons why they took the nonfluencies of their own children to be unusual; they may not have understood very clearly what is unusual and what is to be expected in the speech of preschool-age children under various kinds of conditions.

The findings indicate that the two groups of parents had made crucially different evaluations of essentially the same general kinds of nonfluent childhood speech. The experimental group parents had expressed their evaluations by deciding their children were stutterers and the control group parents had expressed their evaluations by continuing to regard the speech of their children as normal. In contemplating the possible theoretical implications of these findings, it is important to appreciate that among the nonfluencies which the control group parents regarded as normal there were some that they described as involving more than ordinary tension and various sorts of "emotional" reaction. In apparently about the same proportions, such nonfluencies were among those classified by the experimental group parents as stuttering. It is not that the children classified as stutterers never did anything except effortlessly repeat syllables, words, and phrases — even though this seems to be what they mainly did — but that the other things they did which involved tension and "emotionality" were also done reportedly by the control group children, who were not classified as stutterers for doing them.

The term "normal nonfluency" represents, according to the usages sampled in this study, a relatively broad category. It is to be considered that along with all else that it covered, the category included the types of nonfluency described as syllable repetition and sound prolongation, the ones reported, as shown in Table 39, for significantly more experimental than control group children. What seems particularly noteworthy is that these types of nonfluency, especially the repetition of syllables, are evidently more likely to be classified as stuttering," at least by listeners within our culture.* More information is needed concerning individual differences among listeners in perceiving and evaluating syllable repetitions in the speech of various sorts and ages of speakers under various kinds of circumstances. Apparently some listeners do not even perceive them, at least when produced by certain speakers in some situations; after all, a substantial proportion of the control group parents indicated that they had never heard repetitions in the speech of their children, and as was said above this would

* Boehmler (R16) and Giolas and Williams (R35) have reported on the basis of laboratory studies that the repetition of syllables is regarded as "stuttering" relatively more often than are repetitions of words and phrases. Glasner and Rosenthal (R36) have reported that repetition (type not indicated) "was clearly the nonfluency most frequently associated with a diagnosis of stuttering and prolongation [of sounds] was noted least frequently" by their sample of 153 parents who "said that their children had stuttered at some time."

seem to be an observation concerning their own perceptual reactions rather than the speech of their children, since it has been well established that repetition is a characteristic of the speech of children generally (R8). The matter of individual differences among speakers in producing nonfluencies is to be most meaningfully investigated in relation to the question of individual differences among listeners — and the variability of specific listeners — in perceiving, as well as evaluating and classifying, nonfluencies in speech.

Reactions to the Speech Behavior That Was Regarded as First Stutterings

The interview items designed to explore the parents' reactions to what they took to be the stuttering of their children — or to their own feelings that their children were stuttering — are to be found particularly in the section of the interview that extends from 238 through 324. Most of the questions were also addressed to the control group parents, and again their answers were made with reference to what they had reported as the nonfluencies of their children.

In 238, the parents were asked, "How soon after it was first noticed did someone say something to the child about his stuttering?" In the control group approximately 80 per cent of the respondents indicated either that nothing had ever been said to the child about the nonfluencies, or else that they were uncertain about this. In the experimental group, however, two thirds of the fathers and three fourths of the mothers indicated that something had been said to the child about what was referred to as his stuttering, and of these about three fourths reported that something had been said either immediately or soon — that is, within one month. The difference between the control and experimental groups with respect to the number of children to whom something was said (238) was, for both the fathers and mothers, significant at the 1 per cent level, according to the obtained value of chi-square.

As shown in 239, it had nearly always been someone within the family, usually the parents and most frequently the mother, who had said something to the child. These persons had made a great variety of comments to the child, as indicated in 240, the most common of which were suggestions that he slow down, take it easy, and stop and start over. Such comments or suggestions were said to have been made as often as from 5 times a day to 25 times a month in roughly one third of the cases in the experimental group (246). All the parents in all four subgroups who responded to 238 by saying that nothing was ever said to the child were consistent in stating, in response to 239, that no one had said anything to the child and in giving the response of "nothing" to 240, "What was first said to the child?" Moreover, all those who answered "nothing" to 240 also answered "never" when asked, in 241, how frequently "such comments were made."

In another series of four questions only the experimental group parents were asked when the child was told he was thought to have a speech defect (252); who told him (253); how the child was told, under what circumstances, and precisely what he was told (253); and what the child's own first reaction was to being informed that he was thought to have a speech defect (255). Scarcely one out of six fathers and about one out of three mothers indicated that the child had been told that he was thought to have a speech defect or difficulty (252). Most of those who were told were informed by their parents, usually in the form of a direct statement or in connection with an explanation of a planned visit to a doctor or speech correctionist. Most of the children had not appeared to be bothered by being told, according to their parents. Both the fathers and mothers were completely consistent in their responses to items 252, 253, and 255; all those who said the child had not been told he had a speech defect (252) gave corresponding answers to 253 and 255. So far as reliability may be equated with consistency, then, the responses to these items, as well as the responses to 238–241, as previously noted, were reliable.

The responses to these questions were spontaneous, or self-formulated by the informants. The parents were also asked, in a series of eight questions, 264–273, whether specific comments had been made to the child by anyone. The percentages of those control and experimental group fathers and mothers who had stated (240) that nothing was said to the child about his stuttering (control group: nonfluency) and who responded, consistently with this, to each of the items 264–273 by saying that the child had "never" been asked to talk slowly (264), or to think about what he was going to say (265), etc., are shown in Table 48. The consistency of response in both groups, as thus measured, was quite high, fourteen of the twenty percentages for the control group and thirteen of the twenty for the experimental group being above 90. There was some tendency for more of the informants to indicate in response to the specific questions than in response to the general one (240) that certain comments or reactions had been made. This was especially the case with respect to asking the child to slow down (264) and "saying the difficult words for" the child (270). Practically identical results were obtained when the "never" responses to 264–273 were compared with the "never" responses to 241, "How often were such comments made?" ("such comments" as those listed in 240).

Table 49 is similar to Table 48. In it are shown the percentages of informants in each subgroup whose "no" responses to items 276–283 were consistent with their statement, in response to 238, that nothing was ever said to the child about his or her stuttering (control group: nonfluency). For the control group all sixteen percentages were 90 or above, thirteen being 98 or 100. Half of the percentages for the experi-

Table 48. Percentages of Control and Experimental Group Fathers and Mothers Whose Responses to 264–273 (Concerned with Frequency with Which Parents Made Certain Reactions or Told the Child to Do Certain Things, Such as "Slow Down," "Stop and Start Over," and "Take It Easy" When They First Felt the Child Had a Speech Problem) Agreed with Their Self-Formulated Statement That Nothing Was Said to the Child (240) (Control Group Parents Answered with Reference to What They Reported as the Nonfluencies of Their Children)

	Control Group				Experimental Group			
	Fathers		Mothers		Fathers		Mothers	
Item	%	N	%	N	%	N	%	N
264	93	57	80	56	68	28	78	32
265	91	57	89	56	89	28	91	32
266	100	57	100	56	100	28	100	32
267	98	57	96	56	96	28	97	32
268	89	57	88	56	93	28	81	32
269	96	57	88	56	96	28	81	32
270	96	57	87	55	75	28	81	32
271	100	14	100	13	100	17	95	21
272	96	57	100	55	100	28	97	31
273	100	57	100	56	100	28	100	32

Table 49. Percentages of Control and Experimental Group Fathers and Mothers Whose Responses to 276–283 (Concerned with Whether Parents or Others Listening to the Child, When Parents First Felt the Child Had a Speech Problem (235), Reacted in Specified Ways "to the Fact That the Child Seemed to Be Having Difficulty") Agreed with Their Self-Formulated Statement That Nothing Was Ever Said to the Child about His or Her Stuttering (238) (Control Group Parents Answered with Reference to What They Reported as the Nonfluencies of Their Children)

	Control Group				Experimental Group			
	Fathers		Mothers		Fathers		Mothers	
Item	%	N	%	N	%	N	%	N
276	94	48	90	50	66	29	48	25
277	98	48	98	50	89	28	72	25
278	100	48	96	50	97	29	88	25
279	100	48	98	50	97	29	88	25
280	100	48	100	50	97	29	96	25
281	98	48	98	50	97	29	96	25
282	98	48	98	50	90	29	96	25
283	98	48	98	50	86	28	80	25

mental group were 90 or higher, and the only notable discrepancy lay in the fact that, when asked (276), "Did you or anyone else listening to the child react in any way to the fact that he seemed to be having difficulty?" only 66 per cent of the fathers and 48 per cent of the mothers in the experimental group who had stated that "nothing" had been said to the child (238) answered, "No." The reactions specified in 276–283 were wholly or for the most part — at least potentially — nonverbal, such as "Did you avert your gaze?" (277), or "Did you try to change the subject?" (278), or "Did you register surprise?" (279), or "Did you look worried?" (238). The relatively high degree of agreement between the responses to these questions and the response to 238, which was concerned with what was *said* to the child about his speech, is to be interpreted, accordingly, as indicating a general consistency of parents' reactions, verbal or nonverbal, to what they took to be the child's stuttering. Essentially the same array of percentages of agreement, or consistency, was obtained when the "no" responses to 276–283 were compared with the corresponding negative responses to 239, 240, and 252.

The parents were asked to rate the degree of concern they felt when they first thought the child had a speech problem (262) and at the time of interview (321), as well as their degree of shame over the child's stuttering (control group: nonfluencies) at the time of interview. The responses are summarized in Table 50. Roughly 90 per cent of the parents in the experimental group, as against 10 to 15 per cent of the parents in the control group, indicated that they had been slightly to very much concerned at "onset" and that they still were at the time of interview. Similar percentages were obtained in response to 263 and 322, in which each informant was asked to rate the concern felt by the spouse. The differences between the control and experimental group fathers and mothers, respectively, for 262 and 263 were significant at the 1 per cent level, as indicated by chi-square values (Table 51). There had been a slight shift of both the fathers and mothers in the experimental group in the direction of more concern at the time of interview, although the small degree of this shift is to be stressed. Somewhat less than 10 per cent of the experimental group fathers and about 13 per cent of the mothers expressed some degree of shame, mostly slight, with respect to what they regarded as their children's stuttering.

It is readily apparent from the data summarized in Table 51 that the experimental group parents reacted more often, more strongly, and more negatively to what they took to be their children's stuttering

152

Table 50. Percentages of Control and Experimental Group Fathers and Mothers Expressing Designated Degrees of Concern over the Child's Stuttering When They First Felt the Child Had a Speech Problem (262) and at the Time of Interview (321), and of Shame over the Child's Stuttering at the Time of Interview (323) (Control Group Parents Answered with Reference to the Nonfluencies of Their Children) *

Degree of Concern (262, 321) or Shame (323)	Control Group						Experimental Group					
	Fathers			Mothers			Fathers (N = 150)			Mothers (N = 150)		
	262 (N = 75)	321 (N = 75)	323 (N = 88)	262 (N = 84)	321 (N = 84)	323 (N = 96)	262	321	323	262	321	323
Very much	0	1	0	2	1	0	21	26	2	31	32	1
Moderate	4	1	0	1	0	0	18	27	1	27	31	4
Slight	11	7	1	13	11	0	48	36	4	36	29	8
None	85	90	99	84	88	100	13	11	93	6	8	87
Uncertain	0	0	1	0	0	0	1	0	0	0	0	0

*See the second and third items in Table 51 for statements of statistical significance of group differences with respect to 262 and the related item, 263.

153

Table 51. Results of Chi-Square Analysis of Responses to Items Pertaining to Parents' Attitudes and Reactions toward Stuttering (or Nonfluency) or Which the Experimental and Control Group Parents Differed Significantly

Item	Direction of Difference	Level of Confidence	Remarks
How frequently was something said to the child about speech? (241)	Something was said more often to experimental than control group children, according to mothers	1%	Fathers followed similar trend, significant at 2% level
How did you feel when you first felt your child had a speech problem? (262)	More control than experimental group mothers reported having felt no concern	1%	Fathers followed similar trend, significant at 1% level
How did your wife (husband) feel? (263)	More control than experimental group fathers felt no concern, according to their wives	1%	Fathers' statements concerning their wives followed similar trend, significant at 1% level
How often was the child told to slow down? (264)	Experimental group mothers reported higher frequencies than control group mothers	1%	Fathers followed similar trend, significant at 1% level
How often was the child told to stop and think about what he was going to say? (265)	Experimental group mothers reported higher frequencies than control group mothers	1%	Fathers followed similar trend, significant at 1% level
How often was the child told to stop and start over? (268)	Experimental group mothers reported higher frequencies than control group mothers	1%	Fathers followed similar trend, significant at 1% level
How often was the child told to relax and take it easy? (269)	Experimental group mothers reported higher frequencies than control group mothers	1%	Fathers followed similar trend, significant at 1% level

Table 51 — *continued*

Item	Direction of Difference	Level of Confidence	Remarks
How often did you say the "difficult" words for the child? (270)	Experimental group mothers reported higher frequencies than control group mothers	1%	Fathers followed similar trend, significant at 1% level
How often was the child told to try to keep from stuttering/nonfluency? (273)	Experimental group mothers reported higher frequencies than control group mothers	1%	Fathers followed similar trend, significant at 2% level
How frequently were other similar suggestions made? (275)	Experimental group mothers reported higher frequencies than control group mothers	1%	Fathers followed similar trend, significant at 1% level
Did anyone react in any way to the fact that the child seemed to be having difficulty? (276)	More experimental than control group mothers answered "yes"	1%	Fathers followed similar trend, significant at 1% level
Did you avert your gaze when the child was "having trouble"? (277)	More experimental than control group mothers answered "yes"	1%	Fathers followed similar trend, significant at 1% level
Did you register surprise when the child was "having trouble"? (279)	More experimental than control group mothers answered "yes"	2%	Distribution of fathers' responses unsuitable for chi-square analysis
Did you look worried when the child was "having trouble"? (283)	More experimental than control group mothers answered "yes"	1%	Fathers followed similar trend, significant at 1% level
Did you react in any other way when the child was "having trouble"? (284)	More experimental than control group mothers answered "yes"	1%	Distribution of fathers' responses unsuitable for chi-square analysis
Have you made other suggestions to help the child speak well? (274)	More experimental than control group mothers answered "yes"	1%	Fathers followed similar trend, significant at 1% level

155

than did the control group parents to what they looked upon as the nonfluencies of their children.

Development of the Stuttering Problem Subsequent to Onset

Both the control and experimental group parents were asked (285), "What has been the general course of the problem since you first noticed it?" In the experimental group roughly 30 per cent said the problem had become worse, nearly the same proportion said it had become better, and about one out of four stated that it had stayed about the same. The rest gave varying reports to the effect that it had got worse and then better or the reverse. Roughly two thirds of the mothers and half of the fathers, when asked specifically, in 290, whether there had been a time when they felt "the stuttering became more severe," answered, "Yes." Over two thirds of the mothers and about 40 per cent of the fathers in the experimental group reported, on the other hand, in response to 286, that after they had first noticed the stuttering there had been "a time when the speech improved greatly." Approximately one third of the mothers and one fourth of the fathers stated, in fact, in response to 288, that there had been a time when they felt "the stuttering had completely disappeared." In the control group the great majority of the parents said the problem had become better, stayed the same, or disappeared. Group differences are summarized in Table 52.

In 293 the experimental group parents were asked to describe and imitate "the present pattern of stuttering," just as they had been asked in 217 to describe and imitate "what the child was doing in his speech when he first stuttered," and, in 236, when they first felt the child had a speech problem. A breakdown of the responses to these items is given in Table 38, and significance values of certain differences among them are presented in Table 39. The degree of similarity among the three distributions of responses, in combination with the pattern of differences among them, is of very considerable interest. In general, the responses at the time of interview were more like those made with reference to the time when it was first felt that a problem existed (236) than those made with reference to the time of "first stuttering" (217). The shift in pattern of responses from 217 to 236 was in the direction of more fathers and mothers reporting silent intervals or pauses and interjections, and fewer reporting "repetitions only." To the degree that there was a further shift in pattern between the time when it was first thought that a problem existed (236) and the time of interview (293), it was in the direction of some additional increase in cases involving sound prolongations and a tendency for more mothers to re-

Table 52. Results of Chi-Square Analysis of Responses to Items Concerning the Development of Stuttering, or Nonfluencies, on Which the Control and Experimental Group Parents Differed Significantly

Item	Direction of Difference	Level of Confidence	Remarks
What has been the general course of the stuttering/nonfluency since you first noticed it? (285)	More control than experimental group mothers said it was same or better	1%	Fathers followed similar trend, significant at 1% level
After you first noticed that the child was stuttering/nonfluent was there ever a time when you felt the stuttering/nonfluency had completely disappeared? (286)	More experimental than control group mothers answered "yes"	1%	Fathers followed similar trend, significant at 1% level
After you first noticed that the child was stuttering/nonfluent was there ever a time when you felt the stuttering/nonfluency became more severe? (290)	More experimental than control group mothers answered "yes"	1%	Fathers followed similar trend, significant at 1% level
What was the child's usual attitude toward being called upon to perform as a speaker for outsiders? (315)	More experimental than control group mothers reported unfavorable reactions ("refusal," for example)	2%	Fathers did not differ significantly
How sensitive was the child about the speech defect/nonfluency? (318)	More experimental than control group mothers rated children as being sensitive	1%	Fathers followed similar trend, significant at 1% level

157

port word repetition and for more of both mothers and fathers to report syllable repetition. On the other hand, the numbers of experimental group fathers reporting "repetitions only" and silent intervals or pauses at the time of onset and at the time of interview were not significantly different. It is to be observed that even at the time of interview syllable and word repetitions were reported by much larger proportions of experimental group respondents than were "blocks," silent intervals or pauses, interjections, or sound prolongations. The number of experimental group informants reporting phrase repetitions remained essentially constant (217, 236, 293), and markedly under the number of control group informants reporting phrase repetitions (217).

The experimental group parents were asked how many times their children repeated each repeated word (219) or syllable (222) at the time of "onset," and at the time of interview they were asked (294), "How many repetitions are there as a rule now before the word is finally spoken?" The approximate mean that could be computed from the responses as coded was, for each of these three items, roughly 3.3.

As was shown in Table 47, about the same proportions of experimental group parents reported that their children manifested tension in speaking at "onset" and at the time of interview, respectively (250 and 305). It is of interest, therefore, that about half the fathers and two fifths of the mothers stated (295) that their children were showing about the same degree of "force or effort" at the time of interview as "when stuttering was first noticed," while about one third of the fathers and two fifths of the mothers said their children were showing more tension and the remainder, roughly 15 per cent of all experimental group informants, said their children were speaking with less tension at the time of interview.

In response to 296, over half the fathers and two fifths of the mothers said their children made "no reaction," at the time of interview, when they had "a lot of trouble saying a word," and the others gave reports indicating varying degrees of tension and kinds of affective or evaluative reactions. Nearly three fifths of the mothers and about two fifths of the fathers said their children had "especially difficult periods." Over half of the parents reporting such periods indicated (298) that they were brief in that they occurred "at least once a day" or "two or three times a week," and the causes to which they were attributed by the larger proportions of respondents (299) were fatigue and excitement, presumably transient states.

In 300 the attempt was made to ascertain the conditions under which the informant had "personally observed the child stuttering more than usual." A large variety of responses was obtained; the most frequently given were "none," "don't know, can't say," "when excited," and "describing something; telling a story," these four responses being given by 91 mothers and 110 fathers. In 301 each informant was asked, "During the past month in what situations have you personally observed that the child has had little or no trouble speaking?" Again, a great variety of responses was obtained. The following six responses were given by a total of 92 mothers and 87 fathers: "none," "don't know, can't say," "when calm, relaxed," "when talking, playing with other children," "when alone with father or mother," and "when playing alone; talking to himself." Approximately similar distributions of responses were given to 302 and 303, in which the informants were asked to identify the persons to whom the child stuttered more and less than usual, respectively, during the month preceding the interview. To both questions over two thirds of the informants gave the response "none." Similarly, when asked (304) which topics of conversation had given the child the most trouble, over two thirds of the experimental group parents gave the response "none in particular."

In 305 the informants were asked whether, at the time of interview, their children when stuttering (control group: when speaking nonfluently) "make any grimaces or odd bodily movements, or . . . do anything else out of the ordinary." About three fifths of the experimental group parents said they did not, and the rest gave a great variety of answers, only three of which, however, were given by as many as three or more of either the fathers or mothers. About three fourths of those who reported such reactions evaluated them negatively but most of these made the claim, the validity of which was not readily ascertainable, that they "overtly ignored" these reactions of the child which they said they disliked in some degree.

It is of interest that when asked (309), "How much does the child talk now as compared with other children?" over 90 per cent of both the experimental and control group parents said their children did an average amount of talking or more. About the same proportions stated that their children were permitted, at the dinner table (310) and when guests were present (312), to speak an average or greater than average amount. On the other hand, nearly 90 per cent of both groups said that their children were "taught to speak pieces" (313) and "called on to perform before outsiders" (314) about an average amount or less. The usual attitudes of the two groups of children toward requests to perform before outsiders (315) were reportedly more or less the same, with more of the experimental group children having "refused," as indicated in Table 52, and a few more of the control group children having exhibited shyness.

The Onset of Stuttering

Since there would appear to be a reasonable doubt that most of the informants were clearly aware of "the average amount" of talking done by other children under the conditions in question, their responses might judiciously be interpreted as representing, in some measure, their wishes and ideals. Even so, the general similarity of the responses given by the experimental and control groups suggests that, even eighteen months, on the average, after onset of the problem the allegedly stuttering children had not yet experienced sufficient "difficulty" to become conditioned appreciably against speaking. These data also suggest that the parents, although concerned to the degrees that have been indicated, had not been sufficiently impressed by their children's manner of speaking to modify their policies, as acknowledged, toward their speech behavior, so far as the items under consideration might reflect these policies.

This general inference would appear to be supported by the sorts of reactions elicited by the Iowa Scale of Attitude toward Stuttering.* This instrument samples the respondent's more or less general attitude toward stuttering. It was administered to the parents at the time of interview. As indicated in Table 53, the mean group differences were not statistically significant for either the fathers or mothers, nor were the means of the fathers and mothers within each group significantly different. These facts would seem to strengthen the implication of the

Table 53. Mean Scores of the Experimental and Control Group Fathers and Mothers on the Iowa Scale of Attitude toward Stuttering

Item	Experimental Group			Control Group			Diff.	t
	N	Mean	S.D.	N	Mean	S.D.		
Mothers	146	1.91	.47	149	1.86	.45	.05	NS
Fathers	138	1.85	.47	149	1.85	.47	0.00	NS
Difference		.06			.01			
t		NS			NS			

rest of the relevant data to the effect that the experimental group parents, while sufficiently disturbed to seek clinical service, were not for the most part extreme in their reactions to whatever it was their children were doing, nor, presumably, were the children doing anything that was, to their parents, extraordinary in any gravely alarming sense.

One question (318) was addressed directly to the matter of the child's sensitivity about his so-called speech defect, or nonfluencies.

---

* This scale, with instructions for administration and scoring, and with a summary of normative data reported by Ammons and Johnson (1), is to be found in Johnson, Darley, and Spriestersbach (64, pp. 137–146).

More experimental than control group parents, as shown in Table 52, reported that their children were sensitive. Half of the experimental group fathers and somewhat over one third of the mothers, however, said that their children were not sensitive and that the children apparently did not feel there was anything wrong with their speech. Nearly a third of the mothers and a fifth of the fathers expressed the judgment that their children were "mildly" to "very" sensitive, mostly "mildly," and somewhat less than a third of the experimental group parents gave the response that their children were not sensitive "but probably feel there is something wrong" with their speech.

Comparison of "Clinical" and "Nonclinical" Subgroups of Experimental Group Mothers

As indicated in 614, 47 of the 150 experimental group children were not considered by the interviewers to be stutterers in a clinically significant sense on the basis of their observations of the children at the time of interview. Ratings were not made in 7 cases. The interviewers agreed with the parents that the remaining 96 children were to be classified as stutterers, on the basis of such observations as the interviewers made of them, at the time of interview. These 47 "nonclinical" and 96 "clinical" experimental group children were treated, for purposes of the analysis presently to be described, as subgroups of the experimental group as a whole.

The mothers of these two subgroups of children were compared with respect to their responses to 136 items for which it had been possible to record responses in a single column of an IBM card. Nineteen of these had yielded distributions unfavorable for computation of chi-square values. Statistically significant chi-square values were obtained for 9 of the remaining 117 items, and these are presented in Table 54. The direction of the difference between the two subgroups was, for each of the 9 items, the same as it had been for the complete groups.

As indicated in Table 54, the experimental group mothers whose children's speech justified their being diagnosed as stutterers at the time of interview, according to the interviewers, differed significantly in the following ways from the experimental group mothers whose children's speech did not appear to the interviewers to justify the stuttering classification: they had given their children more attention when ill; more of them had told their children to stop speaking and start over, and to relax and take it easy in speaking; they rated their children as more sensitive about the speech problem; they had been more concerned about their children's stuttering; fewer of them had done some reading about stuttering before deciding that their children had

Table 54. Results of Chi-Square Analysis of Responses to Items on Which Experimental Subgroup Mothers Differed Significantly*

Item	Direction of Difference	Level of Confidence	Remarks
At times when the child has been ill, how much attention did he get? (163)	"Experimental" subgroup mothers gave their children more attention than "control" subgroup mothers gave their children	1%	Difference in same direction as that between full experimental and control groups in main study
How often did you tell him (the child) to stop and start over? (268)	More "control" than "experimental" subgroup mothers answered, "Never"	5%	Difference in same direction as found in main study
How often did you tell him to relax and take it easy? (269)	More "control" than "experimental" subgroup mothers answered, "Never"	5%	Difference in same direction as found in main study
How sensitive was the child about his speech defect? (318)	"Control" subgroup mothers rated their children as less sensitive than "experimental" subgroup mothers rated their children	1%	Difference in same direction as found in main study
How concerned are you now about the child's stuttering? (322)	"Experimental" subgroup mothers more concerned than "control" subgroup mothers	5%	Difference in same direction as found in main study
Had you read about stuttering before your child began to stutter? (338)	More "control" than "experimental" subgroup mothers had done some reading	1%	Difference in same direction as found in main study
Have you ever consulted a speech expert about your child's speech? (359)	More "experimental" than "control" subgroup mothers answered, "Yes"	1%	Difference in same direction as found in main study

Table 54 — *continued*

Item	Direction of Difference	Level of Confidence	Remarks
Do you encourage or discourage or say nothing about the child's playing alone? (508)	More "control" than "experimental" subgroup mothers said nothing	5%	Difference in same direction as found in main study
How well satisfied are you with your present marital relationship? (696)	More "control" than "experimental" subgroup mothers completely satisfied	1%	Difference in same direction as found in main study

* The interviewers indicated by their ratings that they clearly regarded 47 of the 150 experimental group children not to be stutterers in a clinically significant sense, and that they classified 96 of the children as stutterers at some level of severity. These 47 "nonclinical" and 96 "clinical" experimental group children were treated, for purposes of a special analysis of certain data represented by this table, as subgroups of the experimental group as a whole. The data summarized in this table were obtained from the mothers of these children.

The statistically significant values of chi-square and associated degrees of freedom are as follows:

Summary Table Item No.	Value of Chi-Square	df
163	10.96	2
268	10.73	3
269	6.98	2
318	18.95	2
322	8.37	2

Summary Table Item No.	Value of Chi-Square	df
338	4.42	1
359	8.49	1
508	3.87	1
696	8.35	1

begun to stutter; and more of them had consulted a speech expert about the child's speech. Also, more of the "control" subgroup mothers had neither encouraged their children to play alone nor discouraged them. And finally, more of the "control" subgroup mothers were completely satisfied with their present marital relationship. These findings appear to reinforce the significance of the corresponding differences between the full experimental and control groups of mothers.

Ratings of Severity of Stuttering at Time of Interview

The basic orientation of the experimental group parents seems to have been particularly well represented in the ratings they made of their children's alleged stuttering at the time of the interview (292). On a seven-point scale of severity, with 1 representing no stuttering, 4 stuttering of average severity, and 7 very severe stuttering, the mean ratings of the mothers and fathers were nearly identical, being 3.6 and 3.5, respectively.* Each of these means, however, was significantly different, at the 1 per cent level, from the mean severity rating of 2.5 made by the interviewers ($t = 6.99$ and 6.16, respectively; df $= 290$ in both cases). These figures presumably indicate that the parents were evaluating their children's speech on the basis of motivations or with reference to standards that were different from those of the interviewers, and that were conducive to relatively more dissatisfaction with, or concern over, their children's speech than they would have been likely to feel on the basis of standards such as the interviewers' ratings implied.

Parents' Explanations of Stuttering

At the same time, most of the experimental group parents seemed either not to be in all respects functionally aware of their own evaluative reactions, or not to be wholly or consistently inclined to acknowledge the possibility that they could be important in relation to their children's speech behavior. When asked, for example, "How do you think stuttering can be overcome?" the respondents gave a variety of specific answers, several of which are of special interest. These are the ones numbered 4, 5, 6, 10, 13, 14, 15, 16, 17, 18, 20, and 22 under 345 in the Summary Table. They are answers that express or imply the general point of view that it is helpful to a so-called stuttering child to be encouraged to do more speaking, to have the nonfluency in his speech disregarded, and to be loved and dealt with patiently and calmly, under home conditions likely to give the child a sense of security. These

---

*In Study II the experimental group mothers made a mean severity rating of 3.9 and the fathers made a mean rating of 3.4 of their children's stuttering.

Table 55. Numbers and Percentages of Experimental and Control Group Fathers (F) and Mothers (M) Who Gave Designated Types of Responses to 343, "What Do You Think Causes Stuttering?"; the Numbers and Percentages of Experimental Group Parents Who Gave Designated Responses to 344, "What Do You Think Caused Your Child's Stuttering?"; and the Numbers and Percentages of Experimental Group Parents Who Agreed and Disagreed with Themselves in Responding to the Two Questions

	Experimental Group												Control Group, 343			
	343				344				Same Response to 343 and 344							
	F		M		F		M		F		M		F		M	
R*	N	%	N	%	N	%	N	%	N	%	N	%	N	%	N	%
1	14	9.3	11	7.3	12	8	15	10	5 (1)†	3.3	3 (4)	2	10	6.6	10	6.6
2	38	25.5	52	34.6	30	20	48	32	10 (9)	6.6	18 (6)	12	44	29.3	58	38
3	28	18	40	26.6	12	8	19	12.6	4 (6)	2.6	11 (4)	7.3	31	20.6	29	19.3
4	0	0	1	0.6	8	5.3	3	2	0	0	1	0.6	1	0.6	1	0.6
5	23	15.5	6	4	30	20	11	7.3	12 (5)	8	3	2	11	7.3	8	5.3
6	1	0.6	3	0.2	1	0.6	1	0.6	0	0	0	0	5	3.3	8	5.3
7	4	2.6	9	6	17	11.3	21	14	2	1.4	3 (2)	2	21	14	28	18
8	41	27.3	27	18	40	26.6	32	21.3	18 (2)	12	9 (2)	6	27	18	8	5.3
9	1	0.6	1	0.6												
10									6	4	9	6				
11									57 (23)	38	57 (18)	38				
12									80	53.3	75	50				
13									93	62	93	62				

* R symbolizes the types of response, and these are, as numbered: 1, physical; 2, emotional, behavioral; 3, nervousness; 4, imitation; 5, discrepancy between talking and thinking; 6, handedness; 7, parental policies, parent-child relationship; 8, ? ("Don't know," "Have no idea," etc.); 9, "multicausal"; 10, same pattern of two or more responses to 343 and 344; 11, wholly same single responses to 343 and 344; 12, partly same responses to 343 and 344 (the same single response to both questions, plus an additional response to one but not to the other); 13, wholly or partly different responses to 343 and 344. See the accompanying text for definitions of the designated categories of response.

† Numbers in parentheses represent informants who agreed with themselves in giving the same type of response to 343 and 344 but who made a fuller response to one item than to the other. For example, the person represented in the parentheses beside which the dagger is placed indicated a physical type of cause in answer to 343 and also one of the emotional and behavioral type. As shown in row No. 12, if the numbers in parentheses are added to the corresponding numbers that are not in parentheses, a total of 80 fathers and 75 mothers, roughly half of all the parents, in the experimental group gave responses to 343 and 344 that were partly or wholly the same. This means, as shown in row No. 13, that 93, or 62 per cent, of the fathers and of the mothers gave responses to these two items that were partly or wholly different; the numbers in parentheses are included in the totals and are represented in the percentages given both in row No. 12 and in row No. 13.

particular responses were given by 85, or nearly three fifths, of the control group mothers, and only 32, or about one fifth, of the experimental group mothers, with the corresponding numbers of fathers being 53 and 33. It seems especially interesting that 27 control group mothers and only one experimental group mother said that the child should be given security, attention, and affection (No. 17) and that pressures should be removed and conflicts solved (No. 18). Also, three times as many control as experimental group mothers, 21 to 7, said that the stuttering should be ignored (No. 22).

It is of interest to consider these data in relation to the responses of both groups of parents to 343, "What do you think causes stuttering?" and those of the experimental group parents to 344, "What do you think caused your child's stuttering?" In Table 55 the distribution of these responses among several different categories is presented. The categories in Table 55 include these actual responses as recorded and coded by the interviewers:

1. Physical:
   a. Shock to mother
   b. Change of handedness
   c. Physically inferior speech mechanism
   d. Heredity
   e. Mental deficiency
   f. Birth injury
   g. Hearing deficiency
   h. Difference in other bodily functions
   i. Some illness of child
   j. Being tired
   k. Being tickled
   l. Because he has cerebral palsy, perhaps
   m. Polio
2. Emotional, or Behavioral:
   a. Shock to child
   b. Inferiority complex
   c. Pressures of speaking situations
   d. Carelessness; lack of attention
   e. Excitement; emotional upset
   f. Emotional disturbance
   g. Excitement
   h. Fear
   i. Emotional insecurity; being around someone who stutters
   j. Bad scare

k. Too much competition with sibs for attention
l. Frustration at the table — competing in talking
3. Nervousness:
   a. Nervousness
   b. Being generally high-strung
   c. Form of nervous tension
4. Imitation:
   a. Imitation
5. Discrepancy between Talking and Thinking:
   a. Thinks faster than can talk
   b. Talks faster than can think
   c. Inadequate vocabulary
   d. Immaturity; wants to talk faster than mind works and has inadequate vocabulary, so repeats until he finds the next word
   e. Talking too fast
   f. Not thinking before talking
   g. Talking too fast; can't get one word out so keeps saying it until he can
6. Handedness:
   a. Change of handedness
   b. Left-handedness
   c. Lack of cerebral balance
7. Parental Involvement:
   a. Punishment of child

166

b. Semantogenic or diagnosogenic factors
c. Influenced by conditions in home
d. Parental overconcern
e. Parents; associates

f. Result of father's strictness; got all tied up because tries so hard to say words
8. "Have no idea"
   a. ? ("Don't know," "Have no idea")

Aside from category No. 8 ("have no idea," etc.), only category No. 7 contains responses which indicate recognition by the informant that the interaction between parents and children might be important in relation to the stuttering problem. The other six types of response appear definitely to presuppose that "the cause," however designated, is to be found wholly within the physical or psychological makeup of the speaker. In terms of this distinction, 217, or 76 per cent, of the experimental group parents and 203, or 68 per cent, of those in the control group expressed, in response to 343, some form of the belief that the cause of stuttering is to be found wholly within the body or "personality" or "behavior pattern" of the speaker. "Heredity," suggested by 8 control and 9 experimental group parents, was the most frequently proposed "cause" classified as physical. Excitement and "emotional upset" or "disturbance" constituted most of the responses classified as emotional or behavioral. The relatively high numbers who attributed stuttering to "nervousness" and the low frequencies of response in the categories of imitation and handedness are of special interest, as is the comparatively large number, especially in the experimental group, and particularly in response to 344, who expressed, in a variety of forms, the general notion that stuttering is caused by talking faster than one can think, or thinking faster than one can talk, or talking too fast, or not thinking before speaking, or speaking with an inadequate vocabulary. Only 13, or 4 per cent, of the parents in the experimental group, compared with 49, or 16 per cent, of those in the control group may be assumed to have expressed a belief that "the cause" of stuttering is to be found in the interaction of the speaker and his listeners — in this case, the child and his parents.

One hypothesis that is suggested by these figures is that such a belief was less attractive to the parents for whom it was a possible source of feelings of guilt, or chagrin, or self-reproach. This hypothesis might be considered by some observers to be indicated also by the fact that in response to 343, 68, or 23 per cent, of the experimental group parents professed to "have no idea" of what the cause of stuttering might be, while only 35, or 12 per cent, of the control group parents were motivated to make this response. It is to be observed, too, that although the "I have no idea" response was given by 68 experimental group parents to the impersonal question, 343, and by 72 in reacting to the pointed question, 344, it was made by only 27 in response to both questions. This means that 113, 63 fathers and 50 mothers, were inconsistently "innocent," saying they had no notion of what "the cause" might be in answering one of the two questions, but then stating what they thought "the cause" to be in reply to the other question. These figures intimate, of course, that at least the 113 respondents who stated one time but not the other that they "had no idea" of what the cause might be were not very sure of the one positive opinion they did express.* Interestingly enough, moreover, the hypothesis that the "I have no idea" response was in some measure self-defensive or self-protective might be inferred indirectly from the fact that more experimental group parents indicated in response to the more pointed question "What do you think caused your child's stuttering?" than in response to the more general and impersonal question "What do you think causes stuttering?" (13 per cent to 4 per cent) that they thought their policies and reactions as parents, and their relations with the child, could have had something to do with bringing about the problem of stuttering. Five gave this type of response to 343 but not to 344, while thirty gave the response to 344 but not to 343. That is, more parents denied or disregarded the proposition on a relatively abstract level than when it was clearly related to their own specific situations.

In the meantime, the comparatively few parents who felt there had been sufficient improvement in their children's speech to justify an answer to 346 ("How do you account for any improvement in the child's speech?") were largely those who were of the opinion that such improvement as had occurred was due to a calmer home atmosphere, to the children being more relaxed, and to the parents disregarding the speech repetitions and being more easygoing, attentive, and patient. Moreover, in indicating what they would do differently if they were to meet the speech problem again (349), those experimental group parents who said they would do anything differently gave most frequently a type of response indicating awareness of the importance of their own negative or critical reactions to nonfluency in their children's speech, such as "would do nothing," "have more patience," "ignore it more at the start," and "wouldn't correct him."

Slightly more than half of the experimental group parents, however,

* The main implication of this — and of the proportions of respondents attributing stuttering to "heredity," "nervousness," "excitement," and "thinking faster than one speaks" or "speaking faster than one thinks" — would seem to be that the data in Table 55 are fundamentally anthropological or sociological, representing primarily "the folk mind," or "folk thinking," rather than rigorously reasoned conclusions drawn from sufficient and carefully gathered data by disciplined and independent observers.

indicated that if they had it to do over again (348) they would do "about the same." And, in response to 347, "How well do you feel you have handled the speech problem?" only twenty fathers and twenty-two mothers said they had not done well or had not done enough; all the rest said they had done the best they knew how, or that they had done very well, the best possible, or moderately well.

Follow-up Study

Twenty-eight and one-half months, on the average, after the original investigative interviews an attempt was made to gather certain follow-up data. Information was obtained from the parents of 118 experimental group children; 108 were interviewed in their homes, 4 were reached by telephone, and 6 by mail. Three sets of parents preferred not to be interviewed and 29 could not be located by means of the available facilities.* Observations of the children's speech, in the 50 cases in which such observations were possible, were carried out informally by the interviewers, chiefly by conversing with the children; the data resulting from these observations are summarized in Tables 57 and 58.†

The interview was conducted in each case in accordance with the following outline:

1. Sometime ago you felt that your child (name) had a speech problem, and at that time we interviewed you about it. Do you feel that he (she) has the same kind of speech problem now?
   (1) Yes (2) No (3) ? (Write answer given.)
2. If yes, how would you rate it now as compared with the way it seemed to you at the time of our interview?
   (1) Much worse now (2) Somewhat worse now (3) About the same now as it was then (4) Somewhat better now (5) Much better now
3. In your own words, what did we recommend that you do about the problem at the time of our interview? (Write answer given.)
4. Did you carry out these recommendations?
   (1) Very thoroughly and consistently (2) Fairly well (3) Only slightly (4) No
5. After our interview were you given advice by any other speech clinic, or doctor, teacher, speech correctionist, or anyone else?
   (1) Yes (2) No (3) ? (Write answer given.)

* The mother was the sole or major informant in every case. There were two investigators, James Neelley and Martin Young; the former worked in the Iowa and Minnesota areas and the latter in Illinois. Both were experienced clinical and research workers and advanced graduate students in speech pathology at the University of Iowa.

† It did not prove feasible to make a return visit for the purpose of observing the speech of any child who was away from home, attending school or summer camp, or for any other reason, at the time of the follow-up interview.

6. If yes, what in your own words was this advice? (Write answer given.)
7. Did you follow this advice?
   (1) Very thoroughly and consistently (2) Fairly well (3) Only slightly (4) No
8. Why do you think your child's speech problem
   (1) is worse (2) is better (3) has not changed (4) has disappeared? (Write answer given.)
9. Interviewer's personal report of observations of the child:
   (1) Did not observe child's speech.
   (2) Observed child's speech:
      (a) Do not regard child as a stutterer.
      (b) Do not regard child as significantly nonfluent in speech.
      (c) Regard child as significantly nonfluent but not as showing the tension and anxiety reactions characteristic of stuttering.
      (d) Regard child as a stutterer.
10. Interviewer's rating of the child's speech problem:
    (1) No stuttering; speech normal (2) Very mild (3) Mild
    (4) Average (5) Moderately severe (6) Severe (7) Very severe
11. Informant's rating of the child's speech problem:
    (1) No stuttering; speech normal (2) Very mild (3) Mild
    (4) Average (5) Moderately severe (6) Severe (7) Very severe

As shown in Tables 56–59, about one third of the 118 experimental group children surveyed no longer had a stuttering problem, according to information obtained, at the time of the follow-up study. It is to be appreciated that "speech problem," the term used in the question which elicited this information, could be, but was not necessarily, equivalent, for any given respondent, to the term "stuttering" (see the responses made to 196 and 235, respectively, and the relevant discussion in the preceding and present chapters). Basic interest was in the presence or absence of a speech problem, regardless of the words used to refer to it, and, if a speech problem was present, it was important to determine, so far as possible, whether or not it was the "same" one that had been investigated at the time of first interview. Questions 9, 10, and 11 of the interview were of a different sort and were so worded as to provide for use of the term "stuttering" in making responses; the answers to these questions are summarized in Tables 57–59.

These distinctions noted, it is to be observed in Table 56 that the percentage of parents reporting "no problem" at the time of follow-up was significantly different for the Minnesota sample and the combined Iowa and Illinois samples, but the difference between the Iowa and Illinois samples was not significant. In the Iowa-Illinois sample 45 per cent and in the Minnesota sample 23 per cent of the parents reported "no problem." In the Minnesota area the interviewers worked in the

Table 56. Data Obtained from Parents of 118 Experimental Group Children in Response to Follow-up Question No. 1: "Sometime Ago You Felt That your Child Had a Speech Problem, and at That Time We Interviewed You about It. Do You Feel That He (She) Has the Same Kind of Speech Problem Now?"

Sample*	N	Response			
		Yes		No	
		No.	%	No.	%
Total	118	75	64	43	36
Iowa	47	27	57	20	43
Illinois	27	14	52	13	48
Iowa-Illinois	74	41	55	33	45
Minnesota	44	34	77	10	23

* The difference between the percentages who responded "No" in the Iowa and Illinois samples, respectively, was not significant $(z = 1.04)$. The difference between the percentages who responded "No" in the combined Iowa-Illinois and Minnesota samples, respectively, was significant at the 5 per cent level $(z = 2.33)$.

Table 57. Data Obtained from 118 Experimental Group Parents Who Indicated in Response to Follow-up Question No. 1 Whether or Not Their Children Still Had a Speech Problem (See Table 56), and from the 75 Who, Having Stated Their Children Still Did Have a Problem, Were Then Asked How They Would "Rate It Now as Compared with the Way It Seemed to You at the Time of Our Interview"

Follow-up Rating	No.	% (N = 118)
Much worse now	1	0.8
Somewhat worse now	3	2.5
About same now as then	10	8.5
Somewhat better now	13	11.0
Much better now	48	40.7
No problem now (see Table 56)	43	36.4
Much better plus "no problem"	91	77.1
Somewhat and much better plus "no problem" . . .	104	88.1

Table 58. Summary of Observations of Children's Speech by Interviewers in the Follow-up Study (See Table 59 for Fluency Ratings)

Item	Problem Group (N = 75)	No-Problem Group (N = 43)	Both Groups (N = 118)
Child's speech not observed by interviewer	40	27	67
Child's speech observed and judged by interviewer	35	16	51
Child not a stutterer	31	16	47
Not significantly nonfluent	22	16	38
Significantly nonfluent	9	0	9
Child a stutterer	4	0	4

Table 59. Data Derived from Ratings Made by Interviewers and Experimental Group Mothers of Severity of Stuttering in the Speech of Experimental Group Children at the Time of the Follow-up Study, after an Average Interval of 28.5 Months following Initial Interviews (Mean Values of Corresponding Ratings Made at the Time of the Initial Interview Are Also Shown)

Ratings of Severity of Stuttering	Interviewers' Ratings		Mothers' Ratings			
	Problem Group, A* (N = 34)	No-Problem Group, A (N = 16)	Problem Group		No-Problem Group	
			A (N = 34)	B* (N = 39)	A (N = 16)	B (N = 27)
1. None; speech normal	30	16	3	7	14	25
2. Very mild	3	0	8	11	1	0
3. Mild	1	0	14	14	1	1
4. Average	0	0	5	4	0	1
5. Moderately severe	0	0	4	3	0	0
6. Severe	0	0	0	0	0	0
7. Very severe	0	0	0	0	0	0
Mean	1.15	1.0	2.97	2.62	1.19	1.19
Mean, A and B			2.78		1.19	
Mean, total group	1.06		2.19			
Mean, first interview	2.60	2.51	3.60	3.54	3.56	3.42
Mean, A and B, first interview			3.57		3.48	
Mean, total group of 118, first interview	2.57		3.53			

* A refers to those children whose speech was observed by the interviewers and B refers to those children whose speech was not observed by the interviewers at the time of the follow-up interview.

172

homes or in an office removed from a speech clinic, not as members of the staff of any speech clinic in the area, and necessarily, therefore, they did no remedial counseling of parents; in some cases general recommendations were made in consultations requested by some of the public school speech correctionists who were working with certain children in the experimental group. In the Iowa and Illinois areas the interviewers were either officially affiliated with the speech clinic in which they did the interviewing and were authorized, therefore, to do essential counseling, or they did the interviewing as part of a clinical program which included counseling of the experimental group parents by a duly authorized member of the clinic staff.

In general, counseling at the time of the original interview was restricted to that which could be done in the limited time available during the one day devoted in each case to the interview and related testing. It was of necessity, therefore, rather brief, although in nearly all cases relatively good rapport was established with the parents, and nearly all the experimental group parents were motivated to want advice and information. The interview itself may have had a therapeutic effect so far as it facilitated a more or less objective facing up to the facts which it was designed to bring into focus. In any case, the counseling that was provided consisted essentially of an attempt to help the parents recall and acknowledge such facts concerning the beginnings of the problem as they were able to remember and describe, to evaluate these facts by reference to research-based standards of child development and of the speech behavior known to be generally characteristic of young children, to recognize the apparent importance of relevant environmental circumstances, and to become effectively conscious of their own roles in the development of the problem so far as these could be indicated and interpreted.* No speech therapy, as such, or any other type of therapy, was administered to the children themselves.

As a check on how the parents had interpreted what had been said to them, they were asked at the time of follow-up what had been recommended at the time of the first interview. Approximately 80 per cent of the responses indicated at least some degree of understanding of the suggestions that had been given. Such responses as the following, for example, were obtained: "spend more time with the child and listen to him more"; "read to the child"; "have the child talk more often, express himself"; "give the child more responsibility." For the most part the responses were brief or fragmentary, vague, and unde-

---

* The kinds of information and recommendations given to these parents are fairly well indicated in Chapter 5, "Stuttering," and Appendix VII, "An Open Letter to the Mother of a Stuttering Child," in *Speech Handicapped School Children* (61), revised edition, 1956.

veloped, though of a kind that might be roughly evaluated by the phrase "so far, so good." A comparison of these responses with those made in the initial interview to 345, "How do you think stuttering can be overcome?" indicates that the counseling that had been done and the experience of the interview and its subsequent effects must have occasioned generally substantial changes in the relevant aspects of the thinking of most of the experimental group parents. Although the Problem and No-Problem subgroups gave generally similar accounts of the recommendations that they recalled having been made to them, it is noteworthy that about two thirds of the No-Problem group as compared with 40 per cent of the Problem group parents said they had carried out the recommendations "very thoroughly and consistently."

After the first interview, about 27 per cent of the Problem group and 20 per cent of the No-Problem group had been given advice by some other clinic, doctor, or teacher; these included mostly public school speech therapists and psychologists, together with a few psychiatrists and pediatricians. Most of those who had received such further help had been advised by the interviewers to seek additional counseling. The majority of those who had obtained additional advice said they had followed it "very thoroughly" or "fairly well."

The parents in the No-Problem group were asked for their opinions as to why their children no longer had the speech problem, and the most frequently given responses were these: "don't know," 8; "child outgrew it," 7; "child more mature," 6; "less criticism by the parents," 5; "parents ignored it," 4; "child has more confidence now," 3; "child given more attention, more chance to talk," 3; and "parental attitudes improved," 3. The Problem group parents gave essentially the same types of reason for the improvement of their children's speech, with fifteen saying they didn't know why the child had improved, eleven referring to the child's increased maturity, and ten to better parent-child relations. Of the ten mothers who said their children's speech had not changed, seven could give no reason, one blamed "poor parent-child relationship," one said the mother "was very busy," and one said the father had had a heart attack. Five parents who reported the problem to be worse gave a total of six responses when asked for their explanations. Three had no opinion, one attributed the greater severity of the problem to "poor parent-child relationship," one said the child had become "more aware of his speech," and one said, "It has become a stronger habit."

The counseling that was done at the time of the initial interview was carried out with due sensitivity to the possibility that the facts to be acknowledged by the parents concerned could be conducive to feelings of guilt, self-accusation, and remorse, and that reactions to such feelings might include various forms and degrees of self-defensiveness, resentment, discouragement, conflict between the mother and father, various forms of rationalizing, rejection of the facts, and rejection of the counselor and the counseling and its premises and objectives. The degree to which such feelings and reactions occurred, and the success with which the problems occasioned by them were handled, cannot be clearly indicated from the data that could be secured. Most of the parents who were counseled seemed to react more or less positively, and, while it is difficult to gauge the degree to which they understood operationally what was being said, it seems clear that the attitudes and opinions expressed by them in the follow-up interviews were considerably different from corresponding views and feelings evidenced in the initial interviews in response to such items as 345, "How do you think stuttering can be overcome?"; 343 and 344, which concerned the informant's opinions as to the causes of stuttering; 346, "How do you account for any improvement in the child's speech?"; and 348 and 349, which were designed to explore the informant's evaluations of the ways in which they had handled the problem before seeking clinical service. All presumably relevant information considered, it seems reasonable to infer that one possible explanation of the fact that a larger proportion of the parents in the Iowa-Illinois sample than in the Minnesota sample reported that their children no longer had a speech problem at the time of the follow-up study was that it had been possible to provide more counseling for the Iowa-Illinois parents at the time of the first interview.

The parents who said that their children still had a speech problem were asked to rate its severity at the time of the follow-up study as compared with its severity at the time of the first interview. The results are shown in Table 57, and they would seem to have hopeful implications. Only 4, roughly 3 per cent, of the 118 were said to have more of a problem at time of follow-up; 10, or 8.5 per cent, were reported to be "about the same"; and the rest, 104, or 88 per cent, were reported either to have no problem or to be somewhat better or much better. Of the 75 who still had a problem, according to their mothers, 61, or 81 per cent, were said to be better, and 48, or 64 per cent, of the 75 were reported to be "much better."

These figures are to be compared with the data obtained in the initial interview in response to those items designed to indicate the course of development of the problem from its inception to the time of interview, especially 285, "What has been the general course of the problem since you first noticed it?" (See the section of this chapter entitled

Table 60. Values of t and Chi-Square for Differences between
Mean Values Shown in Table 59

Item	t	Chi-Square (df)	Significance Level
Total group, follow-up: interviewers vs. mothers		33.34 (1)	1%
Problem group, follow-up: interviewers vs. mothers		51.89 (1)	1%
Mothers, follow-up: problem vs. no-problem group		62.64 (1)	1%
Mothers, total group: interview vs. follow-up	8.59		1%
Interviewers, total group: interview vs. follow-up		47.87 (1)	1%
Mothers, problem group: interview vs. follow-up	4.48		1%
Interviewers, problem group: interview vs. follow-up		2.62 (1)	NS
Mothers, no-problem group: interview vs. follow-up		59.41 (1)	1%
Interviewers, no-problem group: interview vs. follow-up		14.89 (1)	1%
Mothers, interview: problem vs. no-problem group	0.41		NS
Fathers, interview: problem vs. no-problem group	0.56		NS
Interviewers, interview: problem vs. no-problem group	0.30		NS
Mothers, follow-up, problem group: A vs. B	1.34		NS

"Development of the Stuttering Problem Subsequent to Onset.") In response to 285, about 30 per cent of the experimental group informants said the problem had become worse, roughly 30 per cent said it had become better, about 25 per cent stated that it had stayed about the same, and the rest gave varying answers indicating that the severity of the problem had fluctuated. In general, the amount of improvement for the group as a whole was evidently much greater after the initial interview than it had been before that time.

Notable improvement was also reflected in the severity ratings made at the time of initial interview and at the time of the follow-up study. Using a seven-point scale of severity, the mothers, as shown in Table 59, made a mean rating at follow-up of 2.19 for all children rated, 2.78 for the Problem children, and 1.19 for the No-Problem children, and they gave the same children corresponding mean ratings of 3.53, 3.57, and 3.48 at the time of initial interview. The interviewers rated 50 children at the time of follow-up, with resulting means of 1.06 for the total group, 1.15 for 34 Problem children, and 1.0 for 16 No-Problem children. At the time of initial interview the same children were given corresponding mean ratings of 2.57, 2.60, and 2.51. Differences between the mean ratings for both the mothers and the interviewers, at the time of follow-up and the time of initial interview, for all children rated at the time of follow-up, were statistically significant at the 1 per cent level.*

Of the thirty Problem children rated by the interviewers, only four were judged by them to be classifiable as stutterers. As indicated in Table 58, the interviewers judged an additional nine, whom they did not believe to be "showing the tension and anxiety reactions characteristic of stuttering," to be "significantly nonfluent." If there was any difference between the children observed and those not observed by the follow-up interviewers, the parents' ratings summarized in Table 59 suggest that those not observed by the interviewers were speaking somewhat better than those who were observed. It may reasonably be inferred that by the interviewers' standards approximately 7 per cent of the experimental group children were classifiable as stutterers, an additional 15 per cent were "significantly nonfluent," and roughly three fourths presented normally fluent speech at the time of the follow-up study.

A search was made for differences between the children in the Problem and No-Problem groups, and the results are summarized in Table 61. Of thirteen comparisons nine yielded nonsignificant values. The Problem and No-Problem groups did not differ significantly with respect to proportions of males and females; length of the mean interval between the initial and follow-up interviews; mean ratings of severity of stuttering made by the parents and by the interviewers at the time of initial interview; parents' mean self-ratings, at the time of initial interview, of concern over the children's stuttering; parents' mean self-ratings, at the time of initial interview, of how much they cared about what outsiders knew and thought about the children's speech; mothers' mean self-ratings, at the time of the initial interview, of how much they cared about the impression they made on others; or number of children in the family. The direction of difference for these items, as indicated in Table 61, may warrant some consideration, however. It is of particular interest that the two groups did not differ with regard to the severity ratings made at the time of the initial interview.

In addition to the differences so far noted with respect to the reactions to counseling of the parents in the Problem and No-Problem groups, and the differences in amount of counseling and corresponding differences in the proportions that reported no problem at follow-up in

---

* See Table 60 for results of tests of significance of differences between designated pairs of values shown in Table 59.

Table 61. Data Concerning Designated Group Differences Obtained in Follow-up Study of 118 Experimental Group Children Reported by Their Parents (a) Still to Have a Stuttering Problem or (b) No Longer to Have a Stuttering Problem

Item	Problem Group (N = 75)	No-Problem Group (N = 43)	t	Chi-Square (df)	Significance Level
Sex (5)					
Male	57	30		0.27 (1)	NS
Female	18	13			
Mean age, in months, at the time of the initial interview (4)	64.56	55.63	3.06		1%
Mean interval, in months, between onset and the initial interview (813)	22.47	14.95	3.60		1%
Mean interval, in months, between the initial interview and follow-up	28.13	29.26	0.64		NS
Mean severity rating by interviewers at the time of the initial interview (614)	2.60	2.51	0.30		NS
Mean severity rating by parents at the time of the initial interview (292)					
Fathers	3.57	3.44	0.56		NS
Mothers	3.57	3.48	0.41		NS
Parents' mean self-ratings, at the time of the initial interview, of concern over the child's stuttering (321)					
Fathers				1.69 (1)	NS
Very much or moderately	43	21			
Mildly	25	18			
Not concerned	7	4			
Mothers				2.25 (1)	NS
Very much or moderately	50	23			
Mildly	19	15			
Not concerned	6	5			

178

Table 61 – continued

Item	Problem Group (N = 75)	No-Problem Group (N = 43)	t	Chi-Square (df)	Significance Level
Parents' mean self-ratings, at the time of the initial interview, of how much they cared about what outsiders knew and thought about their children's speech (362)					
Fathers					
Do care	25	15		0.03 (1)	NS
Do not care	50	28			
Mothers					
Do care	27	19		0.77 (1)	NS
Do not care	48	24			
Mothers' mean self-ratings, at the time of the initial interview, of how much they cared about the impression made on others (668)					
Do care	53	23		3.06 (1)	NS
Do not care	22	20			
Number of children in family (725)					
One or two	52	25		1.51 (1)	NS
Three or more	23	18			
Mean index of status characteristics (622) *	49.35	44.42	2.43		2%
Social class (623) †					
Upper and middle	42	35		6.69 (1)	1%
Lower	33	8			

* The lower the numerical value of this index, the higher the socioeconomic status indicated.

† The full distributions were, for the problem group and no-problem group, respectively: upper class, 1 and 1; upper middle, 12 and 10; lower middle, 29 and 24; upper lower, 30 and 8; lower lower, 3 and 0.

the Iowa-Illinois and Minnesota subgroups, there were four statistically significant differences between the two groups represented in Table 61, and these reflected three factors: age, length of the interval between the onset of the problem and the initial interview, and socioeconomic status. The No-Problem group had a lower mean age at the time of first interview, and the mean interval between onset of the problem and the first interview was significantly shorter for this group. These facts would seem to indicate that whenever parents feel that a stuttering problem exists, the sooner their concern is dealt with clinically, and the earlier in the life of the child this is done, the better. The difference with respect to socioeconomic status was almost wholly due to the comparatively larger number of Problem than of No-Problem group families in the upper lower class (see footnote, Table 61). Of the various possible implications of this difference, none seems unequivocally indicated. The difference does suggest the conjecture that while families in the middle or upper class are probably more likely than those of lower class status to develop the problem of stuttering, they are also more likely to contend with it effectively, given at least minimal appropriate counseling.*

* These findings are in substantial agreement with those obtained in Study I. See p. 35 and the footnote on p. 235.

CHAPTER 7

Parental Responses to the MMPI

THIS chapter reports the findings of a comparative investigation of some aspects of the personalities of the experimental and control group parents by means of a self-report personality inventory, one of the most widely used approaches to personality measurement. Such inventories are composed of statements concerning attitude and overt behavior, to each of which the subject is instructed to respond by indicating whether it is "true" or "false" as applied to himself. Items such as the following are typically included in these inventories: When I get bored I like to stir up some excitement. While in trains, buses, etc., I often talk to strangers. I dislike to take a bath. I am afraid of the dark.

Early types of self-report inventories have been severely criticized for their rationale, the obviousness of the questions, and the consequently limited usefulness of the instrument. The authors of these early instruments assumed that respondents would be frank and truthful, and that a person answering "True" to the question about fear of the dark, for example, would, in fact, show such fear. There is considerable research evidence that such assumptions were unwarranted and that inventories developed on the basis of these assumptions should be used with the utmost caution, if at all.*

Identification, measurement, and evaluation of the various facets of human personality are extremely complex and difficult (R2, 33). Much of the recent work in the behavioral sciences of psychology, so-

---

* See Anastasi (2, Chapter 20) and Ferguson (33) for summaries of such studies together with much general criticism.

NOTE. This chapter was prepared by Leonard D. Goodstein and W. Grant Dahlstrom, who served successively as consultants in clinical psychology in the program of research reported in this volume and were responsible for the aspect of the program presented in this chapter. Leonard D. Goodstein (Ph.D., Columbia University) is associate professor of psychology and director of the University Counseling Service, University of Iowa. W. Grant Dahlstrom (Ph.D., University of Minnesota), formerly on

ciology, and speech pathology has been devoted to the methodological problems involved in such work. One recent approach to the difficulties encountered in the use of the self-report inventory has involved the development of empirical personality scales. These empirically derived inventories treat the test items as standardized verbal stimuli, and regard the responses to these stimuli as useful information about the respondent with no assumption about the "truthfulness" of the content of the responses (R81). Thus, it is taken to be of interest that a person *says* he fears the dark, regardless of whether or not he would act fearfully in a darkened place. Inventories may be developed by determining whether there are behavioral differences between persons who do and do not admit a fear of the dark, for example. If it can be reliably demonstrated that there are such differences in verbal response to specified questions between clinically meaningful groups of persons, then we may assume that an inventory developed on the basis of these differences is a useful psychometric instrument. The Minnesota Multiphasic Personality Inventory (MMPI), the instrument used in this study, is such an empirically derived inventory (R50).

The MMPI was developed by empirically demonstrating that differences in the responses elicited by means of it could be used to differentiate normal persons from a variety of types of psychiatric patients.† It was further shown that members of various psychiatric groups could be differentiated from each other on the basis of their test responses. As a result of the original standardization and subsequent research, the MMPI has been used in clinical settings to "assay those traits that are commonly characteristic of disabling psychological abnormality" (R50, p. 5). It has been successfully used also in the description and evaluation of *normal* persons.

The MMPI

The MMPI consists of 550 questions such as those listed above. The questions, all of which are to be answered as either "True," "False," or "Cannot say," cover a wide range of subject matter, from the physical health and fitness of the subject to his social, moral, and religious

the faculty of the University of Iowa, is associate professor of psychology, University of North Carolina. This chapter is, with editorial adaptations, an extended and elaborated version of an article by the same authors, "Some Personality Test Differences between Parents of Stuttering and Nonstuttering Children," *Journal of Consulting Psychology*, 20:365–370 (1956), and is reprinted as edited with the permission of the authors and the American Psychological Association.

† It is beyond the scope of this report to present a detailed account of the standardization of the MMPI or of the subsequent research dealing with its clinical usefulness. A recent volume edited by Welsh and Dahlstrom (120) reprints many of the journal articles reporting research with this instrument and includes a very comprehensive bibliography.

attitudes. In the initial form of the test, each question was printed on a separate card and the subject was told to sort the questions into the three response categories. Another form is now also available in which the questions are printed in a test booklet and the subject indicates his responses on a separate answer sheet. The two forms are regarded as interchangeable. The test is virtually self-administering and is untimed; the time required by most subjects for completing it is about one hour.

It has become usual to score the MMPI routinely for four validity and nine clinical scales. There are a number of additional scales which can also be scored for evaluating additional psychological characteristics that may be of special interest to the investigator or clinician. While it is not possible here to give a complete description of the several MMPI scales and their interpretations, the following may serve as a brief introduction to the scales used in the present investigation.

THE VALIDITY SCALES

The validity scales of the MMPI are built-in checks on carelessness, misunderstanding, malingering, and the presence of such test-taking attitudes as overdefensiveness or overcriticalness. There are four such validity scales.

The Question Score (?). This score is determined by the total number of questions placed in the "Cannot say" category, in effect those the subject did not answer. High ? scores affect the scores on all other scales and may invalidate the entire test.

The Lie Score (L). This score is based upon items which, if answered in the scored direction, indicate a naive attempt to place oneself in a favorable light, especially in regard to personal ethics and social conduct. The scored response is rarely true; an example is the response of "False" to "Once in a while I put off until tomorrow what I ought to do today." A high L score is indicative of a defensive attitude which may invalidate the remainder of the scores by keeping the clinical scores low.

The F Score. This score is determined from a set of items rarely answered in the scored direction, such as the response of "True" to "I have nightmares every few nights." Although responses in the scored direction do represent an admission of strange or socially undesirable behavior, such an admission does not represent the typical response of even definitely pathological persons. High F scores are, consequently, regarded as indicative of malingering or "faking bad." Occasionally carelessness in responding to the test items also results in a high F score. A high score on this scale is usually interpreted as meaning that the person is trying to place himself in an unfavorable light and may also result in an invalid profile.

The K Score. This score is also based upon a special set of items and reflects the subject's general test-taking attitudes in much the same way as the L and F scales do, but it represents an attempt to tap the more subtle aspects of these attitudes. High K scores are interpreted as indicating a defensiveness against admitting psychological weaknesses and may, in extreme cases, represent deliberate distortion in the favorable direction. High scores on this scale are obtained by responding "True" to items such as "I have never felt better in my life than I do now." The raw K score is used as a corrective or suppressor variable with five of the clinical scales (Hs, Pd, Pt, Sc, and Ma) and is used, in interpreting these scales, to correct for the presence of the indicated attitudes. This use of the K score has been shown to increase the discriminatory power of these scales in the crucial middle range of score values. The appropriate amount of the K score has been added in scoring these scales in the present study.

THE CLINICAL SCALES

While the names of the clinical scales are derived from the classical Kraepelinian nomenclature as modified by contemporary American psychiatric practice, high scores on these scales cannot and should not be directly translated into diagnostic statements. Considerable training, both in using the MMPI and in abnormal psychology, is required for interpretive competence. It should be noted also that high scores on the scales are not sufficient evidence of psychopathology to warrant definite diagnostic judgments and extreme caution must be used in test interpretation.

The Hypochondriasis Scale (Hs). This scale was developed by comparing the responses of normal persons to those of patients having many physical complaints with no demonstrable organic basis. Persons who score high on this scale tend to be unduly worried about illness and to have many generalized fears about their health. They are characteristically immature in their approach to life and demonstrate little insight into their problems.

The Depression Scale (D). This scale was derived from the responses of persons who suffer from feelings of depression; they are sad and unsure of themselves and their future, and are characterized by lack of self-confidence, tendencies to worry, narrow interests, and introversion. Within the normal limits, high scores on this scale reflect social shyness and sensitivity.

The Hysteria Scale (Hy). This scale was derived from the responses

184

of persons who have developed conversion hysteria symptoms. While this scale is much like the Hs scale, it involves more culturally respectable symptomatology such as low back pains or functional heart disease, illnesses which often involve psychosomatic disturbances. Persons who score high on this scale tend to have little insight into their psychological difficulties and to be reluctant to face their difficulties directly. They show an overcompensatory rejection of the possibility that they may be neurotic. Within groups of normal persons high scores on this scale reflect irritability, lack of dependability, and desire for social approval.

The Psychopathic Deviate Scale (Pd). This scale was developed from studies of persons who did not conform to the mores of society and consequently came into direct conflict with the law. While superficially likable, they do not have deep emotional responses and do not seem to profit by experience. They most frequently get into difficulties by lying, stealing, alcohol or drug addiction, and sexual immorality.

The Interest Scale (Mf). This scale provides a measure of the masculinity or femininity of the subject's interest pattern. High scores indicate a deviation of the basic interest pattern in the direction of the opposite sex.

The Paranoia Scale (Pa). This scale was developed by contrasting the responses of normal persons with those of a group of patients characterized by suspiciousness, oversensitivity, and delusions. Persons making high scores on this scale tend to show undue interpersonal sensitivity which, in extreme degrees, may involve paranoid feelings about other people and feelings of being mistreated or threatened. High scores within the normal range reflect aloofness and to some degree arrogance. Persons making such scores are frequently seen as affected, emotionally cold, and somewhat contradictory in their attitudes.

The Psychasthenia Scale (Pt). This scale provides a measure of the similarity of the subject to psychiatric patients who are troubled by phobias or compulsive behavior. Persons scoring high on this scale tend to be overly conscientious or excessively meticulous; high scores may also indicate worry, anxiety, and feelings of overcriticalness or of ruminative self-doubt.

The Schizophrenia Scale (Sc). This scale was derived by contrasting the responses of normal persons with those of patients with bizarre and unusual thoughts or behavior. Subjects who score high on this scale tend to be regarded as peculiar or withdrawn. They are likely to distort some aspect of the world around them and this tendency, in extreme degrees, may be indicative of schizophrenia. High scores within the normal range reflect apathy and seclusiveness, as well as serious

185

intellectual and esthetic interests. Persons making such scores may also be rather undependable and lacking in responsibility and maturity of judgment.

The Mania Scale (Ma). This scale affords a measure of the similarity of the subject to patients with marked overproductivity in thought and action. Those making high scores are persons who easily become interested in things and approach life with much zest. Such tendencies, when carried to extremes, may lead to irrational manic behavior or antisocial acts. High scores within the normal range reflect egocentricity and social exhibitionism as well as energetic and enterprising modes of solving problems and dealing with others.

THE SPECIAL SCALES

As has been mentioned, a large number of additional scales can be scored from the 550 items. Four of these scales were used in the present study since it was thought, on an a priori basis, that these might represent variables important in relation to the onset of stuttering.

The Anxiety Scale (A). This scale provides a measure of the manifest anxiety experienced by the subject. High scores result from the admission of feelings of tension, discomfort, worry, and a variety of physiological concomitants of anxiety, such as sweating or flushing (R108).

The Achievement Scale (Ac). This scale was developed by comparing the responses of high and low achievers in academic situations, with intelligence held constant. High scores indicate interest and motivational patterns typical of persons who do well in school and college work (R42).

The Dominance Scale (Do). This scale provides a measure of "strength" in face-to-face relationships. A high score indicates that the person is able to exert a personal influence on others. Persons making high scores on this scale are seen as forceful, strong, confident and sure of themselves (R43).

The Status Scale (St). This scale affords a measure of the personal qualities and attitudes that are associated with social status, rather than social status as typically measured by social scientists. High scores indicate literary and esthetic interests, social poise and self-confidence, and persons making such scores are likely to be regarded as being "broadminded" and having positive opinions about their social environment (R41).

THE MMPI PROFILE

The T Scores. Each of the clinical scales is transformed, by the use of tables, into standard score equivalents called T scores; these are arbitrarily derived with the mean set at 50 and the standard deviation

186

set at 10. The higher the score the greater the degree of abnormality. A T score of 70, two standard deviations above the mean, is made by only 5 per cent of presumably normal persons and is generally regarded as the cut-off score for identifying pathological deviations. The scores on the validity scales and the special scales are typically reported in raw score units.

Coding the Profile. Contemporary clinical use of the MMPI emphasizes that the pattern of T scores rather than the individual T score is of chief importance in interpreting a profile. It has been suggested (R49, 119) that a "high point" coding system be used for analyzing the pattern. In such a system the MMPI clinical scale having the highest T score is placed first in the code and the remainder of the clinical scales are then ranked in descending order according to the obtained T scores. The pattern is thus indicated without regard to the level of the score elevation for each scale. The absolute elevation of the profile, however, is indicated by inserting symbols in the code indicating those scores above 90, those between 80 and 89, those between 70 and 79, etc.

Purpose of Present Investigation

The purpose of this investigation was to compare, by means of the MMPI, the relative psychological adjustment and personality characteristics of the parents in the experimental and control groups. The selection of these two groups of parents as well as the procedures used in matching the groups has been discussed in Chapter 1.

The MMPI has been used in a similar way by Williams (129) for evaluating parental adjustment in its relation to child behavior in a number of families in each of which there was a cerebral-palsied child. Grossman (45) has used the test in a study of a small group of parents of chronically stuttering and nonstuttering children.

Subjects and Procedures

The routine administration of the booklet form of the MMPI was part of the standard interview procedure that was followed with each parent who had agreed to participate in the over-all study. Usually one parent took the test while the other parent was being interviewed. If the tests were not completed during the full clinical session, arrangements were made to have the booklets and answer sheets picked up at some later time.

While it had been planned to secure an MMPI profile from each parent, this goal was not realized because of a number of uncontrollable factors such as lack of time and refusal of some subjects to cooperate. Profiles were, however, obtained from 224 of the 300 experimental group parents and from 223 of the 300 control group parents in Study III. An inspection of the other data did not suggest that those parents who had failed to complete the MMPI were different in any obvious ways from those parents for whom profiles were secured.

All answer sheets were hand scored by the interviewers, in accordance with the usual scoring procedures, for the seventeen scales discussed above. All profiles were also coded by means of the high-point coding system which has been previously discussed. For ease in tabulation and statistical analysis the scores on the seventeen scales as well as the high-point codes were then coded by reference to a predetermined system and punched on standard IBM cards.

Findings

Four groups of 100 profiles each, obtained from the experimental group mothers and fathers and the control group mothers and fathers, respectively, were selected from the 447 available MMPI profiles by excluding the 47 profiles whose validity scale scores suggested the most significant degrees of dissimulation. The cutting score for exclusion was L scale raw score of 7 or higher, or F scale raw score of 17 or higher, or K scale raw score of 28 or higher. The numbers of cases excluded on the basis of these criteria were 17, 22, and 8 respectively; there were no obvious differences between the control and experimental group parents with respect to these validity criteria.

The means and standard deviations obtained on the seventeen MMPI scales for the experimental and control group parents, respectively, together with the significance levels of the differences between the experimental and control group means, are presented in Table 62. For ease in communication the scores in Table 62 are reported in values based on the original distributions of scores rather than the coded score distributions. The reported values are, consequently, approximate rather than exact; all statistical tests, however, were based upon the more exact coded score values.

A prior comparison of the means of the experimental group mothers and fathers and of the control group mothers and fathers gave no notable evidence of any sex differences in the scores, and so the data from the two sexes were combined. The only exception to this finding was for the Mf scale on which both groups of fathers had significantly higher $(p < .01)$ mean T scores than the corresponding groups of mothers; there were, however, no significant differences between the experimental and control groups and therefore the data were combined in this case as well.

There were only three statistically significant mean differences be-

Table 62. Means and Standard Deviations* of MMPI Scales for Parents of Allegedly Stuttering Children (Experimental Group) and Parents of Allegedly Nonstuttering Children (Control Group) and the Significance Levels of the Differences between the Means (N = 200 in Each Cell)

Scale†	Experimental Group Parents		Control Group Parents		p‡
	Mean	S.D.	Mean	S.D.	
?	6.5	7.9	5.8	4.6	NS
L	3.3	1.9	3.6	1.8	NS
F	3.2	2.5	2.8	1.8	NS
K	15.5	5.2	16.9	4.8	.05
Hs	51.6	8.7	53.0	7.4	NS
D	53.9	10.3	52.4	9.2	NS
Hy	55.5	7.9	56.1	7.7	NS
Pd	53.2	9.6	54.8	9.0	NS
Mf§	52.5	10.1	52.7	10.1	NS
Pa	52.8	7.8	52.3	6.8	NS
Pt	53.0	8.6	51.9	7.7	NS
Sc	51.7	9.0	52.2	7.8	NS
Ma	51.9	10.1	51.2	9.1	NS
A	14.3	7.6	11.8	6.9	.01
Ac	16.9	2.9	16.8	2.6	NS
Do	17.3	3.3	18.8	3.3	.01
St	21.4	3.9	22.5	4.0	NS

* These values are approximate, having been derived from the coded scores.

† The scores on the clinical scales (Hs, D, Hy, Pd, Mf, Pa, Pt, Sc, and Ma) are in T-score units; all the others are expressed in raw score units. K-scale corrections have been included where appropriate.

‡ The t tests for mean differences as well as the significance levels for these differences were based upon the more precise coded score values rather than the values reported in this table.

§ Both groups of fathers scored significantly higher $(p < .01)$ than the corresponding groups of mothers; there were, however, no significant differences between the experimental and control groups.

Table 63. The Number of Experimental and Control Group Mothers and Fathers Who Presented Their Highest Scores on Each of the MMPI Clinical Scales*

Group	MMPI Clinical Scales									Total
	Hs	D	Hy	Pd	Mf	Pa	Pt	Sc	Ma	
Experimental mothers . .	4	13	18	12	15	12	8	6	12	100
Experimental fathers . .	5	17	16	8	23	4	5	4	18	100
Subtotal	9	30	34	20	38	16	13	10	30	200
Control mothers	3	18	27	22	6	7	7	5	5	100
Control fathers	1	10	17	18	27	4	5	3	15	100
Subtotal	4	28	44	40	33	11	12	8	20	200
Grand total	13	58	78	60	71	27	25	18	50	400

* Only the nine clinical scales were used in this analysis.

tween the experimental and the control group parents on the seventeen MMPI scales. The control parents had significantly higher mean scores on the K and Dominance (Do) scales ($p < .05$ and $p < .01$, respectively) while the experimental parents had a significantly higher mean score on the Anxiety (A) scale ($p < .01$). None of the other mean differences were significant at an acceptable level of confidence.

The number of experimental and control group mothers and fathers who presented their highest scores on each of the MMPI clinical scales is shown in Table 63. The differences between the obtained frequencies were then analyzed by means of the chi-square test for a two-by-nine table. There were no significant differences between the experimental and control group fathers, between the experimental and control group mothers, or between the experimental and control group parents without regard to sex. There were, however, significant differences between the total male group and the total female group when the experimental and control groups were combined ($p < .001$). It may be seen in Table 62 that the Mf and Ma scales occurred relatively more frequently in the initial position in the male codes while the Pa and Sc scales were the more frequent initial points in the female codes.

The relative frequencies in the four groups of subjects of the secondary scale in the high-point code, that is, the clinical scale in each case with the second highest T-score value in the individual profiles, are presented in Table 64. The differences between the obtained frequencies were again analyzed by means of the chi-square test for a two-by-nine table. Again there were no differences between the experimental and control group fathers, the experimental and control group mothers, or the total experimental and the total control group. And again there were significant differences between the total male group and the total female group when the experimental and control groups

Table 64. The Number of Experimental and Control Group Mothers and Fathers Who Presented Their Second Highest Scores on Each of the MMPI Scales*

Group	MMPI Clinical Scales									Total
	Hs	D	Hy	Pd	Mf	Pa	Pt	Sc	Ma	
Experimental mothers . .	9	11	21	12	6	14	12	9	6	100
Experimental fathers . .	4	18	13	14	15	11	8	5	12	100
Subtotal	13	29	34	26	21	25	20	14	18	200
Control mothers	9	6	20	14	13	12	8	7	11	100
Control fathers	2	13	18	16	16	9	6	9	11	100
Subtotal	11	19	38	30	29	21	14	16	22	200
Grand total	24	48	72	56	50	46	34	30	40	400

* Only the nine clinical scales were used in this analysis.

were combined ($p < .02$). It may be seen in Table 64 that the D, Mf, and Ma scales occurred relatively more frequently in the secondary position in the male codes while the Hs and Hy scales were the more frequent secondary scales in the female codes.

The number of parents in the two groups with one or more T scores above 70 on the clinical scales (the usual cutting score) was obtained in an effort to evaluate the relative frequency of "severe disturbance" in the two groups. There were forty-seven persons in the control group and forty-nine in the experimental group with one or more T scores above 70; by eliminating from consideration those cases in which both parents in the family had scores above 70, these numbers were reduced to forty-one and forty-two, respectively. An inspection of the high-point codes of these "severely disturbed" persons did not reveal any differences between the experimental and control groups although the sex differences that were discussed above (see Tables 63 and 64) were again present.

In an attempt to evaluate the differences in the severity of stuttering as a function of the "abnormality" of the MMPI scores, the 224 experimental group children for whom parental MMPI profiles were available were divided into two subgroups, those children who had one or both parents with one or more clinical scale T scores above 70 (the disturbed group) and those children for whom neither parent had a clinical scale T score above 70 (the nondisturbed group). Independent ratings by the interviewers of the experimental group children on the Iowa Scale for Rating the Severity of Stuttering (R64, pp. 129–136) were available for thirty-eight children whose parents were placed in the disturbed group and seventy-seven children whose parents were in the nondisturbed group. The mean rating for the children of the disturbed parents was 1.97 (S.D. = .97) while the mean rating for the children of the nondisturbed parents was 3.13 (S.D. = .71); the difference between these means is highly significant ($t = 6.4$, $p < .001$) and indicates that the children of the nondisturbed parents were rated as being the *more* severe stutterers. (Since a rating of 1 on the Iowa Scale indicates normal, fluent speech, 7 represents extremely severe stuttering, and 4 an average degree of severity, a rating of 3 indicates a relatively mild degree of stuttering.)

Discussion

The most striking finding of this portion of Study III was the failure to establish any major personality test differences between the experimental and control group parents. Although certain differences between the two groups of parents were statistically significant and psychologically provocative, the over-all impression left by the results is that whatever important differences exist between these groups they are not clearly reflected in their MMPI scores. Certainly the small absolute differences between the means and the large amount of overlap between the two distributions of scores would prohibit the use of MMPI as an instrument for differentiating these groups in clinical work.

The present results are in substantial agreement with those of Grossman (45) although she interprets her results somewhat differently. Grossman had secured MMPI profiles from twenty-one married couples whose school-age children were receiving speech therapy for stuttering and a matched control group of twenty-one couples. She compared the mean scores of the two groups on the four validity and nine clinical scales of the MMPI; while only one of these thirteen comparisons was statistically significant (the stutterers' parents were higher on the F scale), Grossman concluded that the stutterers' parents respond to the MMPI more "atypically" than the nonstutterers' parents. Since twelve of her thirteen differences were not statistically significant and all the differences were small in absolute magnitude, her conclusions do not seem to be justified by her data.

It is essential to note that not only are the two sets of parents in the present study very similar to each other in their mean MMPI profiles but they are also very similar to the original Minnesota standardization group of presumably normal subjects (R50, 120). The highest clinical scale mean for either group is 56.1 for the control parents on the Hy scale; this represents a deviation of only 0.6 of a standard deviation from the expected mean score of 50.0 for a group of psychiatrically normal persons. The highest clinical scale mean for the experimental group is 55.5, also on the Hy scale. These are the largest differences from the expected normal mean scores and all the other obtained means are, of course, even closer to the expected value of 50.0. While some of these differences may be of statistical significance, they lie within the normal limits and are not, in all probability, psychologically important in a clinical sense. It is more reasonable to ascribe such small differences to sampling factors than to any "real" differences between experimental and control groups or between the persons studied in the present investigation and the Minnesota standardization group. These differences certainly do not provide a sound basis for regarding either the control or the experimental group of parents as psychiatrically abnormal or more maladjusted than adult persons in general.

The absence of evidence of abnormality in these mean profiles is even more strikingly brought home when they are compared with the mean profiles of various neurotic and psychotic groups and of college students receiving psychological counseling (R120). Each of the latter groups have characteristic mean profiles with very marked peaks and valleys differing greatly from the flat mean profiles obtained from these parents. Such comparisons strongly support the contention that these are, for the most part, essentially normal persons who differ little, if at all, from the Minnesota group of normal adults who comprised the standardization sample.

While the present results offer no evidence for concluding that these two groups of parents are very different from each other or from normal persons generally, it should be recalled that three of the seventeen mean differences, although absolutely quite small and within the normal range, were statistically significant and deserve further comment. On the K scale the control group parents' mean was significantly higher than that of the experimental group parents. This would indicate that the control group parents were somewhat more defensive, less likely to admit psychological defects or problems. These control group parents had not been asked, as had the experimental group parents, to admit *as part of the selection procedure* that they regarded their children as deviant, and certainly might be expected to be less open and more defensive in such a clinical situation.

The finding that the control group mean on the dominance (Do) scale was significantly higher than that of the experimental group, suggesting greater dominance in face-to-face personal relationships, is rather difficult to interpret and fit into the other findings and conclusions about the onset of stuttering. Little is known about the interpretation and usefulness of the Do scale as it is a recent addition to the MMPI scales and perhaps any more elaborate interpretation of this result should be postponed until additional information about the Do scale is available.

The experimental group parents scored significantly higher on the Anxiety (A) scale than did the control group parents. Certainly the admission of greater tension and anxiety on the part of the stutterers' parents may be regarded as an important finding, but great care should be exercised in relating this finding to the onset of stuttering. The heightened anxiety on the part of the experimental group parents may be an important etiological factor in the development of stuttering, or it may be a subsequent reaction by these parents to what they regarded as the development of stuttering by their children. The present data do not permit a resolution of these alternative interpretations.

Perhaps the best evidence that the experimental group of parents was essentially normal from a psychiatric point of view was the finding that the "deviant" group of experimental group parents, those with one or more T scores above 70, had children with generally less severe stuttering, as rated, than that of the children whose parents were in the nondeviant experimental group. On the other hand, the MMPI profiles of the parents of the more severe stutterers were almost uniformly within normal limits and gave no indication of severe psychological pathology of any sort. It may be that these deviant parents volunteered for participation because they were concerned not so much with nonfluencies in their children's speech, as with their own problems; they may have regarded participation in the experiment as one way of receiving help with these more general problems, rather than as an opportunity to discuss their children's speech. Such an interpretation would indicate a need for caution on the part of the speech therapist when he does find a presumably stuttering child's parent with a deviant MMPI profile.

Following the conclusion of this study it seemed worthwhile to cross-validate these results with a group of presumably typical speech clinic patients. This was done by selecting from the files of the Iowa Speech Clinic the case records of fifty chronically stuttering children for whom the MMPI profiles of both parents were available. These 100 profiles were then compared with the mean profiles given in Table 61 (R 40). Only three significant mean differences between the cross-validation group and the two original groups were found, with all the differences in the direction of more "normal" responses for the cross-validation group, and with all group means lying within 0.5 S.D. of the theoretical mean value of 50. The cross-validation group was significantly lower on the Ma scale than either of the original groups and significantly lower on the Pd scale than the original control group parents. Comparisons of the high-point codes of the cross-validation parents and the two original groups revealed no significant differences between the three groups. The children of the cross-validation parents with one or more T scores above 70 were independently rated as having the same severity of stuttering as the children of the parents with no clinical scale scores above 70. These results were interpreted as indicating that the responses of the cross-validation group were not significantly different from those of the two earlier groups and as lending additional support to the prior conclusions that the etiology of stuttering is not related to severe psychopathology on the part of the stutterers' parents.

The MMPI results are in general agreement with those of the overall investigation in that they do not support the notion that the par-

194

ents who regard their children as stutterers are very different in their behavior and attitudes from the parents who judge their children to be nonstutterers. Rather, these results support the suggestion that those parental group differences that are important in the etiology of stuttering are rather limited and probably related quite specifically to certain evaluations and reactions of the parents to the nonfluency aspects of the speech of their children in particular speech situations, or under particular circumstances.

CHAPTER 8

Analysis of Recorded Speech Samples

I$_T$ is difficult, as was indicated in Chapters 5 and 6, to obtain, after the fact, a descriptive account of the speaking done by a child at the very first moment, or during the first hours, or even the first weeks or months, when the parents or others began to suspect or judge or take for granted that the way in which he was talking was "not right" and that, as they told themselves, he was stuttering. It is difficult to obtain such an account because the words of the informants are not descriptive exclusively of the child and the child's speech. On the contrary, their statements appear to be considerably, or even in some instances solely, projective of their own inner states, and are more or less elaborately influenced by the vagaries and compulsions of memory, the rigidity of habitual language patterns, a relative lack of appreciation of the need for reliably descriptive statements and of what is involved in achieving them, plus varying intensities of anxiety, guilt, regret, and resentment, and associated self-defensiveness, wishful thinking, and obfuscating hopefulness or depression. The definite and imposing fact is that, in consequence, it is extraordinarily hard — indeed, often impossible — to obtain, after any considerable intervening period, substantially objective and detailed information about the way a child was talking at the time when someone entertained the first faint stirrings of the judgment that he was beginning to stutter.

There would appear to be only two possible methods of securing information about the speaking that a child was doing at the moment when he was first regarded as a stutterer, or the equivalent. One of these methods involves the subsequent gathering of testimony or reports from observers, including the speaker himself, or from informants who were not observers. As has been implied, it is to be stressed that the memories out of which the informants speak are more or less clear or blurred, abundant or sketchy, dependable or distorted by self-projection, and this holds whether the informants qualify as firsthand

196

observers or only as relayers of what they presumably have been told by others who supposedly were observers. It is particularly important to note that practically never is the alleged stutterer himself qualified as a firsthand observer. Nearly without exception, in the writer's experience at least, the stutterer himself is unable to recall from his own clear memory the events involved in the beginnings of his speech problem, and so the statement he is prepared to make about those beginnings has, in general, the status of a self-interested account of family legend. In the present investigation the speakers under scrutiny were relatively young children, and it was not feasible to question them concerning what has been termed the onset of their stuttering. The informants in this study were the mothers and fathers of the speakers under investigation, and the data supplied by them have been examined in the preceding chapters.

The second of the two methods available for ascertaining the facts about the speech of a person at the first instant when he is judged to be stuttering is that of making a sound film or a tape or other type of recording of the speaking done by him *at that instant.* It would be ideal to compare such a recording with recorded samples of the same person's speech obtained previously and subsequently under similar and dissimilar circumstances in real life situations as well as in laboratory or contrived settings. It would also be part of the ideal procedure to record, preferably on sound film, the real life situations in which the person produces these samples of his speech, including especially the verbal and nonverbal reactions of his parents, siblings, or other persons present in these situations.

This brief description of the ideal procedure serves the basic purpose of making us aware of the fact that the data to be obtained by means of it do not exist — except possibly in fragmentary form in an isolated instance here or there, and even this would seem to be extremely unlikely — and if any fragments of such data do exist they are, to the best of the writer's knowledge, unanalyzed, uninterpreted, and essentially unknown in any scientifically meaningful sense. Nor are such data likely to be secured in any substantial amounts, if at all. Even so, efforts to approximate as closely as possible the indicated ideal type of speech sampling and investigation are to be encouraged. Indeed, in this and in the previously published book *Stuttering in Children and Adults* (62), and in other relevant publications, a considerable body of information is to be found concerning the aspects of speech that are relevant to the present purposes, and concerning the conditions that affect these aspects of speech, including the ways in which they are evaluated and reacted to by listeners, such as parents and others more or less interested or disinterested in the speaker and his speech. More data of this general sort probably will be gathered, and a vigilant and sustained endeavor to obtain, as early as possible in presumably suitable cases, tape recordings of the speech of individual children, and of the relevant descriptive and evaluative statements of their parents, together with systematic observations of the accompanying behavior of both child and parents in each case, should continue to yield an increasingly illuminating body of information concerning the period more or less closely subsequent to the moment of inception of the problem called stuttering.

It seems unrealistic, however, to expect that very often, if ever, a tape recorder will be luckily located and running at the precise instant when a particular parent first makes the judgment that his or her child is stuttering. To the extent that the kind of data such a recorder would preserve are not to be come by, the question as to what they would be like, if obtained, may be answered as well as it can be only by disciplined inference from the data that have been and will be gathered by available means under accessible conditions.

The Problem and Subjects

In the spirit represented by these comments, an attempt was made in the present study to obtain a tape recording of a sample of the speech of each experimental and control group child for whom this was possible, and it proved to be possible for eighty-nine of the matched pairs of children.* Of these matched pairs, sixty-eight were boys and twenty-one were girls. Age data are summarized in Table 65; the mean age was approximately five years for all four of the subgroups, and the ages ranged from roughly two and one-half to a bit over eight years.

In keeping with the preceding discussion, it is to be recognized, and duly taken into account in making interpretations of findings, that what was recorded was not, in any case, the speech that was originally judged by someone to be stuttering. The only available information about that speech has been presented and discussed in Chapters 5 and 6. The data about to be presented were derived from tape-recorded samples of children's speech obtained from about one month to over three years, and in the average case approximately a year and a half, after the children had first been regarded as stutterers (see Table 66).

---

* If a usable recording was obtained for one child of a matched pair but not for the other, the one obtained was not included in the analysis. Lack of facilities, particularly for those subjects studied in their homes, lack of time, quality of recording, and failure of the children to cooperate adequately were the principle reasons why usable recordings were not obtained in all cases.

Table 65. Ranges, Means, and Standard Deviations of Ages in Months of Male and
Female Subjects in the Experimental and Control Groups from
Whom Tape-Recorded Speech Samples Were Obtained

Group	N	Range	Mean	S.D.
Experimental males	68	29–91	62.2	15.58
Experimental females	21	32–96	59.8	18.77
Control males	68	30–104	62.4	15.93
Control females	21	30–101	60.0	17.90

Table 66. Means, Standard Deviations, and Ranges of the Difference in Months, for
Male and Female Experimental Group Subjects, between the Age at Onset of Stuttering
as Reported by the Mothers and Fathers and the Age at the
Time When Speech Samples Were Tape-Recorded

Informant	Mean	N	S.D.	Range
		Male Subjects		
Mother	18.57	68	10.35	1–39
Father	19.68	63	12.37	0–50
		Female Subjects		
Mother	18.14	21	11.73	2–39
Father	14.67	21	10.05	3–37

It is to be duly considered, therefore, that these speech samples may
reflect changes in the speech behavior of the experimental group children associated with the fact that, in contrast to the control group
children, they had been speaking, for the indicated periods of time, under conditions occasioned by the negative evaluations made of them
and their speech by their dominant authority figures and, in most
cases, by others also. Moreover, these negative evaluations had presumably been adopted in varying degrees by the children themselves.

So far as the speech of the two groups of children was similar just
prior to and at the moment when this negative evaluation of the
speech of the experimental group subjects was first made, the data here
presented constitute the findings of an "undeliberated experiment." In
this experiment, so far as it may be so designated, two groups of children, matched with respect to age, sex, and socioeconomic status of
family, and with speech as much alike as it may be judged to have
been, were subjected at a particular point in time to contrasting conditions. The speech of those in the control group continued presumably
to be as positively evaluated and as fully accepted by their parents
as it had been, whereas the speech of those in the experimental group
was, at and after a given moment, regarded variously by their parents
as a source of concern and distress, evaluated more or less negatively,

199

and reacted to nonverbally by means of postures, facial expressions, bodily tensions, etc., or verbally in the form of suggestions or urgings to speak more slowly, or more smoothly, or to relax and take it easy, or to stop and think, or take a breath, and the like. After a median interval of approximately eighteen months, then, the speech of the control and experimental group subjects was sampled, analyzed with respect to degree of nonfluency, and compared.

In any interpretation of the demonstrated differences between the two groups with respect to nonfluency, it would seem necessary to give due consideration, based on all relevant data presented in this book, to three crucial questions: (1) What might most dependably be said as to the degree of similarity between the two groups with regard to speech nonfluency just before and during the first moments of the "experiment"? (2) To what degree and in what respects were the two groups subjected to dissimilar conditions during the "experiment"? (3) Were there factors other than the ones indicated in the various sections of this book that affected the two groups differently during the "experiment"?

Such answers as one may be able or inclined to give to these questions will presumably govern, in large measure, the explanation that one will make, or accept, of the findings presently to be described.

Speech Recording Procedure

The tape recordings of the speech of the experimental group subjects were made either in their homes or in the speech clinics of the several universities cooperating in this study, depending on convenience to the subject. The control group subjects were recorded, with few exceptions, in their homes. A portable tape recorder was used at a tape speed of 3.75 or 7.5 inches per second.*

According to the original plan of the study, the parents of each child were to be present in the room during the making of the speech recording, but it proved necessary in some cases for one or both parents to be interviewed during this time. The speech samples were recorded, therefore, with or without one or both parents present.

In each case, after essential preliminaries and the achievement of adequate rapport, a recording was made of the child's responses to the

* The procedure used in collecting and analyzing the data presented in this chapter was an adaptation of methods developed by the writer and his associates in previous investigations of nonfluency in the speech of presumably representative preschool children and college-age male and female stutterers and nonstutterers (R18, 25, 30, 60, 69, 78). Much of the previous work on the nonfluency of children's speech has been summarized in Chapter 5 of *Stuttering in Children and Adults: Thirty Years of Research at the University of Iowa* (62).

Children's Apperception Test (CAT) by Bellak (5). In order to obtain adequate speech samples from very young or very reticent children, the CAT was administered with certain departures from the standard procedure, mainly in the form of promptings and suggestions made by the interviewer concerning possible card content. It did not prove possible to secure responses to all the picture cards in all cases; measures of the size of samples obtained are presented in Table 67. Size of

Table 67. Mean Number of Words and Related Measures of Size of Speech Sample for Male and Female Experimental and Control Group Subjects

Group	N	Range	Mean	S.D.	Median	90th Percentile
Experimental males	68	31–1,158	499.8	293.0	452.5	955.7
Experimental females	21	116–1,296	556.0	351.6	389.0	1,156.4
Control males	68	65–1,229	475.3	234.1	445.5	909.7
Control females	21	211–2,044	526.5	385.5	402.7	824.4

sample was defined in each case in terms of number of words spoken. In computing this number, interjected sounds or words were not counted, and each word repeated singly or in a phrase was counted only once. For example, the sentence "He went went went to town" contains four, not six, words. In a nonfluency of the revision type only the words in the final revised form of the utterance were counted.*

The type of speech obtained was essentially propositional, extemporaneous, unrehearsed, unmemorized, and consisted mainly of the child's comments about the actions or the stories represented by the CAT pictures, as he perceived and interpreted them. No attempt was made to conceal the recording equipment.

Analysis of Speech Samples

The recorded speech samples were transcribed and analyzed according to the procedure, described below, developed by the writer and his co-workers (R60) in their studies of speech fluency of college-age male and female stutterers and nonstutterers. The features of speech identified in the evaluation of the samples were those thought to represent the various aspects of speech nonfluency, with the exception of pause

* It is to be noted that this method of counting words yields a smaller total number of words for a given speech sample than the method used in previously published studies of nonfluency (R62). The present method results, therefore, in a correspondingly higher count of nonfluencies per hundred, or per thousand, words, a fact to be taken into account in comparing the findings of the present study with those of earlier investigations (R18, 25, 30, 62, 78). See the section that follows immediately for definitions of revision and other types of nonfluency.

time. This measure was not used because of the practical difficulty of deciding whether or not given pauses were part of meaningful or expressive speech. The following types of speech behavior were counted as nonfluencies:

1. Interjections of syllables, sounds, words, or phrases. Determination was made of the frequency of extraneous sounds such as "uh," "er," and "hmmm" and extraneous words such as "well" which were distinct from sounds and words associated with the fluent or meaningful text, or with other categories of nonfluency. The number of times each interjection occurred within each instance of its occurrence was tabulated as the number of units, and the number of instances of interjection was also determined. "Uh" and "uh uh uh," for example, were each counted as one instance of interjection, and the number of units in the first instance was recorded as one and the number of units in the second instance as three.

2. Repetition of sounds or syllables. Repetitions of a part of a word were placed in this category. Within each repetition instance the number of times the sound or syllable was repeated was counted as the number of units; "r-run" is one unit of repetition, "r-r-run" two units. No distinction was made between sounds and syllables. "B-boy," "ba-ba-baby," and "abou-about" are examples of sound and syllable repetition.

3. Repetition of words. Repetitions of whole words, including one-syllable words, were placed in this category. Both the number of instances and the number of repetition units within each instance were counted. "I-I-I" was recorded as one instance involving two units of word repetition and "going going" was counted as one instance of word repetition involving one unit. If a word was repeated for emphasis, as in "very, very clean," it was not counted as a nonfluency.

4. Repetition of phrases. Repetitions of more than one word, or of one word and part of a second word, were classified as phrase repetitions, provided no modification or revision of the content resulted from the repetition. "I was I was I was" and "He was g- was going" are examples in this category, the former involving two units and the latter one unit of repetition.

5. Revisions. Changes in the content or grammatical form of a phrase, or in the pronunciation of a word, were counted as instances of revision. "I was — I am going" is an example in this category.

6. Incomplete phrases. An incomplete phrase is one in which the thought or content is not completed and which is not an instance of phrase repetition. "I was — and after she got there, he came" contains an example of an incomplete phrase. Incomplete phrases caused by in-

terruptions made by the interviewer or parents were not considered nonfluencies.

7. Broken words. This category includes words not completely pronounced and not classifiable in any other category. It also includes nonfluencies in which the normal or customary rhythm of the word is broken or disturbed so that the flow of speech is definitely affected. "I was g-(pause)-oing home" is an example of a broken word.

8. Prolonged sounds. This category included any unduly prolonged sound. If a sound was prolonged twice it was counted both as a prolonged sound and as a repetition of a sound.

Measures of speaking time or of rate were not feasible, because the speech of the interviewer and of the parents was intermingled with that of the child in such a way as to preclude a valid estimate of the child's speaking rate.

The analysis of each tape-recorded speech sample was made from a verbatim transcript while listening to a playback of the recording. Re-listening, when necessary, was continued until the observer was essentially certain that he had achieved an accurate perception.

Derived Measures

Two types of index were derived from the counts made of the number of units and instances of nonfluency. The first of these is a frequency index, the number of instances of nonfluency per 100 words. This value was computed for each of the eight categories of nonfluency and for all eight categories combined. The second type of index, the number of units per instance of nonfluency, was computed for each of the first four categories — interjections, sound and syllable repetition, word repetition, and phrase repetition. With respect to interjections, as previously explained, "uh," for example, is counted as one unit and "uh uh" as two; it takes only one production of an interjection to constitute a unit. One unit of repetition, however, is made up of two productions of the sound or syllable or word or phrase involved, two units are made up of three productions, etc. Thus, "boy boy" is one unit of word repetition, "boy boy boy" are two units, etc. For each subject, and for each of the four indicated categories of nonfluency, the total number of units was divided by the total number of instances to determine the average number of units of nonfluency per instance, which may be regarded as an index of extent of nonfluency.

Reliability of the Nonfluency Counts

The method of counting nonfluencies used in this study is the same as that employed in related investigations included in a program of research, of which the present study is a part, concerned with speech nonfluency at childhood and adult age levels (R60). The reliability of this method has been determined by using tape recordings of adult female stutterers. These were recordings of each subject's response to card number 10 of the Thematic Apperception Test (R86), description of present or future job, and oral reading of a 300-word passage. Two independent observers listened to twelve such tape recordings picked at random from a larger collection. Four of these were recordings of job descriptions, four of TAT responses, and four of oral reading.

Pearson product moment coefficients of correlation between the counts of instances and units of nonfluency in the various categories made by the two observers are given in Table 68.

Table 68. Pearson Product Moment Coefficients of Correlation between Counts of Units and Instances of Eight Types of Nonfluency Made Independently by Two Observers in Analyzing Twelve Samples of Recorded Speech

Nonfluency Category	Coefficients of Correlation	
	Number of Instances of Nonfluency	Number of Units of Nonfluency
Interjections	.98	.99
Repeated sound and syllable	.90	.77
Word repetition	.99	.96
Phrase repetition	.95	.96
Revisions	.94	
Incomplete phrases	.97	
Broken words	.95	
Prolonged sounds	.93	

With one possible exception, that for the number of units of repeated sounds and syllables, the values in Table 68 indicate levels of reliability that are relatively high. They are of an order comparable with those previously obtained in analyzing samples of the speech of both children and adults (R18, 25, 60). It is assumed that these measures are indicative of the substantial reliability of the data presented in the following sections of this report.

Findings

The data presented in Tables 69 to 80 are pertinent to three basic questions:

1. What are the distributions of the nonfluency measures employed for children, as represented by the samples described, classified as stutterers and nonstutterers, respectively?

2. What group differences in the nonfluency measures used are demonstrable after a mean period of approximately eighteen months during which the two groups of children spoke under presumably different conditions, as previously indicated?

3. Do the various distributions of nonfluency measures for the two groups overlap, and, if so, to what degree, and with what apparent theoretical implications?

NORMATIVE DATA

Frequency Indexes. The data were analyzed separately for the two sexes, and for the experimental and control groups. Decile values of the frequency index determinations for the various groups are presented in Tables 69 and 70. The means and standard deviations for each of the groups are presented in Tables 71 and 72. There were no statistically significant sex differences in the control group (Table 71), and there were no notable sex differences in the experimental group (Table 72).*

For each of the eight nonfluency measures one or more of the subjects in both groups achieved a frequency index of 0.00, representing no nonfluencies, with the exception of the category of interjections for the female experimental subgroup. No child in either group, however, proved to be perfectly fluent; the lowest index for all categories of nonfluency combined was that of a boy in the control group who scored 0.60, the equivalent of six instances of nonfluency per 1,000 words. For the male subjects the first, fifth, and ninth decile values of the frequency index for all categories of nonfluency combined were as follows: experimental group, 6.48, 13.62, and 34.43; control group, 2.05, 7.14, and 13.76. For the female subjects the corresponding decile values were as follows: experimental group, 5.68, 16.31, and 32.03; control group, 2.74, 5.01, and 13.53.

Tables 69 and 70 may be used as normative reference tables in evaluating appropriately derived measures of the nonfluency of children within the indicated sex, age, and socioeconomic groups. They serve to emphasize that nonfluencies occur in the speech of children generally, and that their distribution is dimensional rather than categorical. There are no "natural" lines of demarcation between "normal" and "abnormal" degrees of nonfluency. The data summarized in Tables 69

---

* In the experimental group (Table 72) there was a significant sex difference for the category of broken words, the female group having the higher mean. This difference, however, is to be considered with reference to the fact that two female subjects in the experimental group had atypically high raw scores of 3.64 and 7.76, respectively, for this category compared with a range from 0 to .94 for the scores of all other subjects in both experimental groups.

Table 69. Range and Decile Distribution of the Frequency Indexes of Nonfluency (Number of Nonfluencies per Hundred Words) for Each of the Eight Nonfluency Categories and for All Categories Combined for the Male Experimental (N = 68) and Control (N = 68) Group Subjects

Nonfluency Category and Group	Lowest Index	Deciles									Highest Index
		1	2	3	4	5	6	7	8	9	
Interjections											
E	.00	.33	1.15	1.85	2.19	2.89	3.41	4.52	6.09	7.10	15.25
C	.00	.39	.67	1.20	1.63	2.04	2.71	3.98	5.31	8.40	12.71
Sound and syllable repetitions											
E	.00	.43	.93	1.50	2.41	3.13	4.07	5.70	7.94	13.09	36.63
C	.00	.00	.00	.22	.40	.55	.60	.79	.91	1.51	2.42
Word repetitions											
E	.00	.90	1.66	2.65	3.00	3.23	3.88	5.39	6.11	8.26	14.80
C	.00	.20	.31	.49	.65	.97	1.17	1.42	1.73	2.03	4.62
Phrase repetitions											
E	.00	.00	.37	.54	.87	.95	1.18	1.59	1.85	1.98	7.07
C	.00	.00	.00	.23	.40	.47	.64	.80	.99	1.54	2.52
Revisions											
E	.00	.00	.43	.58	.68	1.08	1.36	1.79	2.18	2.78	4.41
C	.00	.29	.49	.74	.95	1.11	1.41	1.84	2.32	2.66	7.17
Incomplete phrases											
E	.00	.00	.00	.00	.00	.00	.22	.40	.68	.93	2.45
C	.00	.00	.00	.00	.00	.00	.00	.21	.50	.88	1.65
Broken words											
E	.00	.00	.00	.00	.00	.00	.00	.00	.15	.43	.94
C	.00	.00	.00	.00	.00	.00	.00	.00	.00	.12	1.09
Prolonged sounds											
E	.00	.00	.00	.18	.43	.64	.97	1.36	1.98	3.95	19.60
C	.00	.00	.00	.00	.00	.00	.00	.16	.31	.53	1.95
All categories											
E	3.30	6.48	8.27	10.74	12.77	13.62	14.64	22.12	27.15	34.43	46.51
C	.60	2.05	3.42	4.20	4.97	7.14	8.55	9.74	10.81	13.76	18.28

Table 70. Range and Decile Distribution of the Frequency Indexes of Nonfluency (Number of Nonfluencies per Hundred Words) for Each of the Eight Nonfluency Categories and for All Categories Combined for the Female Experimental (N = 21) and Control (N = 21) Group Subjects

Nonfluency Category and Group	Lowest Index	Deciles									Highest Index
		1	2	3	4	5	6	7	8	9	
Interjections											
E	.81	1.07	1.77	2.38	3.24	3.38	4.23	5.91	6.03	8.64	14.66
C	.00	.24	.50	1.04	1.52	1.62	3.33	3.97	5.51	8.46	15.22
Sound and syllable repetitions											
E	.00	.50	.64	1.38	2.13	2.29	3.43	4.42	5.20	8.91	16.61
C	.00	.22	.25	.26	.29	.53	.55	.74	1.10	1.44	6.09
Word repetitions											
E	.00	.32	.81	1.88	2.39	3.45	3.78	4.88	5.74	7.45	9.23
C	.00	.25	.28	.51	.58	.73	1.21	1.42	1.67	2.61	3.47
Phrase repetitions											
E	.00	.00	.15	.32	.38	.50	.62	.86	1.30	2.16	3.11
C	.00	.00	.00	.00	.29	.44	.50	.53	1.04	1.30	2.51
Revisions											
E	.00	.32	.42	.75	.81	1.16	1.19	1.72	2.11	2.78	3.34
C	.00	.36	.67	.88	1.24	1.28	1.46	1.93	2.05	2.25	3.29
Incomplete phrases											
E	.00	.00	.00	.00	.00	.00	.15	.21	.28	.30	2.41
C	.00	.00	.00	.00	.00	.00	.24	.25	.26	1.05	1.74
Broken words											
E	.00	.00	.00	.00	.00	.00	.00	.13	.30	.56	7.76
C	.00	.00	.00	.00	.00	.00	.00	.05	.25	.40	.51
Prolonged sounds											
E	.00	.00	.00	.15	.25	.51	1.04	1.46	1.79	2.48	7.25
C	.00	.00	.00	.00	.00	.00	.00	.16	.25	.53	.87
All categories											
E	4.16	5.68	8.23	9.51	11.38	16.31	17.27	17.47	18.72	32.03	46.55
C	2.61	2.74	3.31	4.36	4.69	5.01	6.87	8.30	11.06	13.53	28.70

Table 71. Mean Differences, with t Values, between Nonfluency Frequency Indexes (Number of Nonfluencies per Hundred Words) of Male ($N = 68$) and Female ($N = 21$) Control Group Subjects

Nonfluency Category and Group	Mean	S.D.	Diff.	S.E.	t^*
Interjections					
M	3.13	3.01			
F	3.45	3.92	.32	.81	.40
Sound and syllable repetitions					
M	.61	.54			
F	.83	1.30	.22	.20	1.10
Word repetitions					
M	1.07	.87			
F	1.14	.96	.07	.22	.32
Phrase repetitions					
M	.61	.59			
F	.58	.62	.03	.15	.20
Revisions					
M	1.43	1.17			
F	1.38	.79	.05	.26	.19
Incomplete phrases					
M	.23	.39			
F	.28	.47	.05	.10	.50
Broken words					
M	.04	.17			
F	.10	.17	.06	.043	1.40
Prolonged sounds					
M	.16	.33			
F	.14	.22	.02	.10	.20
Total (task index)					
M	7.28	4.38			
F	7.90	1.78	.62	.99	.63

* None of the t scores is significant at the 5 per cent level.

208

Table 72. Mean Differences, with t Values, between Nonfluency Frequency Indexes (Number of Nonfluencies per Hundred Words) of Male (N = 68) and Female (N = 21) Experimental Group Subjects

Nonfluency Category and Group	Mean	S.D.	Diff.	S.E.	t
Interjections					
M	3.62	3.11			
F	4.44	3.01	.82	.78	1.05
Sound and syllable repetitions					
M	5.44	6.49			
F	3.93	4.26	1.51	1.50	1.01
Word repetitions					
M	4.28	3.21			
F	3.65	2.78	.63	.78	.81
Phrase repetitions					
M	1.14	1.04			
F	.84	.91	.30	.24	1.24
Revisions					
M	1.30	1.01			
F	1.30	.97	.00		
Incomplete phrases					
M	.34	.53			
F	.22	.51	.12	.14	.86
Broken words					
M	.12	.26			
F	.63	1.77	.51	.22	2.32*
Prolonged sounds					
M	1.67	3.23			
F	1.24	1.80	.43	.74	.58
All categories					
M	17.91	10.87			
F	16.25	4.56	1.66	2.14	.78

*Significant at the 5 per cent level; t .05 (df = 87) = 1.99.

Table 73. Mean Differences, with *t* Values, between Nonfluency Frequency Indexes
(Number of Nonfluencies per Hundred Words) of Male Experimental
(N = 68) and Control (N = 68) Group Subjects

Nonfluency Category and Group	Mean	Diff.	S.E.	t
Interjections				
E	3.62			
C	3.13	.49	.53	.92
Sound and syllable repetitions				
E	5.44			
C	.61	4.83	.79	6.11*
Word repetitions				
E	4.28			
C	1.07	3.21	.41	7.83*
Phrase repetitions				
E	1.14			
C	.61	.53	.14	3.79*
Revisions				
E	1.30			
C	1.43	.13	.19	.68
Incomplete phrases				
E	.34			
C	.23	.11	.80	.14
Broken words				
E	.12			
C	.04	.08	.04	2.11†
Prolonged sounds				
E	1.67			
C	.16	1.51	.39	3.87*
All categories				
E	17.91			
C	7.28	10.63	1.43	7.43*

* Significant at the 1 per cent level; *t* .01 (df = 134) = 2.62.
† Significant at the 5 per cent level; *t* .05 (df = 134) = 1.98.

210

Table 74. Mean Differences, with *t* Values, between Nonfluency Frequency Indexes (Number of Nonfluencies per Hundred Words) of Female Experimental (N = 21) and Control (N = 21) Group Subjects

Nonfluency Category and Group	Mean	Diff.	S.E.	*t*
Interjections				
E	4.44			
C	3.45	.99	1.10	.90
Sound and syllable repetitions				
E	3.93			
C	.83	3.10	.98	3.16*
Word repetitions				
E	3.65			
C	1.14	2.51	.66	3.80*
Phrase repetitions				
E	.84			
C	.58	.26	.25	1.04
Revisions				
E	1.30			
C	1.38	.08	.28	.29
Incomplete phrases				
E	.22			
C	.28	.06	.15	.40
Broken words				
E	.63			
C	.10	.53	.40	1.33
Prolonged sounds				
E	1.24			
C	.14	1.10	.41	2.68†
Total (task index)				
E	16.25			
C	7.90	8.35	1.06	7.88*

* Significant at the 1 per cent level; *t* .01 (df = 40) = 2.71.
† Significant at the 5 per cent level; *t* .05 (df = 40) = 2.02.

Table 75. Average Percentage of the Nonfluencies Classified in Each Category for the Experimental and Control Group Male and Female Subjects

Nonfluency Category	Experimental Group		Control Group	
	Male	Female	Male	Female
Interjections	20.2	27.3	43.0	43.7
Sound and syllable repetitions	30.4	24.2	8.4	10.5
Word repetitions	23.9	22.5	14.7	14.4
Phrase repetitions	6.4	5.7	8.4	7.3
Revisions	7.3	8.0	19.6	17.5
Incomplete phrases	1.9	1.5	3.2	3.5
Broken words	.7	3.9	1.4	1.3
Prolonged sounds	9.3	7.6	1.9	1.8

Table 76. Mean Number of Units per Instance of Nonfluency (Index of Extent of Nonfluency) in Each of Four Categories for the Experimental and Control Male and Female Subjects

Nonfluency Category	Male				Female			
	N*	Range	Mean	S.D.	N	Range	Mean	S.D.
Experimental Group								
Interjections	64	1–2.9	1.21	.33	21	1–2	1.21	.24
Sound and syllable repetitions	64	1–3.4	1.47	.52	20	1–3.4	1.73	.24
Word repetitions . . .	67	1–2.9	1.33	.26	20	1–1.9	1.29	.20
Phrase repetitions . . .	59	1–1.5	1.07	.20	18	1–1.4	1.08	.10
Control Group								
Interjections	63	1–2	1.11	.20	20	1–1.6	1.06	.17
Sound and syllable repetitions	51	1–2	1.08	.17	19	1–2	1.10	.49
Word repetitions . . .	62	1–2	1.10	.17	20	1–2	1.11	.22
Phrase repetitions . . .	50	1–1.3	1.04	.10	13	1–1	1.00	.00

* Persons having zero scores for a particular category were excluded for the purpose of computing the mean and standard deviation for that category. Each mean presented here is the average number of units per instance for those subjects who presented the particular kind of nonfluency indicated. There are zero scores in each instance in which the male N is less than 68 and the female N is less than 21. The minimal values given in the range columns are for subjects whose scores were greater than zero.

Table 77. Mean Differences, with t Values, between Indexes of Extent of Nonfluency (See Table 76) for Control Male and Female Subjects

Nonfluency Category and Group	N	Mean	Diff.	S.E.	t^*
Interjections					
M	63	1.11			
F	20	1.06	.05	.05	1.00
Sound and syllable repetitions					
M	51	1.08			
F	19	1.10	.02	.08	.25
Word repetitions					
M	62	1.10			
F	20	1.11	.01	.08	.13
Phrase repetitions					
M	50	1.04			
F	13	1.00	.04	.03	1.43

* None of the t values is significant at the 5 per cent level.

Table 78. Mean Differences, with *t* Values, between Indexes of Extent of Nonfluency (See Table 76) for Experimental Male and Female Subjects

Nonfluency Category and Group	N	Mean	Diff.	S.E.	t
Interjections					
M	64	1.21			
F	21	1.21	.00		
Sound and syllable repetitions					
M	64	1.47			
F	20	1.73	.26	.12	2.17*
Word repetitions					
M	67	1.33			
F	20	1.29	.04	.06	.62
Phrase repetitions					
M	59	1.07			
F	18	1.08	.01	.05	.20

* Significant at the 5 per cent level; t .05 (df $=82) = 2.00.$

Table 79. Mean Differences, with *t* Values, between Indexes of Extent of Nonfluency (See Table 76) for Male Experimental and Control Subjects

Nonfluency Category and Group	N	Mean	Diff.	S.E.	t
Interjections					
E	64	1.21			
C	63	1.11	.10	.05	2.08*
Sound and syllable repetitions					
E	64	1.47			
C	51	1.08	.39	.08	5.06†
Word repetitions					
E	67	1.33			
C	62	1.10	.23	.04	5.90†
Phrase repetitions					
E	59	1.07			
C	50	1.04	.03	.03	.97

* Significant at the 5 per cent level; t .05 (df $= 125) = 1.98.$
† Significant at the 1 per cent level; t .01 (df $= 113$ or $127) = 2.62.$

Table 80. Mean Differences, with t Values, between Indexes of Extent of Nonfluency
(See Table 76) for Female Experimental and Control Subjects

Nonfluency Category and Group	N	Mean	Diff.	S.E.	t
Interjections					
E	21	1.21			
C	20	1.06	.15	.07	2.21*
Sound and syllable repetitions					
E	20	1.73			
C	19	1.10	.63	.13	5.00†
Word repetitions					
E	20	1.29			
C	20	1.11	.18	.07	2.61†
Phrase repetitions					
E	18	1.08			
C	13	1.00	.08	.03	2.76‡

* Significant at the 5 per cent level; t .05 (df = 38 or 39) = 2.02.
† Significant at the 1 per cent level; t .01 (df = 37) = 2.70.
‡ Significant at the 1 per cent level; t .01 (df = 29) = 2.76.

and 70 serve to focus attention in a crucial sense on the problems involved in defining "stuttering" in terms of nonfluency.

Differential Frequencies of Types of Nonfluency. The mean proportion of nonfluencies classified in each category was computed separately for the experimental and control group males and females (Table 75). Approximately three fourths of the nonfluencies of the experimental group male subjects were sound and syllable repetitions (30.4 per cent), word repetitions (23.9 per cent), and interjections (20.2 per cent). Nearly all of the remainder were distributed among the categories of prolonged sounds, revisions, and phrase repetitions. The findings for the female subjects in the experimental group were similar, a difference being the greater proportion of interjections than of either sound and syllable or word repetitions. Slightly more than three fourths of the nonfluencies of both the male and female subjects in the control group were interjections (male, 43 per cent; female, 43.7 per cent), revisions (male, 19.6 per cent; female, 17.5 per cent), and word repetitions (male, 14.7 per cent; female, 14.4 per cent). Sound and syllable repetitions were fourth in frequency for the control group and phrase repetitions were fifth.

Index of Extent of Nonfluency. The group ranges, means, and standard deviations of the index of extent of nonfluency (mean number of units per instance of nonfluency) are presented in Table 76. As shown in Tables 77 and 78, there were no significant sex differences with respect to this measure, except for a difference significant at the 5 per cent level between the means of the male and female experimental group subjects for sound and syllable repetitions, the females having the higher mean. The means of the experimental group, including both male and female subjects, ranged between 1.07 and 1.73 units of repetition per instance, seven of the eight values falling between 1.07 and 1.47. The range of individual values for the experimental group extended from 1.0 to 3.4. For the control group the eight means ranged from 1.00 to 1.11, the individual values ranging from 1.0 to 2.0. (Values of 1.0, 2.0, and 3.0, respectively, would represent such word repetitions, for example, as the following: "blue blue," "blue blue blue," "blue blue blue blue.") Children's speech, as represented by these data, is characterized by repetitions that are relatively limited in extent.

GROUP DIFFERENCES

Frequency Indexes. Results of *t* tests of the significance of the differences between group frequency index means are summarized in Tables 73 and 74. Differences significant at the 1 per cent level were obtained between the frequency index means of male experimental and control group subjects for the categories of sound and syllable repetition, word repetition, phrase repetition, prolonged sounds, and for all categories combined (Table 73). The difference between the corresponding means for the category of broken words was significant at the 5 per cent level. In all these comparisons the experimental group means are higher. Nonsignificant mean differences were obtained for the categories of interjections, revisions, and incomplete phrases.

Differences between the means of female experimental and control group subjects were significant at the 1 per cent level for the following categories: sound and syllable repetitions, word repetitions, and all categories combined (Table 74). The difference between the means for prolonged sounds was significant at the 5 per cent level. The experimental group means were higher in all these comparisons. Nonsignificant mean differences were obtained for interjections, phrase repetitions, revisions, incomplete phrases and broken words.

Index of Extent of Nonfluency. The mean indexes of extent of nonfluency for the male experimental and control group subjects differ significantly at the 1 per cent level for the categories of sound and syllable repetitions and word repetitions and at the 5 per cent level for interjections (Table 79). The experimental group mean was higher in each case. The differences between the corresponding means of the female experimental and control group subjects were significant at the 1 per cent level for sound and syllable repetitions and phrase repetitions and at the 5 per cent level for interjections and word repetitions, the experimental group means being higher (Table 80).

The small magnitudes of the mean values involved, and the correspondingly limited extent of the differences between them, serve to raise a question concerning the functional significance of the differences. This question, in its most general form, is of concern in all instances in which mathematically derived statements of the significance of a finding, such as the difference between two means, is to be distinguished from the medical or educational or clinical or practical significance of the finding. The mean differences shown in Tables 76, 79, and 80 are to be viewed within the perspective which this consideration provides, since none of them is as much as one unit of repetition in magnitude, the largest being only 0.63 of one unit, less than the full difference between "bl-blue" and "bl-bl-blue." The statistically significant difference between the means of the male experimental and control group subjects for extent of word repetitions was 0.23, about one fourth of the whole difference between "blue blue" and "blue blue blue."

OVERLAP OF GROUP DISTRIBUTIONS

Frequency Indexes. In view of the traditional and current tendency to equate the term "stuttering" with such other terms as "disorder in the rhythm of speech" or "disturbance of fluency" or "nonfluent speech," and to refer to some generally unspecified portion or aspect of childhood nonfluency as "primary stuttering," it is of particular interest to consider the degree to which the distributions of nonfluency measures for the "stuttering" and "nonstuttering" children were found to overlap.

The overlapping of the group distributions indicated in Tables 69 and 70 points up the importance of the consideration that "stuttering" and "nonstuttering" are names for judgments made by listeners of the vocal and phonetic productions made by speakers. The degree of nonfluency of the speaker is evidently but one of the factors determining whether the one or the other judgment will be made of his speech by a given listener. The findings of this study and of the related investigations referred to suggest that most, and possibly all, very young children speak with sufficient nonfluency or fluency to be classified as "stutterers" or as "normal speakers" by appropriately motivated parents, or other listeners.

It is to be observed (Table 69, bottom two rows) that the most nonfluent male "nonstutterer" in the present study was less fluent than nearly two thirds of the male "stutterers," and the most nonfluent female "nonstutterer" (Table 70, bottom two rows) was less fluent than over four fifths of the female "stutterers." Twenty per cent of the males regarded as "nonstutterers" were more nonfluent than 30 per cent of the males who were judged to be "stutterers," and essentially the same statement is to be made concerning the two female groups.

Like comparisons may be made with respect to the various types of nonfluency represented in Tables 69 and 70. The overlapping is nearly complete for the categories of interjections, revisions, incomplete phrases, and broken words; it is to be said that, on practical grounds, these kinds of nonfluency do not serve to differentiate the two groups. The two groups are not as well differentiated with regard to phrase repetitions and prolonged sounds as they are in repetitions of words and parts of words, particularly the latter. Even in frequency of repetition of sounds and syllables (parts of words), with respect to which there was the greatest mean difference between the experimental and control groups, the most nonfluent male "nonstutterer" repeated more than did 40 per cent of the male "stutterers," and approximately 20 per cent of the males regarded as "nonstutterers" presented more sound or syllable repetitions than did 20 per cent of the males judged as "stutterers." As to word repetitions, the most nonfluent male "nonstutterer" showed more than did approximately two thirds of the male "stutterers," and 20 per cent of the males classified by their parents as "nonstutterers" performed more repetitions of words than did 20 per cent of the males whose parents thought of them as "stutterers." Corresponding statements of about the same sort are to be made concerning the two female groups.

Index of Extent of Nonfluency. The overlapping between the experimental and control groups in index of extent of nonfluency is of special interest in view of current usage of the term "primary stuttering" (R15, 113). Presumably this term is usually intended to refer to something distinctively different from that which the term "normal nonfluency" or the equivalent is meant to designate. Meanwhile, the terms seem to be generally employed without clear and consistent reference to any explicit and unambiguous referential or operational definition of "primary stuttering" in contradistinction to "normal nonfluency." There does seem to be evident at times an attempt to differentiate repetitions of syllables or words that are relatively extended — that are, in the terminology of this report, made up of many units — from those that are brief, or comprised of few units, the latter to be regarded presumably as "normal" and the more extended repetitions as "primary stuttering." The data presented in Tables 76, 79, and 80 would seem to be indicative of a relatively limited extensional, or empirical, basis of such a distinction. Although the group mean differences in index of extent of nonfluency (Tables 79 and 80) are statistically significant at the 1 or 5 per cent level, none of them, as has been pointed out, is as large as one whole unit, the mean values themselves are uniformly small, and the group overlap, as indicated by the ranges, means, and standard deviations, is considerable for both the male and female subjects. Indeed, most of the range values are quite similar for the compared groups. A valid assertion of difference between "primary stuttering" and "normal nonfluency," or between "clinically significant" and "clinically nonsignificant" extents or amounts of nonfluency, would seem to presuppose differences dependably perceivable by most listeners. The data presented in Tables 76–80 are to be weighed with respect to the degree to which they probably do or do not represent such readily perceptible differences.*

Concluding Note

In evaluating the data presented in this chapter, it is to be duly considered, as has been stated, that they were obtained in an "undeliberated experiment" in which two groups of children, matched with respect to age, sex, and socioeconomic status of family, were subjected to two different conditions during a mean period of approximately eighteen months extending between mean age levels of about three and a half to five years. At the beginning of this period the speech of the two groups of children was presumably more or less similar, so far as can be determined from the data presented in Chapters 5 and 6. During the period of eighteen months the experimental group children were subjected to varying degrees of negatively evaluative reactions to their speech by listeners who, as parents, served also as their major authority figures, while the control group children spoke under conditions involving presumably as much positive evaluation of their speaking as they had experienced previously. At the end of the "experimental period" samples of the speech of the children were tape-recorded and analyzed, with findings as reported.

From these findings it is to be inferred that the question of whether or not a given child is or is not stuttering at any given moment cannot be answered by measuring or observing the nonfluency of his

---

* Attention is also called to the relevance of other material in preceding sections of this chapter and in the other chapters of this book to the evaluation of other proposed or conceivable extensional or operational distinctions between "primary stuttering" and "normal nonfluency," or generally between clinically "significant" and "nonsignificant" types or degrees of nonfluency, such as those based on the presence or absence of "excessive tension," or of "normal" and "abnormal" frequencies of occurrence of specified types of nonfluency.

speech. There is no agreed-upon procedure for determining an agreed-upon amount of one or more types of nonfluency that may be accepted as constituting stuttering. The study here reported serves to clarify the problem of defining and diagnosing stuttering in the basic sense that it demonstrates the essential lack of synonymity between the words "nonfluency" and "stuttering." This lack of synonymity appears to be due to a fundamental difference between the respective levels of generality on which the two words are customarily used.

The term "nonfluency" turns out to be a word that is definable in more specific terms such as "word repetition" or "prolongation of sounds," which can be employed with a comparatively high degree of reliability in making descriptive statements about samples of speech. It is to be inferred that "stuttering," however, in apparently nearly all its usages, names or indicates a judgment made by a listener in evaluating the vocal, phonetic, and linguistic productions of a speaker. The one term, therefore, serves to name what the speaker does; the other serves to name what the listener does. To put it a bit differently, "nonfluency" is generally employed to indicate an aspect of the speaker's performance; "stuttering," as customarily used, indicates an aspect of the listener's evaluative reaction to that performance. According to the rules of meaningful discourse, therefore, the one term may not be indiscriminately substituted for the other. The question of whether and to what degree a speaker is stuttering may not be answered by making the observations that are required to answer the question of whether and to what degree a speaker is performing nonfluently. This is to be appreciated more readily if the first of these two questions (whether and to what degree a speaker is stuttering) is reworded to read: whether a speaker is judged to be stuttering, and by whom, or by what proportion of any given sample of listeners, and with what degree of severity as rated by those who judge him to be stuttering.

On the basis of the data presented in this chapter, together with those in Chapters 5 and 6, it is to be concluded that the question of whether "the onset of stuttering" has occurred or is occurring is not to be answered by observing the speaker only. The problem that we call "stuttering" involves not only what the speaker does but also what the listener does about it. As shown in Chapters 5 and 6, in most cases when the listener first became concerned about what the speaker was doing, the speaker was apparently doing something essentially ordinary, something commonly done also by the speakers in the control group. It would seem to be very important, however, to appreciate the fact that in any case in which the speaker may have been doing something out of the ordinary, something involving excessive repetition, for example, or unusual muscular tension, it had to be classified by someone as "stuttering," or "a problem," or "something wrong," or "something to worry about," if it were not to be for all practical purposes disregarded. The data indicate that such speech performances by the control group speakers were disregarded, or "taken in stride," and not classified as "stuttering" or the equivalent by the listeners concerned. When first regarded as a "stutterer," a given child may have been speaking with statistically significantly more nonfluencies, and more muscular tension, than the average child in the control group, and yet have been doing something that did not distinguish him from other children in the control group, or something that would be expected of "the ordinary child" under extraordinary circumstances.

The fundamental consideration is that, regardless of how ordinary or extraordinary a speaker's performance may be in a statistical sense, the alternative ways in which it may be evaluated and classified by the listeners, including the speaker himself of course, range from "stuttering," or "something to be concerned about," through "peculiar," or "unusual," to "nothing to worry about," or "understandable under the circumstances," and include the possibility that it could go unnoticed or be essentially disregarded if noticed. It is to be noted particularly that these alternatives were available to the listeners concerned with the speakers in the experimental and control groups whose speech was sampled in this study after the approximately eighteen months during which the speakers in the experimental group had spoken under the "extraordinary circumstances" occasioned by the evaluative reactions of their listeners to their speech. The data presented in this chapter reflect, therefore, not only the nonfluencies in the samples of speech obtained from the speakers, but also the perceptual and evaluative reactions of the listeners who had classified the speakers as "stutterers" and "nonstutterers," respectively.

PART THREE

Summary and Conclusions

CHAPTER 9

Summary

THIS is a report of a series of three investigations, conducted between 1934 and 1957, that were concerned with the onset of the problem of stuttering. A total of 246 children judged by their parents to be stutterers, and their parents — the experimental groups — and 246 children judged by their parents to be nonstutterers, and their parents — the control groups — were studied by means of interview, clinical observation, and test procedures. In Study I each of the experimental and control groups included 46 children and their parents; the ages of the children ranged approximately between two and nine years, and each experimental group child was matched with a control group child in sex, age, and intelligence level. In Study II each group consisted of 50 children and their parents, with the approximate ages of the children extending from two to fourteen years, and with each pair of children matched for sex, age, and socioeconomic level of family. In Study III each group included 150 children and their parents; the children were roughly two to eight years of age, and they were matched, as in Study II, on the basis of sex, age, and socioeconomic level of family.

The interviews comprised 846 items in Study II and 818 in Study III, and each mother and father was interviewed separately. The interview items used in Study III and corresponding items employed in Study II, together with the coding of the responses and a summary of the interview data obtained are presented in the Summary Table in Appendix A. The interview used in Study I was less fully structured than those employed in Studies II and III; it has been described in an earlier publication (R62, pp. 37–71) and in Chapter 1.

Chapter 1 contains a detailed statement of the problem together with a description of the subjects included in the three studies and of the investigative procedures employed. The findings of Studies I and II, which have been reported in full elsewhere (R62, pp. 37–153), are abstracted in Chapter 2. The findings of Study III, which have been presented in detail in Chapters 3–8, are summarized in the following sections.

The Onset of Stuttering

Findings of Study III

THE CHILDREN

In general, the two groups of children in Study III were more similar than different. Data concerning birth and early physical development were not significantly different for the two groups, save in few and seemingly minor respects. There did seem to have been some tendency, however, for the experimental group mothers to experience more concern over the birth of their children, although with the possible, but ambiguous, exception of length of labor, the control group mothers evidently had more substantial objective reasons for anxiety as indicated by the greater numbers of them who reported shorter or longer than normal terms of pregnancy, induced labor, and various sorts of unusual circumstances associated with delivery.

With respect to height and weight and other basic health data the groups were essentially similar, although more may have been made of the illnesses of the experimental group children by their parents, especially their mothers. The two groups did not differ significantly with regard to the numbers of illnesses, injuries, and surgical operations they had had.

There were no statistically significant differences between the two groups of children with regard to the mean ages, as reported by the mothers, at which they met various specified criteria of development, including the ages at which they spoke their first words and sentences. They were essentially alike also in other aspects of speech development and speech behavior. There were no significant group differences with respect to handedness.

The experimental group children were, however, rated somewhat less favorably than were the control group children by their respective parents, particularly with reference to social development. That is, there was a tendency for the experimental group parents to make ratings of their children that were somewhat less favorable than relevant objective data appeared to warrant. For example, more experimental than control group children were rated by their mothers as "much slower than average" in acquiring speech, but, as has been indicated, there were no corresponding group differences reflected in the mean ages, reported by the mothers, at which the children's first words and sentences were spoken. Again, fewer experimental than control group mothers rated their children as sleeping very well, but the mean number of hours each group was reported to sleep per night did not differ significantly.

The experimental group children appeared to have been subjected to somewhat more pressure with respect to various aspects of training.

The mean age at which they started toilet training, for example, and the mean age at which they replaced bottle feeding by cup feeding were significantly earlier. Moreover, more experimental than control group mothers reported the use of coercive or punitive, rather than permissive or rewarding, methods of bowel control training. At the same time there was some evidence that the experimental group children were "fussed over" and worried about somewhat more than were the control group children.

More experimental than control group children had stuttering siblings, parents, or other relatives. Nine mothers (6 per cent) and eight fathers (5.3 per cent) in the control group and thirty-five mothers and thirty-five fathers (23.3 per cent in each case) in the experimental group reported stutterers in the immediate families or among blood relatives. As was stated in Chapter 3, these findings may be explained by either of two hypotheses. According to the one, stuttering, or some as yet undemonstrated physical characteristic responsible for it, is biologically inherited. According to the other, the problem "runs in families," to the degree that it does, because it is chiefly a function of certain attitudes toward childhood speech, and it is these attitudes that are passed on from generation to generation. To the extent that the latter explanation is valid, it implies that in families which have ever been invaded by the relevant attitudes the children's speech behavior is more likely than it would be otherwise to be affected adversely.

In Study II no child in the control group and only one in the experimental group was a twin. Five parents in the control group and three in the experimental group were twins; forty-nine parents in the control group and forty in the experimental group reported relatives who were twins.

A significantly greater proportion of the experimental group, 54 per cent, than of the control group, 37 per cent, were either the only or the oldest children in their families, and there is a possibility that for this reason they were subjected to correspondingly more parental concern.

It is to be stressed that the total mass of information concerning the two groups of children presents a complex picture, and any extended interpretation of it is to be attempted with due care. What there is conservatively to be said is that, in general, such relevant group differences as were found reflected chiefly parental and family influences and evaluations. The two groups of children themselves appeared to be essentially similar.

The Onset of Stuttering

With evident exceptions to be noted, the two groups of parents appeared to be more alike than different. There were almost no significant differences between the two groups with respect to family health, including incidence of such conditions as diabetes, allergies, and epilepsy, and there were no differences so far as handedness was concerned. In their responses to a large majority of the interview items the two parental groups did not differ to a statistically significant degree. Moreover, data obtained by means of the Minnesota Multiphasic Personality Inventory, reported in Chapter 7, did not serve to differentiate notably the experimental and control group parents.

There was a tendency, however, for the experimental group parents, particularly the mothers, to exhibit in certain of their interview responses somewhat more discontent and less satisfaction with their children, their spouses, their circumstances, and themselves. The blurred quality, together with the apparent importance, of these group differences is peculiarly apparent in the data concerning age, for example. The experimental group parents tended to be a bit older, on the average; they had postponed marriage and put off having children a bit longer than had the control group parents. They had also had significantly fewer children and more only children. The question arises as to whether these group differences might be related to the possible tendency noted in Chapter 3 for the experimental group mothers to experience somewhat more anxiety concerning childbirth, to discontinue breast feeding earlier, and to make more frequent use of coercive or punitive methods of toilet training. In considering this question, however, the impressive degree of similiarity between the two groups is to be kept in mind.

Although the two groups were matched for socioeconomic level, the experimental group mothers rated themselves lower than the control group mothers rated themselves with respect to how well-to-do they were — but the fathers did not differ significantly in their corresponding self-ratings. Again, fewer experimental than control group mothers were completely satisfied with their marital relations, while the two groups of fathers did not differ significantly, but both the mothers and fathers in the experimental group rated their neighbors as less friendly than the control group parents rated their neighbors. There were also certain evidences of less family sharing of experiences and less leisure-time companionship in the experimental group.

The child development standards of the experimental group parents, especially the mothers, were higher in certain respects than those of the control group parents. As shown in Table 18, they expected children to walk, talk, and achieve toilet training at earlier ages than the control group parents did. It is of special interest that more control than experimental group parents accepted nonfluencies as characteristic of normal speech. More control than experimental group mothers felt their children were well behaved, and regarded their husbands as neither too strict nor too lax with the children. There was, moreover, a possibly important discrepancy between the attitudes and practices of the experimental group parents where punishment was concerned. By means of a rating scale they expressed the feeling that they punished their children more frequently than the control group parents felt they punished their children, and yet in checking a list of eighteen specific activities they indicated that, compared with the control group parents, they did not, in fact, punish their children for as many of these activities.*

When there was disagreement between parents in responses to items it tended to be the mother in the experimental group and, less decidedly, the father in the control group who expressed the greater dissatisfaction. Moreover, in instances of parental disagreement in the control group the responses that expressed the more favorable evaluations, or the least concern, were made about equally by the mothers and fathers, whereas in the experimental group such responses were made over three times more often by the fathers than by the mothers. The temptation is strong to conclude, therefore, that it is better, or less bad, for a child to have a somewhat unserene father, or even two parents who are companions in discontent, than a disenchanted mother — if he must be allotted one or another of these dismal alternatives.

When these observations are placed in perspective against the background of all the other data presented in this report, there would seem to be two main general findings to be emphasized. The most definite one appears to be that the experimental group parents operated with more demanding expectations regarding the fluency of their children's speech. A second conclusion is that the experimental group parents were somewhat more dissatisfied with their children and with each other, had higher standards of child development in its various aspects, were in general rather more discontented, and seemed more inclined to think, feel, and behave in ways calculated to make for tension in the home. They seemed to be somewhat more perfectionistic and striving than the control group parents.

* It is conceivable that this discrepancy reflects a more or less unconscious, or vaguely acknowledged, sense of guilt on the part of the experimental group parents who, aware of being motivated to punish their children because of feelings of dissatisfaction with them, tended to atone for these feelings by refraining, to a greater degree than they otherwise would have, from the overt act of punishment.

The Onset of Stuttering

The problem of stuttering arose, in the great majority of cases, under conditions that the parents were able to remember only vaguely or not at all, even though the interval between inception of the problem and the interview was in all cases not more than approximately three years and was only about eighteen months in the average case. Only about 15 per cent of the experimental group parents claimed to be able to recall "the very first time" the child stuttered, and not all of these were able to describe "the situation in which the child stuttered the very first time." The few informants whose memories seemed relatively clear indicated that the situations in which the children were first thought to be stuttering were commonplace, as did those also, about two thirds of the parents, who claimed to be able to describe situations in which, they said, their children stuttered "during the period when the stuttering was the same as it had been the very first time it was noticed by anyone." In fact, the conditions reportedly associated with the "first" stutterings of the experimental group children were in the main the same as those associated with the "first" nonfluencies which the control group parents said they observed in their children's speech. In very few cases was the onset of the problem of stuttering reported to have occurred in temporal association with illness or injury, shock or fright, as a consequence of "imitation," or under any other unusual, or memorable, or dramatic circumstance.

AGE OF THE CHILD AT ONSET OF THE PROBLEM OF STUTTERING

The problem of stuttering arose as a rule when the child concerned was in the fourth year of life, probably nearer the third than the fourth birthday in most cases. Those control group parents who said they had observed nonfluencies in their children's speech reported that they first noticed them, in the median case, when the child was thirty-six months, or three years, of age. Evidently both groups of parents were reporting their observations of or reactions to their children's speech during an age period that was roughly the same for both groups of children. This period may be broadly designated for nearly all cases as extending from the second to the fifth birthday. For the large majority of the experimental group cases it extended from the second to the fourth birthday, encompassing the third and fourth years of life, the modal year being the fourth.

THE FIRST OR EARLY STUTTERINGS

Two major facts are indicated by comparison of the responses of the two groups of parents to questions concerning their children's

228

speech nonfluency. The more important is that in general the same kinds of nonfluency were reported for both groups; the extent of overlapping is indicated in Tables 38 and 39. As the overlapping shows, types of speech behavior referred to by the same presumably descriptive terms were classified as "stuttering" by some listeners but not by other listeners. The other, and related, fact is that the great majority of the experimental group children were repeating sounds or syllables, words, or phrases when they were first looked upon as stutterers. According to the fathers 85 per cent, and according to the mothers 90 per cent, of the experimental group children were performing such repetitions when first thought to be stuttering. Moreover, approximately three fourths of the parents did not indicate that the children were doing anything else that they regarded as stuttering, with the exception of a few who were also saying "uh uh" or "well uh" or the equivalent. The overlap between the groups with respect to this repetitive type of nonfluency is indicated by the fact that of the sixty-nine control group fathers who gave unequivocal responses, 79 per cent, and of the eighty mothers who answered definitely, 61 per cent said their children's "first" nonfluencies consisted of repetitions of sounds or syllables, words, or phrases. Roughly two fifths of the control group parents did not report that their children were doing anything except repeating, plus interjecting extraneous sounds such as "uh uh" or "well uh" which was indicated also by twenty-one fathers and eleven mothers.

There were interesting group differences with reference to the various kinds of repetition. Sound or syllable repetitions were reported for significantly more experimental group children, phrase repetitions were reported for significantly more control group children, and there was not a significant group difference for word repetitions.

Prolongations of sounds were reported for significantly more experimental group children; for only eight children, however, did both parents agree in reporting them. Significantly more control than experimental group children were said by their parents to have exhibited silent intervals, or pauses, and interjections such as "well," "and uh," and the like.

Only four fathers and five mothers in the experimental group reported anything that could be classified as "complete blocks" and in no case, moreover, did both parents agree in making such a report. According to the parents' descriptions, there was not much effortfulness or tension or emotional distress in the speech behavior originally classified as stuttering. The experimental group parents made responses that were similar to those made by the parents in the control group to a series of six items designed to yield information concerning tension and reactions of the child indicative of "awareness of something wrong," and feelings of "bewilderment," "unpleasantness," "irritation," or "indifference" associated with the "first stuttering" — or "first nonfluencies." In general, about the same degrees of tension and evident emotionality seemed to be associated with nonfluencies that certain experimental group parents regarded as "stuttering" as were associated with other nonfluencies that certain control group parents disregarded or accepted as "all right" or perhaps as "to be expected under the circumstances."

In evaluating these data, it is to be taken into account that if there was error in the reports obtained from the experimental group parents, it is probable that it was due in most cases to a confusion in memory of relatively recent observations of the child's speech with observations presumably made of the "first" speech reactions regarded as stutterings. As has been suggested in Chapter 5, it is conservative to assume that all or nearly all informants gave accounts covering an extended period of weeks or months, during which they had felt or suspected from time to time, or perhaps continuously but with varying degrees of conviction, that their children were beginning to stutter. Once the parents had decided the child was beginning to stutter (217), about five months passed, in the average case, before they arrived at the judgment that the child had a "speech problem" (236). The problem "came on gradually" — and the evident meanings and implications of this would seem to be of considerable theoretical significance.

In general, the beginning of the problem was reported as a perceptual and judgmental reaction to the child's speech, nearly always by one or both of the parents, usually the mother. So far as the mothers and fathers included in Study III were representative, the findings suggest that roughly half of the parents in the general population are so oriented perceptually that they do not hear the repetitions and other nonfluencies in the speech of their children; nearly all of the remaining half report that they hear them but take for granted that they are normal or acceptable and do not constitute a problem; while the remainder, approximately 1 per cent or fewer, are so oriented perceptually and evaluationally that they hear the repetitions and other nonfluencies and classify them as abnormal, or as stuttering, and as undesirable.*

---

* It is to be considered that in Study III no children were included in the control group who had ever been regarded by their parents as stutterers, and so the control group parents are not representative of all mothers and fathers in the general population who have ever thought of their children as stutterers, particularly those who have held this conviction, or suspicion, momentarily or briefly, vaguely, or with insufficient

With respect to perceptual and evaluational set in this particular sense, then, there appear to be very considerable differences among parents, and further investigation of what determines their perceptual and judgmental orientations to the speech of their children is in order.

THE LATER STUTTERINGS

Once the problem of stuttering had arisen it was reported to have varied considerably. Roughly a third of the experimental group parents stated at the time of the initial interview that the problem had become worse since its onset, about a third said that it had become less marked, roughly a fourth that it had stayed about the same, and the rest indicated it had got worse and then better, or the reverse. While a majority said there had been a time when they felt "the stuttering became more severe," a majority also said there had been "a time when the speech improved greatly" — indeed, about one third of the mothers and one fourth of the fathers stated that there had been a time when they felt for a while that "the stuttering had completely disappeared." In the control group the great majority of the parents said "the problem" had become better, stayed the same, or disappeared.

In general, after the experimental group parents began to feel that their children were stuttering, they tended to become, within limits, increasingly concerned about their children's speech and preoccupied with their feelings about it. Moreover, in most cases they reacted in more or less overt ways. Mainly they urged the child to "slow down," "relax," and "take it easy," but the variety of ways in which they expressed, both verbally and nonverbally, their negative evaluations of the child's nonfluencies was considerable. It would appear that these reactions, verbal and nonverbal, colored the relations between the parents and their children, and while in most cases the effects seemed to be subtle, and some children were not affected in any clearly discernible ways, it appeared that in most cases the first slow turnings of a vicious circle had taken place by the time of the initial interview.

As reported in Chapter 8, the speech of the experimental group children, while presumably essentially similar to that of the control group children at the time of onset of the problem, was significantly

concern to motivate them to seek clinical service. Data reported by Glazner and Rosenthal (36), information communicated to the writer by Dean Williams concerning research in progress with which he is associated, and data obtained from the control groups in Study I and Study II, as indicated in Chapter 2, suggest that considerably more than 1 per cent of children are considered by their parents for varying periods of time, in varied senses, and with differing degrees of conviction and of concern, to be stutterers.

more nonfluent than was that of those in the control group at the time of the interview, according to counts of instances of eight different types of nonfluency in tape-recorded samples of the speech of eighty-nine matched pairs of children. The difference was greatest with respect to repetitions, particularly sound or syllable repetitions. Certain types of nonfluency, however, such as revisions, broken words, and incomplete phrases, did not serve to differentiate the two groups. Moreover, considerable proportions of those who had come to be regarded as stutterers spoke with fewer nonfluencies of various types and of all types combined than corresponding proportions of those who were taken to be normal speakers. The two groups overlapped considerably also in the specific measure of the extent of repetition — that is, the number of units of repetition per instance of it ("th-th-the" would be an example of one instance of sound or syllable repetition made up of two units of repetition). These data serve to raise a formidable question concerning the possibility of an operationally meaningful distinction in terms of nonfluency, as such, between stuttering, including so-called primary stuttering, and what would appear to be the kinds and degrees of nonfluency generally characteristic of the speech of childhood, and to some degree of adult speech.

As was suggested in Chapter 8, the group differences and similarities revealed by this analysis of the recorded speech samples may be evaluated as the findings of an "undeliberated experiment" in which the two groups of children, whose speech behavior was presumably similar, were subjected during the fourth year of life, on the average, to two different conditions. The parents of the control group children and other listeners continued to react to the fluency of their speech with essential acceptance and approval, while the experimental group children were subjected to the experience of having their speech evaluated as "too hesitant and nonfluent" and as "stuttering" and disapproved more or less accordingly by their parents and other significant listeners. After an average period of eighteen months the speech of each child in the two groups was sampled and analyzed, with the results as indicated.

There were many signs of a tendency on the part of the experimental group parents to place comparatively high value on fluency in the speech of their children and to evaluate nonfluency accordingly. This would seem to be suggested, for example, in the ratings made by them of the severity of their children's alleged stuttering at the time of interview, after an average interval of about eighteen months following the beginnings of their concern about their children's speech. On a seven-point scale of severity, with 1 representing no stuttering,

4 stuttering of average severity, and 7 very severe stuttering, the mean ratings of the mothers and fathers were 3.6 and 3.5, respectively, and each of these means was significantly different at the 1 per cent level from the mean severity rating of 2.5 made by the interviewers.

The experimental group parents appeared to take for granted that the cause of the problem lay solely within the child and that it consisted of a fault in either the body or the personality of the child. Indeed, only 4 per cent of them expressed the belief that stuttering might be a problem shared by speaker and listener, and that the problem might arise as a function of the interaction between the child and his parents. At the same time, most of those who felt that their children's speech had improved appreciably since the onset of the problem were of the opinion that the improvement had been due to the bringing about of a calmer home atmosphere, increasing disregard of the nonfluencies, and a tendency for the parents to become more easygoing, attentive to the child, and patient with him.

Findings of the Follow-up Study

This opinion would appear to be borne out in some measure by the findings of a follow-up study carried out nearly two and a half years, on the average, after the interview. Follow-up data were obtainable from the mothers of 118 of the experimental group children, and the interviewers were able to observe and rate the speech of 50 of the children, who were representative of the experimental group as a whole in respect to rated severity of the problem at the time of the initial interview. According to the mothers, about one third of the 118 children surveyed no longer had a stuttering problem at the time of the follow-up study; 88 per cent were reported either to have no problem or to be somewhat or much better than at the time of the initial interview. Of the 75 who still had a problem according to their mothers, 81 per cent were said to be better.

Improvement was also indicated in the mean severity rating of 2.10 made by the mothers at the time of the follow-up as compared with a mean rating of 3.53 for the same children made at the time of the initial interview. The children rated by the interviewers at follow-up were given a mean severity rating of 1.06, as compared with a mean interviewer rating of 2.57 for the same children at the time of the initial interview. In general, the amount of improvement for the group as a whole was evidently much greater after the initial interview than it had been before that time.

Moreover, the 118 children in the follow-up sample were divided into two groups, the 43 who no longer were said by their mothers to

233

have a stuttering problem and the 75 who allegedly still had such a problem, and certain data for these two groups were compared. The children in the No-Problem group were younger on the average at the time of the first interview, the mean interval between onset of the problem and initial interview was shorter for this group, and relatively fewer of the families in the No-Problem group were in the upper lower class (see footnote, Table 60). Severity ratings made by the mothers at the time of the initial interview and at the follow-up yielded means, respectively, of 3.57 and 2.78 for the Problem group and 3.48 and 1.19 for the No-Problem group children. Corresponding means of the interviewer ratings were 2.60 and 1.15 for the Problem group and 2.51 and 1.0 (no stuttering) for the No-Problem group. (Indeed, the interviewers considered only about 7 per cent of the children at the time of the follow-up to be stutterers and an additional 15 per cent to be "significantly nonfluent" but not to be "showing the tension and anxiety reactions characteristic of stuttering.") All the compared mean differences between severity ratings made by the mothers and the interviewers, respectively, at the time of the initial interview and at the follow-up were statistically significant at the 1 per cent level (see Table 59).

It is also to be reported that among the 118 children in the follow-up sample there were 44 who were drawn from a geographical area in which the original investigative interviewing was done under conditions that did not permit counseling of the experimental group parents, whereas such counseling was provided for the parents of the other 74 children in the survey sample. At the time of the follow-up 23 per cent of the non-counseled cases and 45 per cent of the counseled cases reported no problem; the difference between these percentages was significant at the 5 per cent level. The counseling given at the time of the initial interview was brief, confined to the little time available during a single day devoted to interviewing and testing. The interview itself may, of course, have had some degree of therapeutic effect. In any case, such counseling as was done was designed to focus attention on relevant factual information, and to facilitate the parents' evaluation of their relevant policies and practices in light of the evident facts concerning their own child. The parents were assisted in becoming aware of their own roles in the development of the problem so far as these could be ascertained or appreciated. They were also given information having to do generally with child behavior and development. No speech therapy, as such, or any other type of therapy was administered by the investigators to the children themselves.

These positive findings of the follow-up study would appear to imply that whenever parents feel that a stuttering problem is beginning to develop, the sooner their concern is dealt with, and the earlier in the child's life this is done, the better. Even brief counseling of the sort indicated is apparently considerably effective.*

* These findings are in essential agreement with those obtained in Study I; a follow-up investigation was not included in Study II. In Study I, after a median period of two years and four months, following the initial examination, twenty-five, or 54 per cent, of the forty-six children in the experimental group were evaluated by all judges as "normal." An additional eight were regarded as "normal" by some but not all judges or were evaluated by all judges as "nearly normal." Thus, 72 per cent of the children were included in these two categories, and in 39 cases, or 85 per cent of the total group, some degree of improvement or elimination of the problem was reported. "In general, this result was associated with a type of counseling of the parents designed to get them to regard their children as normal, to give major attention not to the child's speech repetitions and hesitancies, as such, but to the conditions affecting the youngster's speech, and to adjust downward their standards of speech and behavior generally, in order to reduce tensions, both for the child and for themselves, and to make it easier for the child to gain essential feelings of success and approval" (R62, pp. 68–71).

CHAPTER 10

Conclusions

THE findings of the research reported in Chapters 2–8 and summarized in Chapter 9 are to be considered in relation to the investigative procedures described in Chapter 1. So far as these findings are reliable and representative of data definitive of the problem under investigation, they appear to warrant or suggest the following interpretive comments.

A General Interaction Hypothesis

The point of origin of the problem of stuttering in a given instance is to be observed, or reported, as a perceptual and judgmental reaction of a listener to something done by a speaker. From its beginning, therefore, the problem involves an interaction of at least two persons, a speaker and a listener. (There may be more than one listener, of course.) At the moment of onset of the problem the speaker is typically a child between two and four years of age, most probably a little over three years old, and the listener is nearly always one of the child's parents, usually the mother. The essential interaction between these two persons is one in which the listener evaluates something done by the speaker as "stuttering," or the equivalent. Then, having decided that the speaker is "stuttering," the listener classifies the speaker as a "stutterer." Moreover, there appears to be a mutually reinforcing interaction between the listener's judgment that the speaker "is a stutterer" and the listener's readiness not only to perceive certain presumably relevant features of the speaker's performance but also to evaluate them as "stuttering." This is to say, in terms of parent and child, the more the mother thinks of her child as a "stutterer" the more attention she gives to what she regards as the child's "stuttering," and also the more readily she regards it as "stuttering"; and the more attention she gives to what she takes to be the child's "stuttering," the more she thinks of her child as a "stutterer," and so on.

There is an interaction also between the primary listener, the one who first decides that the child "is stuttering" and that he "is a

236

stutterer," and the child's other listeners. The conviction of the mother, for example, that the child "is a stutterer" is generally accepted by the father, with the consequence that he too then attends to the supposedly relevant aspects of the child's speech and evaluates them as "stuttering." The mother, taking this as confirmation of her original judgment, strengthens her conviction that the child "is a stutterer." The greater the number of other listeners who agree with her, and so with each other, the stronger the reinforcement of the conviction of the mother, and of all the others as well, that the child "is a stutterer," and so the greater the inclination or perceptual readiness of all concerned to notice whatever the child does in speaking that they have come to think of as "stuttering."

Not only is there an interaction between the perceptual and evaluative processes of each listener, and among those of the various listeners, but there is also an interaction between the speaker and each listener or each group or set of listeners. Again, in terms of parent and child, the child is responsive to the mother's reactions to his speech, and the mother, in turn, reacts to the ways in which the child responds to her reactions. The mother's posture, facial expression, tone of voice, or words and pointedly expressive actions may be interpreted by the child as indicating some degree of disapproval of some unidentified or more or less clearly designated aspect of his speech. If so, the child's reaction may range from rejection of the mother's reaction, through indifference to it, to acceptance of it as valid and with some degree of concern over it. If the child feels concern or insecurity in response to the mother's reaction to his speech, he may respond by speaking less, or more hesitantly and nonfluently, or with decreased spontaneity and expressiveness, or with increased muscular tension. The increased tension or effort is presumably motivated by a desire to "do better" or to "be careful not to make mistakes in speaking" or to "keep from stuttering." To the increasing hesitancy, nonfluency, and tension in the child's speech the mother reacts, in turn, with increasing dissatisfaction with the way the youngster is speaking, a growing doubt of the child's basic ability to speak "normally," and gradually deepening anxiety and general distress accordingly. The child, in consequence, speaks still more hesitantly, with greater tension, and so on. This interaction affects, in ways that range from subtle to gross, the general relation between mother and child, and the resulting changes in this general relation further affect the specific interaction that centers around the child's speech and the mother's reactions to it, per se. There is also to be considered, of course, everything in the way of neurophysiological and psychological background that is brought to this particular interaction by the mother, by the child, and by both together as a function of their comprehensive past and continuing relations with one another and with other persons.

There is, finally, an interaction between the perceptual and evaluative reactions of the speaker to his own speech, on the one hand, and, on the other, what he does in a motor and neuromuscular sense. The basic feelings of doubt and concern about his ability to speak acceptably, which the speaking child adopts from his mother and father and other important listeners, are expressed in some degree of increase in hesitancy, nonfluency, and muscular tension in speaking, as noted above. These consequences of doubt and concern serve, then, to reinforce not only the disturbed, and disturbing, perceptual and evaluative reaction tendencies of the child's listeners, but those of the child as well. Moreover, the degree to which the child attends and reacts to the presumably relevant aspects of his own speaking may be regarded meaningfully as being in part a function of the degree to which his parents and other significant listeners notice and respond to them.

It is to be appreciated that these particular patterns of interaction are to be abstracted in any given case from a complex, self-reflexive, and ever-changing field of events which may never be completely described. Each of the indicated patterns is to be understood in relation to the others; they are to be thought of as interacting among themselves, and, all together, with various situational and social or cultural contexts.

Three Major Variables

By giving attention to three particular variables, the problem may be clarified considerably in any specific instance. The first of these variables is the listener's sensitivity to the speaker's nonfluency — that is, the strength of his set or readiness to perceive it and of his tendency to evaluate it unfavorably, and so to be concerned about it and to classify it as "stuttering" or in some essentially similar disturbing manner. The second is the speaker's degree of nonfluency as objectively determined. The third is the speaker's sensitivity to his own nonfluency, and to the listener's evaluative reactions to his nonfluency. Each of these variables is affected not only by the other two but also by certain other factors.

In general, it may be hypothesized that if the listener's sensitivity to the speaker's nonfluency is sufficiently intense, the problem of stuttering can arise *for the listener*, even though the speaker is insensitive to the listener's reactions to his speech and is, moveover, speaking within the range of fluency, even the more fluent segments of that range, for the relevant population of speakers. Conceivably, the problem of stuttering can develop *for the speaker*, on the other hand, provided he is sufficiently sensitive to his own nonfluency, in the absence of any corresponding sensitivity on the part of the listener, or provided the speaker is sufficiently responsive to the listener's reactions to his nonfluency, even though those reactions are slight or unremarkable. In such a case, moreover, the amount of nonfluency displayed by the speaker can presumably vary from very little to very much.

The relation of the speaker's degree of nonfluency to the other two variables, and so to the probability that the problem of stuttering will arise in a given case, appears to be complex. Certain children who are relatively very nonfluent are not regarded as stutterers. For example, the speech of many cerebral palsied children is markedly labored, hesitant, and tense, but evidently is evaluated by the listeners concerned as "normal" or "to be expected in view of the child's condition." Most children whose speech is temporarily disrupted by clearly justified fright or embarrassment, or by disorienting physical injury, or by bewilderment due to reasons that are readily appreciated by the listeners, are not assumed to be stuttering, even though the nonfluency of their speech may be extreme. It is of particular interest in this connection that the findings of this research show that children are not thought to be stuttering until they are a little past three years old, on the average, and are rarely regarded as stutterers before the age of about two and a half years. Meanwhile, they are generally more nonfluent at earlier ages than they are when, at three or four years of age, or even later, most of them are first classified by their parents or other listeners as stutterers. Indeed, even those control group parents who said that they had noticed nonfluencies in the speech of their children indicated that they had not observed them until the child was about three years old in the average case. All this would seem to imply that if the listener regards the child as "too young to know how to talk" or "too young to talk well," he is not likely to give attention to the child's nonfluencies, and it is improbable, moreover, that if he does notice them he will think of them as "stuttering."

Not only the age but also the sex of the child seems to influence the listener's perceptual and evaluative disposition. The data presented in Chapter 8 show that boys and girls were essentially similar in both the experimental and control groups with respect to nonfluency, as such. Earlier studies of nonfluency in children (R18) have also revealed relatively small, if any, sex differences in various measures of speech fluency. The basic observation to be made is that there is an impressive discrepancy between the magnitude of the difference in the relative proportions of boys and girls who come to be classified as stutterers, on the one hand, and, on the other, the comparatively slight differences between boys and girls in speech nonfluency. The ratio of males to females classified as stutterers varies around a general mean of approximately four to one, according to Schuell (97, 98), the ratio tending to be larger at older than at younger age levels. In Study II of the present research program the ratio was nearly four to one; in Study III, involving younger subjects, the ratio was about two and a half to one. Schuell's findings suggest that in our culture parental attitudes and practices tend to be different for male and female children, especially at early age levels, in ways that probably are reflected in parental evaluations and reactions to the speech of the children. One laboratory study somewhat relevant to this general issue has been reported by Bloodstein and Smith (12). They used recorded speech judged to be relatively ambiguous as to the sex of the child from whom the speech sample was obtained in each case. Two groups of listeners — one group told the speakers were boys and the other told they were girls — classified slightly but not significantly more "boys" than "girls" as stutterers. Male listeners judged more of the speakers to be stutterers than did female listeners. In this study the perception of speech was investigated in isolation from the family and social contexts by which it would ordinarily be affected, and the data are to be evaluated accordingly. Further research is to be done on the sex of the child as a factor affecting the perceptual and evaluational orientation of the parent to the child, particularly to the fluency of the child's speech.

It is to be considered, moreover, that there was, as reported in Chapter 8, considerable overlap of the distributions of measures of nonfluency used in analyzing the tape-recorded samples of speech of the experimental and control group children. That is to say, differences in amount of nonfluency, as such, did not necessarily serve to differentiate a child who had been classified as a stutterer from one who was regarded as a nonstutterer. The interview data presented in Chapters 5 and 6 also showed that on the basis of nonfluency alone the children regarded by their parents as stutterers could not, at the time of onset of the problem, be well differentiated from those who were regarded by their parents as nonstutterers. This is not to say that the experimental group children were remarkably fluent, or were "doing nothing," when first classified as "stutterers," or that the children in the control group were very nonfluent, or were in a "stuttering phase" through which all children presumably must pass. It is to say that the overlap or similarity between the two groups so far as nonfluency is concerned was considerable. It is to say also that, although relatively simple repetitions were most frequently reported for both groups, other types of nonfluency, including those associated with varying degrees of tension and evident emotionality, were also reported for both groups.

So far as the third variable is concerned, that of the speaker's sensitivity to his own nonfluency, and to the listener's reactions to his nonfluency, it is to be reported, first of all, that while it is conceivable that the problem of stuttering could arise for the speaker before it does for the listener by virtue of the speaker's perceptual and evaluative reactions to his own nonfluency, no instances of this were found, so far as is known, in the research here reported. As to whether the experimental group children were appreciably more sensitive than those in the control group to listeners' reactions to their nonfluencies, the data obtained do not provide any clear indication. Some of the control group parents apparently did not observe and so did not react at all to their children's nonfluencies; the rest of the control group parents did perceive the nonfluencies in their children's speech but apparently made no important issue of them. It is not possible to make a clear estimate of how the control group children would have responded had their parents evaluated and reacted to their speech nonfluencies as did the experimental group parents to the nonfluencies in their children's speech. As was indicated in Chapter 4, however, significant differences between experimental and control group responses to relevant interview items appeared to reflect differences, not between the two groups of children, but between the respective attitudes and practices of the two groups of parents. On the basis of this general finding, it cannot be definitely assumed that the experimental group children were more sensitive than were those in the control group to their own nonfluencies or to comparable listener reactions to their nonfluencies.

The most defensible tentative conclusion would appear to be that at the point of origin of the problem of stuttering the most crucial single factor to be considered is that of the listener's sensitivity to the speaker's nonfluencies, his inclination to evaluate them as undesirable and distressing, and particularly his tendency to classify them specifically as "stuttering." It seems reasonable to assume that, for any given listener, the more nonfluent the speaker, as this may be objectively determined, the more likely the listener is to perceive the nonfluencies and, it may be, to evaluate them negatively and regard them as "stuttering." At the same time, it is to be appreciated that degrees and kinds of nonfluency that are so evaluated by one listener are not by another listener. Again, it may seem reasonable to suppose that the more sensitive a given speaker is to his own nonfluencies or to the reactions of other listeners to them, the more likely he is to develop the problem of stuttering for himself, but it is also to be duly considered that amounts of nonfluency and listener reactions to them that are disturbing to one speaker are not to another. The speaker reacts to his own speech as a listener, and it is his sensitivity as a listener to his own nonfluencies, as well as his degree of speech nonfluency, as such, that determines whether he makes an issue of his nonfluencies and creates a problem around them. Moreover, it may well be hypothesized that his perceptual and evaluative reactions to his own nonfluency are patterned to a significant degree after those of his other listeners, especially the ones who are his dominant authority figures.

Factors Related to the Major Variables

The problem of stuttering may be formulated more fully by further discussion of the factors related to the major variables involved in the basic interactions.

FACTORS RELATED TO THE LISTENER'S SENSITIVITY
TO THE SPEAKER'S NONFLUENCY

The degree of the listener's sensitivity to the nonfluency of the speaker appears to be some function of the strength of each of several factors and of their pattern of interrelationship. Among these several factors are the following.

Amount of the Speaker's Nonfluency. As has been suggested, it would seem reasonable to hypothesize that the more nonfluent a speaker is, according to objective determination, the more probable it is that a given listener will perceive his nonfluencies. It is less certain, and yet it would seem to be more or less likely, that the greater the speaker's nonfluency the more inclined a given listener would be to evaluate a specific instance of his nonfluency as "stuttering," and to classify the speaker as a "stutterer." The stimulus value for any particular listener of the sheer amount or frequency of nonfluency is not to be gauged, however, without taking into account other factors such as those to be discussed presently. Moreover, it is to be repeated and duly stressed that there are great individual differences among listeners; amounts of nonfluency to which one listener is very sensitive are not even perceived by other listeners; and what one classifies as "stuttering" (or as "primary stuttering") another evaluates as "normal" or "ordinary." The question of the speaker's nonfluency in relation to the origin of the problem of stuttering is still essentially open and additional rigorous investigation is needed.

Types of Nonfluency. Boehmler (16) found that sound or syllable repetitions were classified by laboratory observers as stuttering more often than were other kinds of nonfluency; revisions and interjections were judged to be stuttering less often than were other nonfluencies. Williams and Kent (128) reported that their laboratory observers, in judging nonfluencies to be stuttered or nonstuttered, classified syllable repetitions and prolongations primarily as stuttered, and revisions primarily as nonstuttered. In a second study, concerned with the reactions of kindergarten and second-grade children to two different types of nonfluency employed systematically by teachers in telling stories, Giolas and Williams (35) found that syllable repetitions appeared to be less acceptable to the children than were interjections of vowel sounds such as "ah."

In a correlational study of ratings of severity of stuttering and computed frequencies of five different types of nonfluency, in fifty tape-recorded 200-word samples of the speech of adult male stutterers, Young (134) found that frequency of syllable repetitions and of sound prolongations correlated more highly than did other nonfluency measures with ratings of severity of stuttering. Frequencies of interjections, word and phrase repetitions (considered in combination as word-phrase repetitions), and revisions were not significantly related to ratings of stuttering severity. Young also found a relatively high correlation between rated severity of stuttering and time required to speak the 200 words.

Boehmler (16) also reported that the degree of agreement among judges in classifying nonfluencies, drawn from the speech samples of both stutterers and nonstutterers, as stuttering was greater for non-fluencies rated severe than for those rated as mild or moderate.

In the present research the experimental group parents were asked to describe the nonfluencies in the child's speech which they first regarded as "stuttering," and the parents in the control group were asked whether their children had shown these same types of non-fluency. As has been stated in Chapter 6, syllable repetitions were reported for significantly more experimental group children, phrase repetitions were reported for significantly more control group children, and there was no significant group difference with respect to word repetition. Prolongations of sounds were also reported for significantly more experimental group children, but for only 8 of the 150 children did both parents agree in reporting this type of nonfluency. The most important finding, however, was that there was impressive similarity between the two groups of children in the information provided by their parents concerning the nonfluencies in their speech; the data summarized in Tables 38 and 39 in Chapter 6 are particularly relevant.

While the probability that any given type of nonfluency will be perceived would seem to depend more or less on its relative frequency of occurrence and its conspicuousness (duration, amount of muscular tension or effort involved, and elaborateness of associated movements or mannerisms, if any), available data seem to indicate that syllable repetitions and sound prolongations are more likely than are other varieties of nonfluency to be noticed and to be evaluated as "stuttering" by a given listener. Again, however, individual differences among listeners are to be duly considered.

The Listener's Perceptual Set. The influence of the perceptual set of the listener has been investigated in two ways. Tuthill (112), Boehmler (16), and Bloodstein, Jaeger, and Tureen (13) employed groups of listeners who differed in professional training and in familiarity or personal experience with the stuttering problem. Williams and Kent (128) approached the matter by giving laboratory judges varied sets of instructions to be followed in evaluating nonfluencies in speech samples.

Tuthill (112) asked different groups of judges — laymen, speech correctionists, and stutterers — to listen to phonograph and sound film recordings of the speech of clinically classified stutterers and speakers generally regarded as nonstutterers. The judges were instructed to mark, on mimeographed copies of the material, the words they judged as stuttered. The stutterers marked the most words as stuttered, the speech correctionists the next highest number, and the laymen, who were college freshmen without training in speech pathology, marked the smallest number. The average stutterer evaluated approximately 40 per cent more words as stuttered than the average layman. It is of incidental interest that the three groups of listeners showed about the same degree of disagreement in marking specific words as stuttered or not stuttered, and, regardless of whether they both saw and heard or only heard the speakers recorded on sound film, the disagreement was impressive. As computed, the obtained agreement among members of a group of listeners amounted on the average to only about 37 per cent of maximum or perfect agreement.

Boehmler (16) used two groups of speech correctionists who differed in the fact that they had been professionally trained at two different institutions, and one group of lay judges consisting of college students with no training in speech pathology. He asked his judges to classify as an example of either "stuttering" or "nonstuttering" each of 804 nonfluencies, 402 selected from tape-recorded samples of the speech of clinically diagnosed stutterers and 402 of comparable severity, as rated, from samples of the speech of persons generally acknowledged to be normal speakers. Boehmler found statistically significant group differences in the number of nonfluencies classified as stuttering. One of the groups of speech correctionists considered significantly more of the nonfluencies to be stuttering than did the other, and both of these groups classified significantly more of the non-fluencies as stuttering than did the lay judges.

Bloodstein, Jaeger, and Tureen (13) recorded twelve two-minute samples of the speech of young children. Some of the children had been brought to a speech clinic by their parents because they regarded them as stutterers, and the others were regarded by their parents as normal speakers. The recorded speech samples were presented to listeners who were parents (not of the children from whom the samples were obtained). Some of the parents had come to regard their own children as stutterers and the others considered their children to be nonstutterers. They were asked to classify the recorded speech samples as stuttered or nonstuttered. Parents who had previously come to consider their own children as stutterers judged more of the speech samples as stuttered than did the parents who thought of their children as normal speakers.

Williams and Kent (128) used two groups of listeners consisting of college undergraduates untrained in speech pathology. These listeners were told that they would hear a recorded speech given by a person who stuttered. Actually what they heard was a carefully contrived sample of speech containing fifty-two speech interruptions distributed by design among six different kinds of nonfluency. Williams and Kent played their contrived speech recording three times for each group of listeners. Group I was told, first, to mark on mimeographed copies each *stuttered* interruption in the speech. On new copies they were then asked to mark *all* interruptions. Finally, again on new mimeographed copies, they were told to mark the *normal* interruptions. The subjects in Group II were instructed first to mark *normal* interruptions, second to mark *all* interruptions, and third to mark *stuttered* interruptions.

The authors stated, "The group of subjects instructed to mark stuttered interruptions first marked more interruptions as stuttered than they subsequently marked as normal. Conversely, the group instructed to mark normal interruptions first marked more as normal than they subsequently marked as stuttered."

Of particular interest was the inconsistency or confusion of the

245

listeners. As the investigators explained, "Under instruction to mark stuttered interruptions, a subject might mark a particular interruption as 'stuttered,' and later under instruction to mark normal interruptions, might judge the same interruption to be 'normal.' " The investigators found that under instructions to mark stuttered interruptions, subjects in both groups tended to have the fewest inconsistent responses on syllable repetitions and prolongations and the most on revisions. When instructed to mark normal interruptions, they made the fewest inconsistent responses on revisions and the most on syllable repetitions and prolongations. The indicated confusion was observed, however, in degrees varying from pronounced to relatively slight for all six types of nonfluency.

The authors, referring to the fact that syllable repetition is the type of nonfluency most likely to be thought of by listeners as "stuttering," raise the fundamental question of whether a child repeats syllables because he is evaluated as a "stutterer" or is considered to be a "stutterer" because he repeats syllables. They offer this answer: "On the basis of this study, it is suggested that the cause and effect relationship may work to a degree in both directions. Apparently, he could become known as a 'stutterer' *because* he repeats syllables. Once, however, he is identified as a 'stutterer,' then his word and phrase repetitions, interjections and even revisions, to a certain extent, also come to be considered as 'stuttering,' seemingly for no other reason than *because* he is now thought of as a 'stutterer.' "

In a footnote, Williams and Kent then make this observation: "One of the objectives in counseling the parents of a child who is considered to be 'stuttering' is to help them re-evaluate some of the child's speech interruptions. It has proved profitable to the present authors, at least, first to acquaint the parents with the concept of normal speech and then to ask them to pay particular attention to and to keep track of the normal interruptions in their child's speaking behavior. Often, the parents, when faced with the task of listening for and noting normal interruptions, not only become more interested in what constitutes a normal interruption, but begin classifying more of the interruptions as 'normal.' As a consequence, the number of interruptions reacted to as 'stuttering' is reduced."

In this connection it is to be recalled that in Study III during the period between the time when the parents had begun to think of the child as a "stutterer" and the time of the interview, there was a general tendency for the parents to feel that the child was doing more "stuttering," and there appeared to be some evidence that the child was responding to the resulting interaction with his parents by speaking with more hesitation and tension. Then at the time of the interview some counseling was provided in most cases. One of the objectives of this counseling was to influence the parents to evaluate the child's nonfluencies more favorably or acceptably, to pay more attention to the circumstances under which the child was speaking more and less nonfluently, and to acknowledge valid justification for regarding the nonfluencies as normal under the circumstances. Although the amount of such counseling was very limited, the data obtained in the follow-up study indicated that to a marked degree the trend had been reversed and that in nearly 90 per cent of the cases the problem was no longer present or had decreased rather than increased in severity since the time of the interview. In general, the other findings also reported in Chapters 5 and 6 suggest that whether or not particular nonfluencies are evaluated by a given listener as "stuttering" depends, in part, on whether the listener's perceptual set has been conditioned by the judgment that the child "is a stutterer."

Much significant further study is to be done on the variable of the listener's perceptual set and the factors functionally related to it.

The Listener's General Level of Aspiration, Sense of Frustration, and Frustration Tolerance. The data presented in Chapters 3 and 4 suggest that by using an appropriately gray language one may indicate that there was a somewhat greater tendency for the experimental than for the control group parents to approach perfectionism in the standards by which they evaluated their children, themselves, each other, and their circumstances. There seemed to be a corresponding degree of difference between the two groups in their sense of frustration in attempting to achieve and maintain their standards, with consequent differences in expression of dissatisfaction and discontent. It is a matter of inference, with an undetermined measure of justification, that the parents' general perfectionism was positively related to their degree of perfectionism in reacting specifically to their children's speech nonfluencies. It is to be conjectured also that their general sense of frustration and their tolerance of frustration were reflected more or less in their tendency to feel and to be distressed by frustration in trying to get their children to speak more fluently.*

It may be that a related consideration is implied in the group difference reported in Chapter 4 in terms of evaluational differences between spouse pairs. Such differences in the control group represented an essentially equal sharing of discontent by the mothers and fathers, whereas in the experimental group the greater degree of discontent

---

* For extended discussions of the problem of frustration see Dollard, Miller, Doob, Mowrer, and Sears (29) and Johnson (58, Chapter 1).

was expressed three times more often by the mothers than by the fathers. So far as it may be assumed that this reflects more "tension in the home" for the experimental group, the generalization may be ventured, again with an undetermined degree of validity, that such "tension" may not only influence the child to speak more hesitantly but also predispose the parent, as listener, to evaluate the nonfluencies in the child's speech as undesirable or unacceptable and to classify them as "stuttering."

Another possibly related consideration is suggested by the fact that a search in Studies II and III for families in which there had been a comparatively recent development of the stuttering problem yielded samples in which a disproportionately high number of the families were classifiable in the middle or upper social classes (see Chapters 2 and 4). There may be a tendency for standards of speech and of other aspects of child behavior to be higher in these classes than on the lower levels, and if so the parents in the middle and upper social classes may be correspondingly more inclined to make the perceptual and evaluational reactions which result in the classification of a child as a "stutterer." More specifically, perhaps, parents who are upwardly mobile in their social class orientation may be particularly motivated to make such reactions.*

Degree of Listener's Concern about Stuttering as a Family Problem. A somewhat greater proportion of speakers classified as stutterers than of those not so classified report that there are other stutterers in their families. In Study III, for example, a little less than 25 per cent of the children in the experimental group, as against 5 to 6 per cent of those in the control group, were reported to have siblings, parents, or other relatives who were said to be stutterers. Other relevant findings suggest that parents who knew the problem of stuttering personally, or as it affected other members of the family, were correspondingly apprehensive about the possibility that their children might "be stutterers" or somehow "develop stuttering." To the extent that this was true, it is to be inferred that they were inclined accordingly to perceive the nonfluencies in their children's speech and to think of them as "stuttering."

The study by Bloodstein, Jaeger, and Tureen (13), previously mentioned, indicated that parents who are accustomed to thinking about the problem of stuttering are more inclined than those who are not to evaluate speech as stuttered. Tuthill's (112) finding, also previously mentioned, that stutterers identified more words as stuttered than

---

* See Morgenstern (85) for a report of relevant data; and see Johnson *et al.* (61, pp. 224–225) for pertinent discussion of these data.

laymen did in listening to the same recorded speech samples, and the finding of both Tuthill and Boehmler (16) that speech correctionists who were familiar with the stuttering problem perceived more words as stuttered than lay listeners did, suggest that preoccupation with stuttering increases the listener's readiness to classify nonfluencies as stuttering. Presumably listeners who stutter or who have stutterers in their families would tend to be more preoccupied with the problem than others.

The tendency for the problem of stuttering "to run in families" needs to be investigated more thoroughly. More information is required concerning the magnitude of the tendency and the variations in it from sample to sample. Specific families should be intensively investigated with attention to the issues in question. Particularly rigorous study needs to be made of the perceptual and evaluational sets which the presence of the problem in a family tends to foster.

The Listener's Sense of Fluency Norms. In general, the parents investigated in this program of research did not appear to have much information about speech fluency norms. This is not to be wondered at in view of the fact that such information is not generally available. The responses made by the two groups of parents when asked to describe their impressions "of what normal speech is like" are especially interesting in this connection (see 364 in the Summary Table, Appendix A). Roughly half of the control group parents, but only one sixth of those in the experimental group, indicated that they considered nonfluencies to be "normal if not excessive." Approximately two thirds of the experimental group parents either did not regard nonfluencies as permissible or else they considered them permissible only if occasional or minimal. On the basis of these and other data it is to be inferred that neither group of parents in Study III had more than meager knowledge about the fluency aspects of childhood speech, and the assumptions of the parents in the experimental group were particularly unrealistic. In view of their evident expectations it is to be assumed that they were more or less predisposed perceptually to notice the hesitations and repetitions in their children's speech and to find them unacceptable. The one sixth of the control group parents who expressed the attitude that nonfluencies are not permissible are peculiarly interesting; the fact that they had not regarded their children as stutterers indicates presumably that either they had not perceived their nonfluencies or else they "did not mean much" by their responses to 364.

General experience in the counseling of parents concerning the fluency aspects of their children's speech, together with the findings of the follow-up investigation in Study III, indicates that most parents welcome information about the nonfluency to be expected in childhood speech and make effective use of such information in achieving a more realistic acceptance of their own children's speech behavior. It would appear to be highly desirable to get information of this kind into the hands of all parents.*

The Listener's Recognition of Factors Contributing to Nonfluency. Examination of dictionaries and textbooks and observation of common usage indicates that "stuttering" is generally defined as a disorder or disturbance in the rhythm of verbal expression, or as hesitant, repetitious, or otherwise nonfluent speech. The findings of the present research serve, of course, to point up the unsatisfactoriness of such a definition. It is to be considered, moreover, that under many different circumstances even extremely dysrhythmic or nonfluent speech is not looked upon as stuttering. After all, hesitant, blocked, repetitive, or labored speech is conspicuously characteristic of certain persons affected by cerebral palsy, aphasia, extreme fatigue, intoxication, certain states induced by drugs, disorienting emotional stress or trauma, physiological shock, and other comparable conditions. Apparently the major reason why the disrupted and nonfluent speech of such persons is not as a rule evaluated as "stuttering" is that the listeners recognize the contributing factors and are inclined, therefore, to regard the nonfluency as "normal" or "to be expected under the circumstances."

It has previously been noted that listeners generally accept, or do not hear or disregard, the nonfluency of children who are considered to be "too young to talk well." Exceedingly few listeners would regard a child as a "stutterer" because his speech was temporarily greatly disturbed by intense fright or shame or rage. Nonfluency that is thought to be understandable or to be expected under the circumstances is not generally classified as stuttering. A crucial consideration is that some circumstances that are conducive to hesitant and nonfluent speech are readily recognized by most persons, while others are subtle and difficult to detect or to appreciate.

This consideration is crucial because the conclusion that a child "is stuttering" seems to be reached as a rule by a process of elimination. That is, if the listener believes the child has an understandable reason for speaking hesitantly, unsmoothly, or even with considerable muscular tension, he seems to assume there is "nothing wrong with

---

* Much of the relevant information so far published is to be found in Chapter 8 of the present volume and Chapter 5 of *Stuttering in Children and Adults* (62). The writer and his associates have completed further studies of nonfluency in the speech of both children and adults and the results are being prepared for publication.

the speech." This is very possibly a major reason why it has been, and in many instances still is, difficult to secure adequate speech services for children with cerebral palsy, mental retardation, or other conditions that affect speech more or less conspicuously. Professionally trained persons as well as laymen appear to reason that something other than speech is of primary importance in such cases, and that until other things are attended to it is essentially normal and to be expected that the speech will be as it is. As a consequence they tend to make no issue of the speech, as such, and so to do nothing about it.

What is true in such cases appears also to be generally true of certain instances of the ordinary nonfluency of childhood. That is to say, if a child, speaking under conditions of fright, lack of vocabulary, or excitement, speaks repetitiously or hesitantly, the listener is likely to be accepting of the nonfluent speech if he is observant of the conditions, attributing it to "good reasons." The listener's reaction in such a case may be thought of as involving an "of course" attitude — "of course a child would be nonfluent under such circumstances." It is when the listener cannot discern or simply overlooks the relevant conditions and so "can see no reason" for the nonfluency that he is most likely to evaluate it as "abnormal" or as something the child "should not do," and to classify it as "stuttering" if this word is one with which he is sufficiently familiar or which he is sufficiently motivated to use.

The conditions conducive to nonfluency which are most likely to be unsuspected and overlooked by a listening parent would seem to be those which the parent creates by the very act of attending to the fluency aspects of the child's speech and judging it as unacceptable in some degree because it is "not as fluent as it should be." As the anthropologist Ruth Benedict phrased it, "It is difficult to be conscious of the eyes through which one looks." A parent who is not very familiar with the facts of childhood speech fluency, who is also not given to observing the sorts of ordinary, as well as unusual, conditions under which children speak more and less smoothly, and who assumes, in addition, that it is not normal for a child to repeat sounds and words or to be nonfluent in other ways — such a parent, happening to notice that her child is speaking nonfluently under what seem to her to be ordinary circumstances, may very well conclude that the child is nonfluent "for no reason" and that, therefore, there must be "something wrong with *his speech.*" Moreover, if to the circumstances which the parent creates by her judgment and reaction the child responds by speaking with increased hesitancy and apparent unsureness, it is not likely that the parent will be perceptive of her own role in the transaction. It is probable that she will, accordingly, simply assume that the child's *speech* "is getting worse."

From these considerations a peculiarly fundamental inference is to be hopefully but warily drawn — in the form of the tentative conjecture that if listeners were always to recognize and understand the circumstances functionally related to nonfluency in speech — or if, like the Bannock and Shoshone Indians (R58) they were to take for granted that it is normal under any circumstances — they would never evaluate it as "stuttering." Given this happy eventuality, the problem of speech fluency per se, so far as it may be a problem in particular instances, would remain, but the problem called "stuttering" presumably would not.

The Listener's Language Behavior. As was noted in Chapter 5, the parents in the experimental group and those in the control group symbolized in crucially different ways the apparently similar speech nonfluencies of their respective children. The difference may be stated essentially by saying that the control group parents made statements that were primarily descriptive of their children's speech, whereas the experimental group parents made statements that were primarily indicative of their own feelings and judgments about their children's speech. That is, the control group parents said their children repeated sounds and words, hesitated in speaking, and the like. The experimental group parents, however, said their children stuttered. Now, "repeating sounds and words," for example, is a description of something being done by the speaker, but "stuttering" is a name for a general classification made by a listener of whatever the speaker may be doing. "The speaker is repeating words" is for all practical purposes a statement about the behavior of the speaker. "The speaker is stuttering," however, is essentially a statement about the behavior of the listener in judging the speaker's behavior.

Lack of awareness of this distinction enables the listener to take for granted that he is talking about the speaker when he is, in fact, talking about himself. This amounts to confusion concerning what is being abstracted and involves a failure to distinguish one level of abstracting (judgment) from another (description). The listener in making this mistake may be said to project his judgment into the speaker, and so to conclude that the speaker is not only repeating words but *also* "is stuttering."

So long as the parent does not make the judgment that the child "is stuttering" (or an equivalent evaluation) this confusion of levels of abstracting, with attendant unconscious projection of judgment, does not occur. It need not occur, moreover, regardless of the specific terms used by the parent in talking about the child's speech, so long as the parent is sufficiently conscious of her own abstracting to be aware of the difference between making a statement about what the child is doing in speaking and a statement about what she herself is doing in perceiving and evaluating the child's speech behavior. From such observations as these it follows that a fundamental objective of the counseling of parents is that of helping them to cultivate an effective awareness of the difference between descriptions of speech and judgments made of it, and, so far as may seem required and feasible, an appreciation of the general principle that perception is affected by the language used in reporting and evaluating what is perceived.*

"Accident." A thorough and thoughtful reading of the preceding chapters would seem to suggest quite strongly that in any relatively full answer to the question of why some parents decide that their children "are stuttering" a place must be reserved for "chance" or "accident." In exercising care not to explain more than actually happened, due attention is to be given to the possibility, if not indeed the probability, that many of the parents had no very good reasons or strong motivations for paying attention to the nonfluency of their children's speech or for classifying it as "stuttering." The chance reading of a magazine article, a casual conversation with a stranger on a train, a fleeting memory of a schoolmate who stuttered — such minor things can undoubtedly influence the way a parent attends for a moment to a child's tottering attempt to negotiate the high, tight wire of spoken language at the fatefully transitional age of three. Once the parent's attention is directed, by whatever turn of chance, to the child's hesitations and repetitions, she may have any one of thousands of specific reasons for "making a problem" of them. The specific reason for concern is probably no more important as a rule than the specific reason for giving attention to the nonfluencies in the first place. What is important is that, for whatever reason, the parent did attend to the nonfluencies, did evaluate them as undesirable, did classify them as "stuttering," and did react accordingly, and in so doing contributed to an interaction in which the child spoke less smoothly and the parent did

* The question of the interaction between the process of symbolization and not only perception but also what we seem ordinarily to mean by thought, feeling, and overt behavior is impressively comprehensive and profound. From a vast literature references to be selected as relatively pertinent to the present considerations are those of Carroll (20), Korzybski (70), Ruesch and Bateson (95), Hayakawa (51), Lee (73), Rapaport (90), Bateson, Jackson, Haley, and Weakland (4), and Johnson (58, 59). A particularly relevant and brief discussion is to be found in the writer's "The Six Men and the Stuttering" (63). Williams (127) has dealt incisively with the interaction of the speaker's language behavior and his so-called stuttering reactions.

not feel as well about the child's speech as she otherwise would have, and so the child spoke even less smoothly, the mother felt still worse about it, and so on.

Much of what is to be said about the speaker's nonfluency and the factors related to it has been stated or implied in the preceding pages. Essential reference has been made to the factors of age and sex of the speaker and to the effect on fluency of a disturbing interaction between the speaker and the listener. Various organic factors have been mentioned. Further relevant discussion will now be presented.

The Speaker's Neurophysiological State. In discussing the listener's recognition of factors contributing to nonfluency, reference was made to such organic conditions as cerebral palsy, aphasia, fatigue, intoxication, certain states produced by drugs, and physiological shock. It is generally recognized that markedly hesitant, blocked, repetitive, or labored speech is commonly associated with these and other comparable conditions. Meanwhile, there appears to have been little investigation of the precise relation between these and other neurophysiological states, including those induced under laboratory conditions, and the various aspects of speech fluency and nonfluency, per se.

There have been, however, many studies designed to determine whether significant neurophysiological differences between persons classified as stutterers and those classified otherwise are demonstrable. Two reviews of some 150 relevant physiological and biochemical studies have been made by Hill (53, 54). The findings of these studies do not appear to identify stutterers as a physiologically distinctive group. They do, however, contribute to the description of certain aspects of the behavior regarded as stuttering. In general, according to Hill, so far as the data serve to distinguish this behavior from the resting state, silence, or speech behavior that is presumably normal, they are indicative of the kinds and degrees of physiological and biochemical reactions associated with the emotionality and struggle ordinarily experienced in contending with threatening, frustrating, or distressing situations. The data may also be said to resemble those characteristic of startle responses and of muscular exertion as observed in human subjects generally. In summing up, Hill said, "An agent in the form of an inner condition . . . is still as distant from discovery as it was four thousand years ago."

The writer has discussed the pertinent issues and data elsewhere (61, pp. 225–260), with the essential conclusion that, to date, no distinctive neurophysiological differences between persons classified as stutterers and those not so classified have been unequivocally demonstrated. The findings of the present research program do not suggest that such differences exist.*

Meanwhile, the scientific investigation of factors, organic and functional, related to fluency and nonfluency in speech, aside from consideration of their relevance to the problem of stuttering, would appear to deserve much more attention than it has so far received.

Conflict Experienced by the Speaker. All who speak understand that conflict in any of its many forms tends to be conducive to hesitant and nonfluent utterance. Conflict may involve necessity of a choice among alternative ways of wording or phrasing or, for bilingual or polylingual speakers, a choice of language. A sense of conflict may arise for the speaker from lack of either essential information or vocabulary, as well as from difficulty in making himself understood because of impaired voice or articulation, unresponsiveness of the listener, or other reasons. Davis (25) reported that the preschool children whose speech she sampled did more repeating of syllables, words, and phrases when attempting to speak while in conflict with their teachers or other children. Findings presented in Chapters 2, 5, and 6 indicate that children tend to be more nonfluent in talking under conditions of conflict involved in speech competition, as at the dinner table of a talkative family, for example. Any conflict present in a speech situation would appear to be heightened by pressure of time or by excitement, factors mentioned by many of the parents in both the experimental and control groups in identifying conditions under which they considered their children to be nonfluent.†

Doubtless the most important kind of conflict, with reference to the problem under consideration, is that which develops as a consequence of parental concern over the child's repetitions and hesitations in speech. To the degree that the child senses the parent's distress over the way he is talking, he appears to react as though in a varying but generally increasing state of conflict over whether to speak at all, or

---

* A comprehensive and critical review of the relevant voluminous experimental and theoretical literature would inordinately extend the present discussion and carry it considerably afield. Among the pertinent references in addition to those indicated are Berry and Eisenson (7), Eisenson (31), Travis (110), Van Riper (113), and West (124, 125).

† The most thoroughly developed conflict theory of stuttering is that of Sheehan (102, 105). Other systematic discussions of conflict in relation to the stuttering problem, as distinguished more or less clearly from the problem of nonfluency per se, are those of Travis (111), Van Riper (113), Wischner (130, 131), Johnson and Knott (65, 66), and Johnson (61). Bloodstein (11) has presented an extended consideration of factors productive of nonfluency in the speech of children, and he has also discussed the problem of stuttering in terms of the speaker's doubt of his ability to speak as well as he feels he must and of his fear of not doing so.

whether to continue speaking once begun. The inference of inner conflict is drawn mainly from observations and informants' reports of a
tendency of the child to talk a bit less and somewhat more hesitantly,
and eventually to talk with some degree of apparent effort or muscular strain.

In this connection, available relevant data and general clinical experience serve to raise the question of possible motivational differences between syllable repetition and the repetition of whole words
and phrases. This question is important because syllable repetition is
evidently the type of nonfluency most likely to be classified as stuttering by most listeners. A possible hypothesis is that syllable repetition
represents a more highly developed conflict between the child's drive
to speak, on the one hand, and, on the other, the effect of his doubt
that he can speak acceptably together with his anticipatory concern
over the possible consequences of failure to do so. With a little less
conflict, he can, we may suppose, attempt a whole word at least before stopping to begin again, but as his sense of conflict increases he is
motivated to stop before he has completed an entire word. The very
act of starting to say the word serves to reactivate the doubt and so
the anxiety about being able to go on satisfactorily, and the child is
immediately motivated to discontinue in order to avoid the anticipated failure. The awareness that he has stopped, however, reacti-
vates his anxiety about not going on, since this also constitutes failure, and so he immediately begins again, only to stop again for the
same reason as before, and once more to begin, again for the same
reason as before, and so on until, as a rule, he finally continues speaking long enough to say the word — unless he reconciles his conflicting
tendencies by neither stopping altogether nor going back to the beginning again, but rather continuing in a sort of stalemate by prolonging the sound produced in beginning to say the word. It will be
recalled that sound prolongation is apparently the only other type of
nonfluency that is evaluated as "stuttering" with distinctive frequency. It may be suspected that the listener tends to sense em-
pathically the speaker's more intense conflict involved in repeating
syllables and in prolonging sounds, and so to conclude more readily
than in reacting to other forms of hesitation and repetition that the
speaker is "having difficulty."

This hypothesis requires extended development and refinement, and
considerable ingenuity would seem to be called for in designing an
adequate operational test of its validity. Meanwhile it may be expected to serve an essential purpose in stimulating further exploration
of the intriguing problem that centers around the differences between

syllable repetition and sound prolongation, which are most often evaluated as "stuttering," and other kinds of nonfluency more commonly regarded as "normal."

A speaker is sensitive to his own nonfluency partly as his own listener and also by virtue of kinesthetic feedback.* (He may respond to his speech visually, too, of course, if he performs before a mirror.) To a considerable degree, therefore, he is affected by the same factors as are his other listeners so far as sensitivity to the nonfluencies in his speech are concerned. Previous discussion of the indicated factors covers, therefore, many aspects of the matter under consideration, but there are some additional observations to be suggested.

The Speaker's Reactions to His Own Nonfluency. The tolerance of presumably normal speakers for their own nonfluency under ordinary conditions of speaking seems not to have been recognized as a problem to be investigated, and there is a consequent lack of laboratory data concerning it. Meanwhile, the fact that such speakers do not appear to "struggle against" their nonfluencies, but perform them with a freedom from avoidant tensions, would seem to imply that they are essentially tolerant of them.† Even stutterers are apparently tolerant of any nonfluencies in their speech which they do not evaluate as "stuttering." Persons who have aphasia or cerebral palsy or comparable conditions sometimes show impatience with their difficulties in speech formulation and production, but the great majority of them seem most of the time to accept their speech even when it is extremely halting and labored.

The production of disturbances in speech by delay in auditory feedback has been reported by many workers including Lee (72), Black (8, 9), Fairbanks and Guttman (32), Atkinson (3), Tiffany and Hanley (109), and Spilka (106). Available data on speakers' reactions to nonfluencies and other modifications of speech behavior induced by delayed auditory feedback are limited to the more or less informal ex-

---

* Van Riper and Irwin (114) have presented a systematic discussion of auditory and kinesthetic feedback with particular reference to implications for speech correction.

† An interesting related problem concerns the tendency of speakers to correct their mistakes. Individual differences in this tendency, and variations in it in relation to kinds of mistake, situational conditions, and other factors, appear to warrant extended investigation. Fairbanks and Guttman (32) reported that their young adult male subjects did not correct most of the errors they made in speaking under conditions of auditory feedback, with time delays of 0, 0.1, 0.2, 0.4, and 0.8 second. They found some tendency to correct errors, however, as evidenced by the repetition of a certain proportion of inaccurate articulations and by the speaker's "tendency to 'stress' syllables in which errors occur, in connection with his efforts to avoid them."

pression of feelings by laboratory subjects and a few observations reported by some of the investigators. The experience is commonly described by laboratory subjects as annoying, unpleasant, and upsetting, or intriguing, interesting, and challenging. Fairbanks and Guttman, as has been stated, reported some indication of attempts to resist or avoid mistakes or disturbances in speech by their subjects. Black and Atkinson demonstrated that the reduced rate of speaking effected by delay of auditory feedback persisted for periods as long as five minutes in continued reading after the condition of delayed feedback was eliminated, suggesting substantial speaker reaction to the induced disturbance. Spilka attempted to relate amount of disturbance produced by delay of auditory feedback to a variety of measured personality variables, and the results, while somewhat too complex to permit an unambiguous summary relevant to the present context, suggest leads for further investigation. Findings of studies reported to date indicate that the speech disturbances induced by delayed auditory feedback, together with the reactions of the speakers to these disturbances, add up to a total effect that is essentially different from the speech behavior generally regarded as stuttering in any significant clinical sense.* The differences, as well as such similarities as there may be, appear to warrant further study.

In general, under usual conditions speakers appear to be for practical purposes tolerant of their own nonfluencies, regardless of type or frequency, provided they do not evaluate them as "stuttering" or the equivalent. It is conceivable, nevertheless, that a speaker, even a young child, might feel frustrated by his nonfluency, particularly if it is extreme, and in reacting to the frustration speak still more hesitantly and even tensely. Through this experience he might also become increasingly attentive to his nonfluencies and more apprehensive of them, evaluating them as unacceptable or as "stuttering," and reacting accordingly with avoidant tensions. In some such way a speaker might conceivably create the problem of stuttering for himself by

* Part of the basis for this statement is the observation of the writer and other persons classified as stutterers that under conditions of delayed auditory feedback the experience recognized by such speakers as their own stuttering is virtually eliminated, and that the speech disturbance induced by the delayed feedback is something distinctively different from it. Moreover, in 1946 the writer directed a study by Shane (101) in which it was demonstrated that stuttering was greatly reduced, and for most subjects it was eliminated, when stutterers read orally while receiving through earphones an approximately 90-decibel masking tone which completely or largely prevented the speaker from hearing his own voice. This basic finding has been confirmed and supplemented in more recent studies by Cherry and Sayers (21), Paruzynski (88), and Maraist and Hutton (79). The possibilities of additional research on the problem of modified auditory feedback are indeed intriguing.

virtue of his intolerance of the nonfluencies in his own speech — and it is an incidental rather than a fundamental observation that any such onset of stuttering seems to be extraordinarily rare. The writer cannot be sure he has ever encountered this sort of origin of the problem, and the present research seems not to have revealed any cases of this kind. According to the findings of this investigation, and related clinical experience, the crucial evaluations are made originally by one or more listeners, and the speaker learns inadvertently from them to regard the nonfluencies in his speech as undesirable and as "stuttering," and then he comes to react to them intolerantly and avoidantly. Regardless of the type or amount of nonfluency, however, it seems clear that it is the evaluation made of it that determines whether either the listener or the speaker, or both, will "make a problem of it."

The Speaker's Sensitivity to the Listener's Reactions to His Nonfluency. Once the parents have begun to show concern over the child's nonfluencies in speaking, the development of the problem for the child would seem to depend, in a significant sense, on his reaction to their concern. The assumption might be ventured that the more sensitive the child is to his parents' reactions to his speech, or the more insecure he feels, or the more dependent he is for his sense of security on his parents' approval of him, the more likely he is to respond to their concern by speaking less, or more hesitantly or cautiously, and with increased conflict over whether, when, and how to speak — the more likely he is to speak, that is, more hesitantly and nonfluently. Further development presumably depends on the parental reaction to the increased nonfluency, and the child's reaction in turn, and so on.

The findings from the present investigation that are relevant to this consideration do not, as has been previously pointed out, unequivocally suggest that the experimental group children were significantly different from those in the control group in being more sensitive to parental reactions. In Study II the Rogers Test of Personality Adjustment did not yield statistically significant differences between the experimental and control group children to whom it was administered. In both Study II and Study III certain of the parents' ratings show that the experimental group children were evaluated less favorably than were those in the control group with respect to certain aspects of social development.* These ratings represent the evaluations of the parents, and the degree to which they reflect the social maturity of

---

* Relevant information about the two groups of children in Study III that was obtained from their parents, primarily in the form of ratings, is presented in Chapter 3, and much of it is summarized in Table 9. Comparable information obtained in Study II is to be found in Chapter 2.

the children in an objective sense is not clearly apparent. They were made, moreover, eighteen months on the average after the stuttering problem was said to have begun and so they presumably reflect in each case the cumulative effects of the interaction of parent and child which the problem involved. The comparative lack of differences between the two groups of children on items involving relatively objective determinations, the degree of overlapping of the groups on parental ratings which did differ significantly, the large number of such ratings that did not show significant differences between the groups, and the marked general improvement of the experimental group children noted in the follow-up phase of Study III suggest caution in concluding that the two groups of children were basically or objectively different in a significant sense with regard to social and emotional development. On the contrary, these findings and considerations indicate that the development of the problem of stuttering in the experimental group families is probably not to be accounted for to any very important extent, if at all, on the basis of a distinctive kind or degree of sensitivity of the experimental group children to their parents' concern over their speech.

It is an important relevant consideration that studies designed to explore personality differences between persons classified as stutterers and nonstutterers, respectively, at both childhood and adult age levels, have yielded no clear evidence of such differences. Sheehan and Zelen (103) found some tendency for stutterers, as compared with control group subjects, to operate, on the tests used, with somewhat lower levels of aspiration, presumably indicative of an inclination to defend themselves against a possible sense of failure. Boland (17), Dahlstrom and Craven (23), and others, including the writer (56), have noted a moderate tendency for stutterers, compared with nonstutterers, to be somewhat withdrawing in certain social situations and to be slightly more discouraged, particularly in regard to tasks or situations involving speech. Such tendencies, so far as they are demonstrable, are understandable as reactions — essentially normal emotional reactions — to the experience of stuttering and of being regarded as a stutterer. With such exceptions, the findings of pertinent studies have been essentially negative. On the basis of a review of twenty studies involving the use of projective tests, Sheehan (104) stated that "no dynamic differences appear between adults who stutter and adults who do not — even by the best tools modern clinical psychology has developed to measure such differences. Moreover, no consistent pattern emerges for the stutterer." Goodstein (39) concluded a comprehensive review of investigations of personality variables in relation to stuttering by saying that children regarded as stutterers have not been shown to be "neurotic or severely maladjusted," and that "there is no general support for the notion that adult stutterers are severely maladjusted or even consistently different from anyone else."

Summary of Conclusions

The program of research reported here has been concerned with this basic question: In what form, at what time, under what conditions, and for whom does the problem of stuttering arise?

The most prevalent answer to this question has been that the problem arises in the form of distinctively disordered speech, at some time between the beginning of speech and adolescence or even adulthood, under unusual conditions such as those of illness, injury, shock, fright, or other neurophysiological or emotional disturbance, and that it arises, therefore, as a problem of and for the speaker.

The research reported in this book appears meanwhile to have yielded an essentially different sort of answer. The data indicate that in the cases investigated the problem was to be described, at its point of origin, not primarily by reference to nonfluent speech, as such, but by reference mainly to an interaction between a listener and a speaker in which the listener made a distinctive perceptual and judgmental reaction to the speaker's nonfluencies. The speaker was characteristically a child between three and four years of age, and the listener was nearly always one of the child's parents, usually the mother. The nonfluencies, as reported, ranged from slight and decidedly ordinary to complex and unusual, and were in general impressively similar to those repetitions, hesitations, and other imperfections of fluency that were reported as having occurred in the speech of a control group of children of comparable age who were not regarded as stutterers. With few if any significant exceptions, the circumstances under which the parents first regarded these nonfluencies as stuttering appeared to be ordinary and unremarkable. What appears to have been crucial was the fact that the parents were motivated to evaluate the nonfluencies as unacceptable, or distressing, to classify them as "stuttering" and to react, nonverbally as a rule but verbally in some cases, to them and to the child accordingly.

On this basis and in this sense, it is to be said that stuttering arose as a problem that involved the interaction of listener and speaker — that is, of the speaking child and those others, chiefly the child's authority figures, his parents primarily, who listened and reacted evaluatively to his speech. The data indicate that by virtue of this interaction the child tended to acquire from his parents and other important listeners the sorts of perceptual and evaluative reaction to his own speech behavior, and to himself as a speaker, which served to inhibit and disrupt his speech reactions in various forms and to varying degrees.

The problem, then, while remaining primarily perceptual for the speaker as well as for his listeners, came also, and significantly, to involve disruption of overt verbal expression in a neuromuscular sense. To recapitulate, characteristically it began primarily as a problem of and for one or more listeners and, through a process of interaction of the listeners' disturbed evaluations and the speaker's responsiveness to them, it became, most fundamentally, a perceptual and evaluative problem of and for the listener who was at the same time the speaker, as well as for his other listeners also. In due course, evidently by virtue of the speaker's disruptive perceptual and evaluative reactions to his own speech behavior, the problem came to involve disturbances of speech, in an overt expressive sense.

It seems necessary to conclude, therefore, that the listener does more than the speaker to set in motion the interactions essential to the creation of the stuttering problem. The speaker's sensitivity to his own nonfluency and to the listener's reactions to it appears to be, like the amount of the speaker's nonfluency per se, decidedly less important in relation to the origin of the problem than is the listener's readiness to attend to the nonfluencies of the speaker and to evaluate them as "stuttering."

Once the crucial interactions have been initiated, however, the speaker's contribution to them and their cumulative effects tends to become more substantial. The speaker's reactions to those nonfluencies in his speech that he takes to be "stuttering" become increasingly important in relation to the problem as a whole. A conspicuous part of the reason for this is that these reactions tend to effect an increase in the frequency and relative complexity of such negatively evaluated nonfluencies. In the bargain the speaker's manifest sensitivity to the listener's reactions to his speech reinforces those reactions, and is, in turn, intensified by them. Moreover, the factors which affect the listener's sensitivity to the speaker's nonfluencies, once they have come to be regarded as "stuttering," affect also the sensitivity of the speaker to them.

It is to be considered especially that the language behavior of the speaker presumably determines to an important degree his beliefs and feelings about speech and particularly the things he does in speaking that he experiences as "stuttering." He shares with his listeners, of course, the basic language structure and usages characteristic of the culture by which they are generally influenced. It follows that the comments previously made in this chapter about the language behavior of the listener are to be applied essentially to that of the speaker as well. The speaker tends to compound the problem by failing to distinguish statements he makes that are descriptive of what he does in speaking from those that are expressive of his evaluations and judgments of what he does. That is, for example, instead of saying descriptively, "I held my breath before I said my name," he tends to say, with implied reference to inferred entities and forces over which he apparently feels he has no control, "My breath stopped," or "I held my breath because I stuttered," or "I had trouble," or "The word wouldn't come out," or "I am a stutterer and I can't say my name without stuttering," or, with deceptive simplicity, "I stuttered." In other words, he tends to confuse inferential statements about what he *is* and what he *has*, and *what there is* to contend with, with descriptive statements about what he *does*. To paraphrase what was said previously about the language behavior of the listener, it is to the advantage of the speaker to be sufficiently conscious of his own abstracting to appreciate the difference between making a statement about what he does as a speaker and a statement about what he does as a listener in evaluating and judging what he does as a speaker.

The findings and their evident implications strongly suggest that the basic rehabilitative need of the speaker, at whatever age level, so far as he may have developed the indicated disruptive perceptual and evaluative reactions to his own speech, is for a reorientation of relevant attitudes, feelings, beliefs, and language behavior tendencies. In any case in which the speaking child has not yet assimilated to a crucial degree the relevant feelings and response patterns of his significant listeners, it is the listeners themselves, as has been emphasized, who appear to require a reorientation of their basic perceptual and evaluative reactions to the child's speech behavior and to the child as a speaker. They need essential information about the fluency aspects of speech development and the factors affecting it, particularly the factors centering in the ways in which they themselves evaluate and react to the nonfluencies in the child's speech. As the speaker becomes a more and more active and important participant in the interactions involved in the problem, he too comes to require appropriate information and counseling, particularly designed to effect a reorientation of relevant perceptual and evaluative reactions and of the related modes of language behavior. In either case the indicated changes are to be attempted with due consideration of the pattern of interpersonal relations that constitute their context.

The Onset of Stuttering

The limits within which implied preventive and rehabilitative principles and procedures may be developed or adapted are relatively broad. The writer and his associates are currently engaged in studies designed to explore and evaluate specific clinical approaches to the problem of stuttering which findings of the present and related research serve to suggest. The nature of the data on the onset of the problem that have been reported in this volume, and the findings of the follow-up investigations, appear to warrant increased attention to preventive measures involving parent education and the dissemination of relevant information to physicians, teachers, child psychologists, family counselors and the general public. It appears possible that through such measures a reduction in the incidence of the problem of stuttering might be brought about in the years ahead.

Finally it is to be considered that the findings here reported, while specific to the problem of stuttering, may suggest leads for investigation of other problems, particularly those of child behavior such as "nervousness," "hostility," "shyness," and other forms of "emotional disturbance," as well as difficulties in learning to read, problems associated with toilet training and eating behavior, and reaction tendencies that tend to culminate in delinquency in its various forms. Intensive study of the origin and early development of such problems in specific cases, within the frame of reference provided by a general interactional theory of the sort outlined in the preceding pages, would seem to be suggested by due contemplation of the data and the interpretative considerations presented in this report.

References and Index

References

1. Ammons, R. A., and W. Johnson. "Studies in the Psychology of Stuttering: XVIII. The Construction and Application of a Test of Attitude toward Stuttering," *Journal of Speech Disorders*, 9: 39–49 (1944).
2. Anastasi, A. *Psychological Testing*. New York: The Macmillan Company, 1954.
3. Atkinson, C. J. "Adaptation to Delayed Side-Tone," *Journal of Speech and Hearing Disorders*, 18: 386–391 (1953).
4. Bateson, G., D. D. Jackson, J. Haley, and J. H. Weakland. "Toward a Theory of Schizophrenia," *Behavioral Science*, 1: 251–264 (1956).
5. Bellak, L. *The Thematic Apperception Test and the Children's Apperception Test in Clinical Use*. New York: Grune and Stratton, 1954.
6. Berry, M. F. "A Common Denominator in Twinning and Stuttering," *Journal of Speech Disorders*, 3: 51–57 (1938).
7. Berry, M. F., and J. Eisenson. *Speech Disorders*. New York: Appleton-Century-Crofts, 1956.
8. Black, J. W. "The Effect of Delayed Side-Tone upon Vocal Rate and Intensity," *Journal of Speech and Hearing Disorders*, 16: 56–60 (1951).
9. Black, J. W. "The Persistence of Effects of Delayed Side-Tone," *Journal of Speech and Hearing Disorders*, 20: 65–68 (1955).
10. Blanton, S. "A Survey of Speech Defects," *Journal of Educational Psychology*, 7: 581–592 (1916).
11. Bloodstein, O. "Stuttering as an Anticipatory-Struggle Reaction," in *Stuttering: A Symposium*, ed. by Jon Eisenson. New York: Harper and Brothers, 1958.
12. Bloodstein, O., and S. M. Smith. "A Study of the Diagnosis of Stuttering with Special Reference to the Sex Ratio," *Journal of Speech and Hearing Disorders*, 19: 459–466 (1954).
13. Bloodstein, O., W. Jaeger, and J. Tureen. "A Study of the Diagnosis of Stuttering by Parents of Stutterers and Nonstutterers," *Journal of Speech and Hearing Disorders*, 17: 308–315 (1952).
14. Bluemel, C. S. *Stammering and Cognate Defects of Speech*. New York: Stechert, 1913.
15. Bluemel, C. S. "Primary and Secondary Stuttering," *Proceedings of the American Speech Correction Association*, 2: 91–102 (1932).
16. Boehmler, R. M. "Listener Responses to Non-Fluencies," *Journal of Speech and Hearing Research*, 1: 132–141 (1958).
17. Boland, J. L. "A Comparison of Stutterers and Nonstutterers on Several Measures of Anxiety," Unpublished Ph.D. thesis, University of Michigan, 1952.
18. Branscom, M. E., Jeannette Hughes, and Eloise Tupper Oxtoby. "Studies of Nonfluency in the Speech of Preschool Children," in *Stuttering in Children and Adults*, ed. by Wendell Johnson, assisted by Ralph Leutenegger. Minneapolis: University of Minnesota Press, 1955.
19. Card, R. E. "A Study of Allergy in Relation to Stuttering," *Journal of Speech Disorders*, 4: 223–230 (1939).

20. Carroll, J. B., ed. *Language, Thought, and Reality: Selected Writings of Benjamin Lee Whorf.* New York: John Wiley and Sons and Cambridge: The Technology Press of the Massachusetts Institute of Technology, 1956.

21. Cherry, C., and B. M. Sayers. "Experiments upon the Total Inhibition of Stammering by External Control, and Some Clinical Results," *Journal of Psychosomatic Research*, 1:233–246 (1956).

22. Committee on Midcentury White House Conference. "Speech Disorders and Speech Correction," *Journal of Speech and Hearing Disorders*, 17:129–137 (1952).

23. Dahlstrom, W. G., and D. D. Craven. "The Minnesota Multiphasic Personality Inventory and Stuttering Phenomena in Young Adults," *American Psychologist*, 7:341 (1952).

24. Darley, F. L. "The Relationship of Parental Attitudes and Adjustments to the Development of Stuttering," Chapter 4 in *Stuttering in Children and Adults*, ed. by Wendell Johnson. Minneapolis: University of Minnesota Press, 1955.

25. Davis, D. M. "The Relation of Repetitions in the Speech of Young Children to Certain Measures of Language Maturity and Situational Factors," Part I, *Journal of Speech Disorders*, 4:303–318 (1939).

26. Davison, A. H. "The Relationship between Unimanual and Bimanual Handedness," *Journal of Experimental Psychology*, 38:276–283 (1948).

27. Despert, J. L. "Stuttering: A Clinical Study," *American Journal of Orthopsychiatry*, 13:517–524 (1943).

28. Despert, J. L. "Psychosomatic Study of Fifty Stuttering Children," *American Journal of Orthopsychiatry*, 16:100–113 (1946).

29. Dollard, J., N. E. Miller, L. W. Doob, O. H. Mowrer, and R. R. Sears. *Frustration and Aggression.* New Haven: Yale University Press, 1939.

30. Egland, G. O. "Repetitions and Prolongations in the Speech of Stuttering and Nonstuttering Children," in *Stuttering in Children and Adults*, ed. by Wendell Johnson. Minneapolis: University of Minnesota Press, 1955.

31. Eisenson, J. "A Perseverative Theory of Stuttering," in *Stuttering: A Symposium*, ed. by Jon Eisenson. New York: Harper and Brothers, 1958.

32. Fairbanks, G., and N. Guttman. "Effects of Delayed Auditory Feedback upon Articulation," *Journal of Speech and Hearing Research*, 1:12–22 (1958).

33. Ferguson, L. W. *Personality Measurement.* New York: McGraw-Hill Book Company, 1952.

34. Froeschels, E. "Beitrage zur Symptomatologie des Stotterns," Monatschi. f. Ohrenheilk, vol. 55 (1921).

35. Giolas, T. G., and D. E. Williams. "Children's Reactions to Nonfluencies in Adult Speech," *Journal of Speech and Hearing Research*, 1:86–93 (1958).

36. Glasner, P. J., and D. Rosenthal. "Parental Diagnosis of Stuttering in Young Children," *Journal of Speech and Hearing Disorders*, 22:288–295 (1957).

37. Glasner, P. J., and F. D. Vermilyea. "An Investigation of the Definition and Use of the Diagnosis, 'Primary Stuttering,'" *Journal of Speech and Hearing Disorders*, 18:161–167 (1953).

38. Goodstein, L. D. "MMPI Profiles of Stutterers' Parents: A Follow-up Study," *Journal of Speech and Hearing Disorders*, 21:430–435 (1956).

39. Goodstein, L. D. "Functional Speech Disorders and Personality: A Survey of the Research," *Journal of Speech and Hearing Research*, 1:359–376 (1958).

40. Goodstein, L. D., and W. G. Dahlstrom, "Some Personality Test Differences between Parents of Stuttering and Nonstuttering Children," *Journal of Consulting Psychology*, 20:365–370 (1956).

41. Gough, H. G. "A New Dimension of Status. I: Development of a Personality Scale," *American Sociological Review*, 13:401–409 (1948).

42. Gough, H. G. "The Construction of a Personality Scale to Predict Academic Achievement," *Journal of Applied Psychology*, 37:361–366 (1953).

43. Gough, H. G., H. McClosky, and P. E. Meehl. "A Personality Scale for Dominance," *Journal of Abnormal and Social Psychology*, 46:360–366 (1951).

References

44. Graf, O. I. "Incidence of Stuttering among Twins," in *Stuttering in Children and Adults*, ed. by Wendell Johnson. Minneapolis: University of Minnesota Press, 1955.
45. Grossman, D. J. "A Study of the Parents of the Stuttering and Nonstuttering Children Using the MMPI and the Minnesota Scale of Parents Opinion." Unpublished M.A. thesis, University of Wisconsin, 1951.
46. Guilford, J. P. *Manual of Directions and Norms, Revised Edition, An Inventory of Factors STDCR*. Beverly Hills, Calif.: Sheridan Supply Company, 1940.
47. Guilford, J. P. *Psychometric Methods*. New York: McGraw-Hill Book Company, 1954.
48. Hamlett, G. W. D. "Human Twinning in the United States: Racial Frequencies, Sex Ratios, and Geographical Variations," *Genetics*, 20:250–258 (1935).
49. Hathaway, S. R. "A Coding System for MMPI Profiles," *Journal of Consulting Psychology*, 11:334–337 (1947).
50. Hathaway, S. R. and J. C. McKinley. *Minnesota Multiphasic Personality Inventory: Manual* (Revised). New York: Psychological Corporation, 1951.
51. Hayakawa, S. I. *Language in Thought and Action*. New York: Harcourt, Brace, 1949.
52. Hill, A. S. "The Use of an Objective Type of Case Study in the Analysis and Prognosis of Pupil Maladjustment Problems," *Educational Administration and Supervision*, 21:611–618 (1935).
53. Hill, H. "Stuttering: I. A Critical Review and Evaluation of Biochemical Investigations," *Journal of Speech Disorders*, 9:245–261 (1944).
54. Hill, H. "Stuttering: II. A Review and Integration of Physiological Data," *Journal of Speech Disorders*, 9:289–324 (1944).
55. Hood, P. N., K. H. Shank, and D. B. Williamson, "Environmental Factors in Relation to the Speech of Cerebral Palsied Children," *Journal of Speech and Hearing Disorders*, 13:325–331 (1948).
56. Johnson, W. *The Influence of Stuttering on the Personality*. University of Iowa Studies in Child Welfare, Vol. 5, No. 5. Iowa City, Iowa: University of Iowa, 1932.
57. Johnson, W., *et al*. "A Study of the Onset and Early Development of Stuttering," *Journal of Speech Disorders*, 7:251–257 (1942).
58. Johnson, W. *People in Quandaries: The Semantics of Personal Adjustment*. New York: Harper and Brothers, 1946.
59. Johnson, W. "Perceptual and Evaluational Factors in Stuttering," Chapter 27 in *Handbook of Speech Pathology*, ed. by Lee Edward Travis. New York: Appleton-Century-Crofts, 1956. Published also in *Folio Phoniatrica*, 8:211–233 (1956).
60. Johnson, W., *et al*. "Speech Fluency Norms," unpublished report of research carried out at the State University of Iowa under a grant from the Louis W. and Maud Hill Family Foundation, St. Paul, Minnesota.
61. Johnson, W., *et al*. *Speech Handicapped School Children*. New York: Harper and Brothers, 1948; revised edition, 1956.
62. Johnson, W., ed., assisted by Ralph Leutenegger. *Stuttering in Children and Adults: Thirty Years of Research at the University of Iowa*. Minneapolis: University of Minnesota Press, 1955.
63. Johnson, W. "The Six Men and the Stuttering," in *Stuttering: A Symposium*, ed. by Jon Eisenson. New York: Harper and Brothers, 1958.
64. Johnson, W., F. L. Darley, and D. C. Spriestersbach. *Diagnostic Manual in Speech Correction*. New York: Harper and Brothers, 1952.
65. Johnson, W., and J. R. Knott, "The Moment of Stuttering," *Journal of Genetic Psychology*, 48:475–480 (1936).
66. Johnson, W., and J. R. Knott. "A Systematic Approach to the Psychology of Stuttering," in *Stuttering in Children and Adults*, ed. by Wendell Johnson, assisted by Ralph Leutenegger. Minneapolis: University of Minnesota Press, 1955.
67. Kinsey, A. C., W. B. Pomeroy, and C. E. Martin. *Sexual Behavior in the Human Male*. Philadelphia: W. B. Saunders Company, 1948.
68. Klingbeil, G. M. "The Historical Background of the Modern Speech Clinic," *Journal of Speech Disorders*, 4:115–132 (1939).

69. Kools, J. A. "Speech Nonfluencies of Stuttering and Nonstuttering Children." Unpublished M.A. thesis, University of Iowa, 1956.
70. Korzybski, A. *Science and Sanity: An Introduction to Non-Aristotelian Systems and General Semantics.* Lancaster: Science Press, 1933; Lakeville, Conn.: Institute of General Semantics, fourth edition, 1958.
71. LaFollette, A. C. "A Study of the Parental Environments of Stuttering Children." Unpublished Ph.D. dissertation, University of Denver, 1948.
72. Lee, B. S. "Artificial Stutter," *Journal of Speech and Hearing Disorders*, 16: 53–55 (1951).
73. Lee, I. J. *Language Habits in Human Affairs.* New York: Harper and Brothers, 1941.
74. Lewis, D., and C. J. Burke. "The Use and Misuse of the Chi-Square Test," *Psychological Bulletin*, 46:433–489 (1949).
75. Luchsinger, H. "Die Sprache und Stimme von ein-und Zweieiigen Zwillingen in Beziehung zur Motorik und zum Erbcharacter," *Julius Klaus, Stiftung fur Vererbungsforschung, Sozialanthropologie and Rassen-hygiene, Archiv., Zurich*, 15:15 (1940).
76. McDowell, E. D. *Educational and Emotional Adjustments of Stuttering Children.* Columbia University Contributions to Education, No. 314. New York: Teachers College, 1928.
77. Makuen, G. H. "A Study of 1,000 Cases of Stammering with Special Reference to the Etiology and Treatment of the Affection," *Therapeutical Gazette*, 38:385–390 (1914).
78. Mann, M. B. "Nonfluencies in the Oral Reading of Stutterers and Nonstutterers of Elementary School Age," in *Stuttering in Children and Adults*, ed. by Wendell Johnson. Minneapolis: University of Minnesota Press, 1955.
79. Mariast, J. A., and C. Hutton. "Effects of Auditory Masking upon the Speech of Stutterers," *Journal of Speech and Hearing Disorders*, 22:385–389 (1957).
80. Mast, V. R. "Level of Aspiration as a Method of Studying the Personality of Adult Stutterers," *Speech Monographs*, 19:196 (1952).
81. Meehl, P. E. "The Dynamics of Structured Personality Tests," *Journal of Clinical Psychology*, 1:296–303 (1945).
82. Milisen, R. L. and W. Johnson. "A Comparative Study of Stutterers, Former Stutterers and Normal Speakers Whose Handedness Has Been Changed," *Archives of Speech*, 1:61–86 (1936).
83. Mills, A. W., and H. Streit, "Report of a Speech Survey, Holyoke, Massachusetts," *Journal of Speech Disorders*, 7:161–167 (1942).
84. Moncur, J. P. "Parental Domination in Stuttering," *Journal of Speech and Hearing Disorders*, 17:155–165 (1952).
85. Morgenstern, J. J. "Psychological and Social Factors in Children's Stammering." Ph.D. thesis, University of Edinburgh, 1953.
86. Murray, H. A. *Thematic Apperception Test.* Cambridge, Mass.: Harvard University Press, 1943.
87. Nelson, S. F., N. Hunter, and M. Walter. "Stuttering in Twin Types," *Journal of Speech Disorders*, 10:335–343 (1945).
88. Paruzynski, T. F. "A Study of the Speech Behavior of Stutterers under the Influence of Circumstances Created by Inhibiting Auditory and Visual Sensation." Unpublished M.A. thesis, Marquette University, 1951.
89. Pflaum, G. R. R. "The Voice Training of the Orators in Antiquity up to the Time of Quintilian." Unpublished Ph.D. thesis, Cornell University, 1924.
90. Rapaport, A. *Operational Philosophy.* New York: Harper and Brothers, 1953.
91. Rogers, C. R. *A Test of Personality Adjustment: Manual of Directions.* New York: Association Press, 1931.
92. Rogers, C. R. *Measuring Personality Adjustment in Children Nine to Thirteen Years of Age.* New York: Teachers College, Columbia University, 1931.
93. Root, A. R. "A Survey of Speech Defectives in the Public Elementary Schools of South Dakota," *Elementary School Journal*, 26:531–541 (1926).

References

94. Rotter, J. B. "Studies in the Psychology of Stuttering: XI. Stuttering in Relation to the Position in the Family," *Journal of Speech Disorders*, 4:143–148 (1939).
95. Ruesch, J., and G. Bateson. *Communication: The Social Matrix of Psychiatry.* New York: W. W. Norton, 1951.
96. Schindler, M. D. "A Study of Educational Adjustments of Stuttering and Non-stuttering Children," in *Stuttering in Children and Adults*, ed. by Wendell Johnson. Minneapolis: University of Minnesota Press, 1955.
97. Schuell, H. "Sex Differences in Relation to Stuttering: Part I," *Journal of Speech Disorders*, 11:277–298 (1946).
98. Schuell, H. "Sex Differences in Relation to Stuttering: Part II," *Journal of Speech Disorders*, 12:23–38 (1947).
99. Scripture, E. W. *Stuttering and Lisping.* New York: The Macmillan Company, 1912.
100. Seeman, M. "The Significance of Twin Pathology for the Investigation of Speech Disorders," *Archiv. für die Gesamte Phonetik*, 1 (Part II):88 (1939).
101. Shane, M. L. S. "Effect on Stuttering of Alteration in Auditory Feedback," in *Stuttering in Children and Adults*, ed. by Wendell Johnson, assisted by Ralph Leutenegger. Minneapolis: University of Minnesota Press, 1955.
102. Sheehan, J. G. "An Integration of Psychotherapy and Speech Therapy through a Conflict Theory of Stuttering," *Journal of Speech and Hearing Disorders*, 19:474–482 (1954).
103. Sheehan, J. G., and S. Zelen. "Levels of Aspiration in Stutterers and Nonstutterers," *Journal of Abnormal and Social Psychology*, 51:83–86 (1955).
104. Sheehan, J. G. "Projection Studies of Stuttering," *Journal of Speech and Hearing Disorders*, 23:18–25 (1958).
105. Sheehan, J. G. "Conflict Theory of Stuttering," in *Stuttering: A Symposium*, ed. by Jon Eisenson. New York: Harper and Brothers, 1958.
106. Spilka, B. "Relationships between Certain Aspects of Personality and Some Vocal Effects of Delayed Speech Feedback," *Journal of Speech and Hearing Disorders*, 19:491–503 (1954).
107. Steer, M. D. "The General Intelligence of College Stutterers," *School and Society*, 44:862–864 (1936).
108. Taylor, J. A. "A Personality Scale of Manifest Anxiety," *Journal of Abnormal and Social Psychology*, 48:285–290 (1953).
109. Tiffany, W. R., and C. N. Hanley. "Adaptation to Delayed Sidetone," *Journal of Speech and Hearing Disorders*, 21:164–172 (1956).
110. Travis, L. E. *Speech Pathology.* New York: D. Appleton and Company, 1931.
111. Travis, L. E., ed. *Handbook of Speech Pathology.* New York: Appleton-Century-Crofts, 1956.
112. Tuthill, C. E. "A Quantitative Study of Extensional Meaning with Special Reference to Stuttering," *Speech Monographs*, 13:81–98 (1946).
113. Van Riper, C. *Speech Correction: Principles and Methods.* New York: Prentice-Hall, 1954.
114. Van Riper, C., and J. V. Irwin. *Voice and Articulation.* Englewood Cliffs, N.J.: Prentice-Hall, 1958.
115. Walker, H. M., and Joseph Lev. *Statistical Inference.* New York: Henry Holt and Company, 1953.
116. Wallin, J. E. "A Census of Speech Defectives among 89,057 Public-School Pupils — a Preliminary Report," *School and Society*, 3:213–214 (1916).
117. Warner, W. L., M. Meeker, and K. Eels. *Social Class in America.* Chicago: Science Research Associates, 1949.
118. Wechsler, D. *The Measurement of Adult Intelligence.* Baltimore: Williams and Wilkins Company, 1944.
119. Welsh, G. S. "An Extension of Hathaway's MMPI Profile Coding System," *Journal of Consulting Psychology*, 12:343–344 (1948).
120. Welsh, G. S. and W. G. Dahlstrom. *Basic MMPI Readings in Psychology and Medicine.* Minneapolis: University of Minnesota Press, 1957.

The Onset of Stuttering

121. Wepman, J. M. "Is Stuttering Inherited?" *Proceedings of the American Speech Correction Association,* 5:39 (1935).
122. Wepman, J. M. "Familial Incidence in Stammering," *Journal of Speech Disorders,* 4:199–204 (1939).
123. West, R., ed. *A Symposium on Stuttering.* Madison, Wisc.: College Typing Company, 1931.
124. West, R. "An Agnostic's Speculations about Stuttering," in *Stuttering: A Symposium,* ed. by Jon Eisenson. New York: Harper and Brothers, 1958.
125. West, R., M. Ansberry, and A. Carr. *The Rehabilitation of Speech.* New York: Harper and Brothers, third edition, 1957.
126. West, R., S. Nelson, and M. Berry. "The Heredity of Stuttering," *Quarterly Journal of Speech,* 25:23–30 (1939).
127. Williams, D. E. "A Point of View about 'Stuttering,'" *Journal of Speech and Hearing Disorders,* 22:390–397 (1957).
128. Williams, D. E., and L. R. Kent. "Listener Evaluations of Speech Interruptions," *Journal of Speech and Hearing Research,* 1:124–131 (1958).
129. Williams, J. T. "A Study of the Parents of Cerebral Palsied and Non-Cerebral Palsied Children Using the MMPI." Unpublished M.A. thesis, University of Wisconsin, 1951.
130. Wischner, G. J. "Stuttering and Learning: A Preliminary Theoretical Formulation," *Journal of Speech and Hearing Disorders,* 15:324–335 (1950).
131. Wischner, G. J. "An Experimental Approach to Expectancy and Anxiety in Stuttering Behavior," *Journal of Speech and Hearing Disorders,* 17:139–154 (1952).
132. Wood, K. S. "Parental Maladjustment and Functional Articulatory Defects in Children," *Journal of Speech Disorders,* 11:255–275 (1946).
133. Yates, F. "Contingency Tables Involving Small Numbers and the χ^2 Test," Supplement, *Journal of the Royal Statistical Society,* 1:217–235 (1934).
134. Young, M. A. "Correlational Analysis of Speech Nonfluencies and Rated Severity of Stuttering." Unpublished M.A. thesis, University of Iowa, 1958.

Index

Abstracting, 44: confusion of levels of, 252–253

"Accident," in relation to onset of stuttering, 253

Age, chronological: of children, 8, 9, 10, 35, 36; of parents, 74–75

Alcohol, use of, 84, 103

Allergies, 84, 226

Ammons, R. A., 24n

Anastasi, A., 181n

Atkinson, C. J., 257

Attitudes of parents: toward speech, 85–88, 106; toward child development, 88–91, 104–105

Auditory feedback, delayed, 257–259

Bannock Indians, 252

Bateson, G., 253n

Bellak, L., 201

Benedict, R., 251

Berry, M., 69n, 71, 255n

Birth: conditions of, 33, 36, 50–52, 96, 224; injuries at, 33, 36, 52; duration of labor, 36, 50; length at, 36; weight at, 36, 50; order of, 39, 72–73, 83, 225

Black, J. W., 257

Bloodstein, O., 240, 244, 245, 248, 255n

Bluemel, C. S., 31

Boehmler, R. M., 148n, 243, 244, 245, 249

Boland, J. L., 260

Breast feeding, 36, 52n, 53

Brown, S. F., 17n

Burke, C. J., 26, 27n

Carroll, J. B., 253n

Case history, projection in, 7, 119–124 *passim*, 136–140 *passim*, 144, 148–149, 164–169 *passim*, 196–199, 219–220, 236–264 *passim*

Cherry, C., 258n

Child development, parents' attitudes toward, 88–91, 104–105

Children's Apperception Test, 201

"Clinical" and "nonclinical" subgroups of experimental group mothers, 161–164

"Complete blocks," 134, 135, 137–139

Conlon, S., 19

Counseling of parents, 35, 173–175, 246–247, 249–250, 253, 263–264

Craven, D. D., 260

Dahlstrom, W. G., 181n, 182n, 260

Darley, F. L., 9, 17n, 20, 23n, 24n, 27, 36n, 45, 46, 51n, 76, 160n

Data analysis, 25–27

Davis, D. M., 35, 255

Davison, A. H., 23n

Demetrius of Phalerum, 4n

Demosthenes, 4

Despert, J. L., 8n

Development: speech, 34, 36, 37, 60–63, 90, 224; physical, 34, 52–56, 224; social, 37, 63–68, 224; expectations of parents, 90

Diabetes, 84, 226

Diagnosogenic factors, 167, and *passim*

Disciplinary practices and attitudes, 37, 40, 91–93, 100, 106, 107, 227

Diseases, *see* Health

Dollard, J., 247n

Doob, L. W., 247n

Drever, J., 3n

Dwyer, S., 16

Education of parents, 37, 38, 75–78, 98

Eels, K., 9, 13, 75

Eisenson, J., 255n

Epilepsy, 84, 226

Evaluative responses of parents, comparative analysis of, 67–68, 93, 115–116

Fairbanks, G., 257, 257n, 258

Family line data: speech disorders, 34, 37–38, 40, 69–70, 168n, 225; handedness, 34, 39, 84–85; twinning, 39, 72, 84, 225

Family size, 34, 39, 52n, 72–73, 82, 226

273

APPENDIXES

Explanatory Note to the Summary Table

The data from Study II and Study III, with exceptions noted, are presented in the following Summary Table. The main purposes of making the findings available in this detailed fashion are to allow essential reference to them in the body of the report and to encourage further evaluation of them and continued development of their implications, not only by students of the stuttering problem but also by child psychologists, cultural anthropologists, medical investigators, and others interested in the broad area of child development and family life.

With a view to the economical and effective use of space, certain deletions have been made. For example, data such as those obtained by means of the Minnesota Multiphasic Personality Inventory (see item 615) have not been included in the table because they have been presented comprehensively in Chapter 7. Certain questions elicited responses that were highly varied and difficult to classify; some of these responses, such as those to items 94, 217, 236, appeared to be sufficiently important to warrant their being reported in full, while others are included in partial or condensed form (e.g., items 720 and 721), with explanatory footnotes. A few items elicited information that proved, in either Study II or Study III or both, to be too fragmentary to justify presentation (see the footnote to items 573-583 and 587-595, for example), or to consist of lists or details summarized elsewhere in the table or in the text (e.g., items 616, 647, and 651), or that were used in deriving certain scores or indexes to be found in the table (see, for example, the footnote to items 617-621). For such items essential explanation is provided in footnotes.

The data from Study II have been included in the Summary Table only to the extent that they were comparable with those from Study III. Codings for Study II that are different from codings used for corresponding questions in Study III are set off by a dagger (†) preceding the number, as in item 55.

The items are numbered consecutively throughout the table; after the colon following each item number in the first column of the table the IBM card and column number is also given. The deletion of a few items from the interview after the coding system had been set up is indicated by corresponding gaps in the IBM numbering. Single asterisks designate items for which responses were not punched for IBM processing but are on file in the University of Iowa Speech Clinic. Responses to most of these items are summarized in this table. Double asterisks designate items that are operational, such as case number; responses to these were punched on IBM cards. Some items, such as No. 4, child's age, were presented only to one parent and responses are summarized accordingly in the corresponding column; F refers to fathers, M to mothers. The numbers in the columns are either computed values, as for item No. 4, or numbers of informants giving each indicated response, as for item No. 5. With occasional exceptions, only those responses to any question are listed that were reported by or for three or more of the respondents represented in one or more columns of the table; indication is given in a footnote of the number of responses reported by or for one or both parents in only one or two cases in either the control or experimental group, or in both, in either Study II or Study III, and it is to be understood that the two parents in any case may or may not have agreed in their responses (e.g., footnotes to items 16 and 51).

For any item with respect to which each respondent gave one and only one response the total number of responses entered in each column of the table is 50 for Study II and 150 for Study III. For any item with respect to which all informants responded and one or more respondents gave more than one answer the column totals affected are correspondingly greater than 50 for Study II or 150 for Study III. Column totals less than 50 for Study II or 150 for Study III are accountable by reference to the rule, stated above, that, with few exceptions, only those responses to any question are listed that were reported by or for three or more of the respondents represented in one or more columns, or on the basis of one or another of the following explanations: (a) the item did not apply to certain respondents, for reasons that are to be ascertained by examining responses entered for preceding questions (e.g., certain questions, such as Nos. 16, 23, and 62, were asked or not depending on responses to preceding items); (b) certain questions in Study II were regarded as "family response items" to be answered by either the mother or father, and they were not asked, accordingly, of some or all of the fathers, or of the mothers; (c) in a very few instances an item was not used because of unavoidable pressure of time or other circumstances, and in an occasional case an item was inadvertently omitted; (d) the "?" or "uncertain" code was used to record responses of "uncertain" or "don't know" or "can't say" for certain items, but for some of these items, such as No. 59, such responses were not included in computing means or other group measures.

Certain items refer to events that occurred at or before "the age of onset of stuttering," and the corresponding age is used as the point of reference for the matched control group child in each case (see, for example, item 125).

Data are on file in the Speech Clinic and, on IBM cards, in the Statistical Service Office of the University of Iowa.

SUMMARY TABLE. Interview data obtained in two separate investigations from mothers (M) and fathers (F) of 200 allegedly stuttering children (experimental groups) and 200 allegedly nonstuttering children (control groups), matched in each investigation for age, sex, and socioeconomic status of the family. The subjects and investigative procedures employed in Study II and Study III are described in Chapter 1. The findings of Study II are summarized in Chapter 2 and are reported in detail by Darley (11). The findings of Study III are presented and discussed in Chapters 3-9 of this volume.

Item No.: IBM Card and Column No.	Item; or Question and Response Codings; or Computed Values	Study II Control Group (N = 50)		Study II Experimental Group (N = 50)		Study III Control Group (N = 150)		Study III Experimental Group (N = 150)	
		F	M	F	M	F	M	F	M
1:A2-5	Case number**								
2*	Interview date								
3*	Child's birth date								
4:A6-7	Child's age (years:months)								
	a. Minimum	2:2		2:4		2:4		2:3	
	b. Maximum	14:0		14:4		8:7		8:0	
	c. Mean	9:0		8:8		5:0		5:0	
	d. Median	8:9		8:3		5:0		5:0	
	e. 90th percentile	12:11		13:0		6:8		6:10	
	f. N	50		50		150		150	
5:A8	Child's sex								
	1. Male	39		39		107		107	
	2. Female	11		11		43		43	
6*	Parent's birth date								
7:A10-13	Parent's present age to nearest month (years:months)								
	a. Minimum	25:10	23:6	24:11	22:10	25:2	22:11	24:2	21:5
	b. Maximum	54:8	57:8	55:11	53:2	50:3	48:4	55:0	46:6
	c. Mean	39:1	36:0	40:8	37:6	34:5	32:3	35:10	33:0
	d. Median	38:5	35:6	40:0	37:4	34:0	32:5	35:2	33:0
	e. 90th percentile	47:6	43:7	49:6	47:5	41:5	38:4	43:6	40:2
	f. N	50	50	50	50	150	150	150	150
8:A14-17	Parent's age at birth of child to nearest month (years:months)								
	a. Minimum	20:10	18:6	20:3	19:11	19:1	19:3	19:10	19:2
	b. Maximum	44:2	44:10	49:2	44:0	43:11	42:4	49:6	40:1

c. Mean	30:1	27:0	32:0	29:1	29:6	27:4	30:10	28:1
d. Median	26:10	27:10	31:3	28:9	28:7	26:10	29:6	27:9
e. 90th percentile	32:1	37:6	40:9	44:10	35:11	34:4	38:2	35:3
f. N	50	50	50	50	150	150	150	150
9* State or country of birth								
10* States lived in for one year or more (states and number of years)								
11:A18 Primary residence								
1. Never lived on a farm; urban	16	21	20	22	80	83	99	101
2. Incidental residence of at least a year but not any long period of years in rural areas	8	6	6	3	23	11	12	8
3. Primarily rural during childhood (up to 11)	0	4	6	5	13	12	3	9
4. Primarily rural during childhood and youth (up to 18)	18	16	3	7	20	27	19	18
5. Primarily rural during youth (12 to 18)	5	0	0	1	4	6	3	2
6. Primarily rural during youth and later (12 and older)	0	0	0	0	1	1	0	0
7. Primarily rural after 18	1	0	1	1	1	3	2	0
8. Primarily rural all of life	1	2	14	11	8	6	10	9
9. Primarily rural during late childhood and early youth (6 to 11)					0	0	0	0
10. Rural up to 24 years					0	1	1	0
12:A19-20 Number of years of school completed (or equivalent in private tutoring)								
a. Minimum	4	3	5	8	8	8	4	6
b. Maximum	22	18	21	20	30	21	21	19
c. Mean	14.1	12.7	12.7	13.5	14.6	13.4	13.3	12.6
d. Median	14.5	12	12	12	14	13	13	12
e. 90th percentile	19	16	17	16	19	16	17	16
f. N	50	50	50	50	150	150	150	150
13* Level of education								
1. Completed one or more years of graduate work at college or university	15	3	7	1	36	4	17	2

Item No.: IBM Card and Column No.	Item; or Question and Response Codings; or Computed Values	Study II Control Group (N = 50) F	M	Study II Experimental Group (N = 50) F	M	Study III Control Group (N = 150) F	M	Study III Experimental Group (N = 150) F	M
	2. Graduated from four-year college, university, or professional school	9	10	6	11	25	36	22	16
	3. Attended college two or more years, or equivalent higher education	6	8	5	8	14	23	25	31
	4. Graduated from high school, or equivalent secondary education	9	20	19	26	58	72	60	82
	5. Attended high school; completed at least one year but did not graduate	4	2	4	2	14	10	15	12
	6. Third to eighth year (older persons), shifting to eighth grade (young adults)[1]	7	7	9	2	3	5	9	6
	7. Below third grade (older persons), shifting to below eighth grade (young adults)[1]	0	0	0	0	0	0	2	1
14:A21	Were you a social fraternity or sorority member in college?								
	1. Yes	15	8	8	7	26	19	18	13
	2. No	15	17	12	17	56	51	53	50
	3. No; correspondence study, no college residence	0	0	0	0	0	0	1	0
15:A22	What is your religion?								
	1. Protestant	37	34	38	44	116	119	91	95
	2. Roman Catholic	12	15	7	5	25	25	35	33
	3. Greek Orthodox	0	0	0	0	0	0	2	1
	4. Jewish	0	0	1	0	5	5	16	17
	5. None--indifferent	1	1	4	1	4	1	5	4
	6. None--anti	1	0	0	0	0	0	0	0
	7. Russian Orthodox	0	0	0	0	0	0	1	0

[1] Identifications of "older persons" and "young adults" in categories 6 and 7 may be found in the files of the University of Iowa Speech Clinic.

16:A23-24 If Protestant, what is your denomination?								
1. Baptist	5	3	2	3	10	8	5	9
2. Methodist	10	10	11	14	40	41	24	25
3. Presbyterian	10	9	8	9	23	22	10	10
4. Lutheran	1	1	6	5	15	17	36	35
5. Episcopal	1	5	0	1	7	8	4	3
6. Others²	7	9	8	11	23	23	12	16
7. No preference	1	1	3	1	8	2	1	0
17:A25 Degree of formal religious adherence within last five years								
1. Actively concerned as regular attendant, or participant in organized church activities, more than once a month	16	27	19	27	83	97	71	83
2. Fairly frequent attendance; about once a month	5	3	7	8	16	15	19	21
3. Infrequent church attendance; about once every 2 or 3 months	7	11	6	4	11	18	25	14
4. Practically no attendance or activity; once or twice a year	15	6	9	5	30	12	25	26
5. None	7	2	9	6	10	7	9	5
18:A26 How was mother's health during pregnancy?								
1. Good	44			36	138	137	123	120
2. Fair	3			6	9	11	17	13
3. Poor	2			7	1	2	3	10
4. ?	1			1	2	0	7	7
19:A27-28 What illnesses did she have during pregnancy?³								
1. None	39			29	111	111	115	115

²There were 27 additional denominations represented in both Study II and Study III. Thirteen of these were reported by the control and 15 by the experimental group respondents.

³In addition to the illnesses specified, each of 49 different illnesses or combinations of illnesses was reported in both Study II and Study III by fewer than three of the informants represented in any one column of the table; 21 of these 49 were reported by the control and 30 by the experimental group respondents.

Item No.; or Question and Response IBM Card and Codings; or Computed Values Column No.	Study II Control Group (N = 50)		Study II Experimental Group (N = 50)		Study III Control Group (N = 150)		Study III Experimental Group (N = 150)	
	F	M	F	M	F	M	F	M
2. Cold						3		2
3. Varicose veins						6		0
4. Anemia						0		5
5. Toxic poisoning		1		2		3		2
6. ?						0		6
7. Nausea		2		0		10		9
20:A29 Was she able to eat regularly and retain food during most of the pregnancy?								
1. Yes		42		40	146	144	131	124
2. No		6		8	3	6	11	19
3. ?		2		2	1	0	8	7
21:A30 Specify any shocks she suffered during the pregnancy[4]								
1. In accident		4		5	1	1	4	4
2. Death in family		0		2	2	1	0	0
3. Bitten by a dog					0	0	3	3
4. Others		0		3	2	4	4	6
5. None		45		38	145	144	133	132
6. Uncertain		1		2	0	0	6	5
22:A31 Specify any falls suffered during the pregnancy (Study II: Specify any falls or severe injuries suffered during the pregnancy)								
1. None		43		40	136	127	132	128
2. 1		3		6	8	18	4	9
3. 2		1		1	1	3	1	2

[4] In addition to the 3 kinds of shock specified, each of 19 different kinds was reported in both Study II and Study III by one informant; 6 of these were reported by the control and 13 by the experimental group respondents. One father in the control group in Study II did not respond to this question; the mother's response was "uncertain." The child in this case was adopted.

Item		1	2	3	4	5	6
4. 3 to 5		2	0	0	2	0	0
5. ?		9	13	5	0	3	3
23:A32 Do you see any connection between these shocks or injuries and any characteristic of the child?							
1. Strongly believes or suspects direct or indirect causal relationship		1	2	0	1	1	0
2. Believes no relationship, direct or indirect		12	19	5	11	24	14
3. ?		2	3	5	1	2	1
24:A33 Does the other parent see any connection?							
1. Strongly believes or suspects direct or indirect causal relationship		0	0	0	0	1	2
2. Believes no relationship, direct or indirect		14	21	6	11	24	12
3. ?		2	3	7	1	2	2
25:A34 Length of pregnancy							
1. Over 9.5 months		2	5	4	2		
2. 9 to 9.5 months		10	10	47	36		
3. Exactly 9 months and 1 day		11	13	51	71		
4. 8 to 9 months		9	1	36	34		
5. 7 to 8 months		2	1	8	0		
6. 6 to 7 months		1	1	0	0		
7. ?		15	19	4	7		
†8. Just 9 months							
26:A35 Was the child considered premature by the doctor?							
1. Yes		13	15		13	3	
2. No		134	133		141	142	
3. ?		3	2		4	2	
27:A36 What anesthetic was administered at childbirth?[5]							
1. None		4	10	4	10		5

[5]In addition to the anesthetics specified, each of 18 different kinds or combinations of kinds was reported in both Study II and Study III by fewer than three of the informants represented in any one column in the table; 12 of these 18 were reported by the control and 7 by the experimental group respondents.

		Study II				Study III			
		Control Group (N = 50)		Experimental Group (N = 50)		Control Group (N = 150)		Experimental Group (N = 150)	
Item No.: IBM Card and Column No.	Item; or Question and Response Codings; or Computed Values	F	M	F	M	F	M	F	M
	2. ?		4		4		24		33
	3. "Spinal"		5		1		10		5
	4. "Gas"		13		12		33		52
	5. Ether		16		23		35		34
	6. "Twilight sleep"		5		3		5		4
	7. Chloroform		1		2		9		2
	8. "Gas" and ether		1		0		5		4
	9. Scopolamine						3		4
	10. Demerol and scopolamine						3		0
28:A37-38	Length of labor in hours								
	a. Minimum						1		1
	b. Maximum						96		72
	c. Mean						5.9		11.4
	d. Median								7.2
	e. 90th percentile						20.4		27.0
	f. N						148		140
29:A39	Was labor induced?								
	1. Yes						35		18
	2. No						111		122
	3. ?						2		7
30:A40	What was position of baby at birth?								
	1. Head first		45		45		138		128
	2. Feet first		1		0		2		0
	3. Breech (hip)		0		1		3		7
	4. Caesarean		2		3		5		7
	5. ?		2		1		1		7
	6. Head first but face reversed						0		1
	7. Caesarean in breech position						1		0
31:A41	Were instruments used?								
	1. Yes		14		7	30	39	28	43
	2. No		35		43	98	104	86	94
	3. ?		1			22	7	33	10

	C1	C2	C3	C4	C5	C6
32:A42 Were there any injuries to the baby?						
1. Yes	4	2	0	3	6	6
2. No	45	47	148	147	140	139
3. ?	1	1	2	0	4	5
33:A43 If yes, where?						
1. Back of head	1	0	0	1	1	0
2. Right side of head	1	0	0	1	1	0
3. Left side of head	0	0	0	0	2	3
4. Forehead	1	0	0	0	0	0
5. Face	0	2	0	0	0	1
6. Right eye muscle	1	0	0	0	1	1
7. Lung (adhered)	0	0	0	0	1	0
8. Neck muscle ruptured	0	0	0	1	0	0
9. Both sides of head	0	0	0	0	0	1
†10. ?	0	0	0	0	0	0
34:A44 If there was injury, how severe was it?						
1. Very severe	0	0	0	0	1	0
2. Moderately severe	1	0	0	1	1	2
3. Average	1	0	0	1	1	0
4. Mild	1	0	0	1	2	0
5. Of no importance	1	2	0	0	1	4
35:A45 Was the mother injured at the birth?						
1. Yes	3	9	1	4	0	4
2. No	46	40	148	146	140	139
3. ?	0	1	0	0	7	5
36:A46–48 Birth weight of baby (in pounds)						
a. Minimum	4.0	4.0	4.3			3.9
b. Maximum	9.6	11.1	10.7			10.1
c. Mean	7.2	7.3	7.4			7.4
d. Median		7.5	7.3			7.4
e. 90th percentile			8.8			8.7
f. N	50	49	150	150	140	146
37:A49 Was the child in question one of twins?						
1. Yes	1	2	0	0	0	0
2. No	49	47	150	150	140	149

Item No.: IBM Card and Column No.	Item; or Question and Response Codings; or Computed Values	Study II				Study III			
		Control Group (N = 50)		Experimental Group (N = 50)		Control Group (N = 150)		Experimental Group (N = 150)	
		F	M	F	M	F	M	F	M
	3. Yes, but other was lost during pregnancy				0		0		1
	†4. Twin supposedly miscarried at 3 months		0		1				
38:A50	If yes, was he the strong or the weak one?								
	1. Strong one	1		1	1				
	2. Weak one	0		1	0				
39:A51	Were the twins								
	1. Like-sexed; can't say whether identical or not (one of twin pair lost during pregnancy)								
	2. Not like-sexed					0	0	1	0
40-47[6]	Were any of the following noted at birth? (In Study II: "Were there any unusual circumstances or conditions connected with birth?" Informants were not asked whether any specific conditions had been present; the conditions reported by them were recorded. See Item 50.)								
40:A52	Cyanosis; blueness								
	1. Yes	0	0	0	0	4	6	3	7
	2. No					141	143	134	140
	3. ?					5	1	11	1
41:A53	Difficulty initiating breathing								
	1. Yes	1	1	0	2	4	9	3	3
	2. No					144	141	137	143
	3. ?					2	0	8	2

[6] Where the same wording applies to several items, underscoring indicates the inclusive item numbers and the wording to be repeated or understood in each.

42:A54 Umbilical cord around neck

1. Yes	0	0	1	1	1	1	2	2
2. No					135	145	140	145
3. ?					14	4	6	1

43:A55 Unusually quiet the first few days

1. Yes	0	0	0	0	9	8	1	5
2. No					124	135	141	138
3. ?					17	7	6	5

44:A56 Pulse slow

1. Yes	0	0	0	0	1	2	0	1
2. No					119	134	134	142
3. ?					30	14	14	5

45:A57 Pulse weak

1. Yes	0	0	0	0	0	4	0	1
2. No					122	137	134	142
3. ?					28	9	14	5

46:A58 Jaundice

1. Yes	1	1	2	3	1	4	1	5
2. No					145	144	141	141
3. ?					4	2	6	2

47:A59 Convulsions

1. Yes	0	0	0	0	0	0	1	0
2. No					148	149	142	147
3. ?					2	1	5	1

48:A60 Was there a history of RH incompatability?

1. Yes	0	1	15	11
2. No			127	130
3. ?			8	7

49:A61 How difficult was the labor?

1. Much more than average	5	6
2. Somewhat more than average	19	23
3. About average	59	70
4. Somewhat less than average	33	21
5. Much less than average	22	20
6. ?	7	5

11

Item No.: IBM Card and Column No.	Item; or Question and Response Codings; or Computed Values	Study II				Study III			
		Control Group (N = 50)		Experimental Group (N = 50)		Control Group (N = 150)		Experimental Group (N = 150)	
		F	M	F	M	F	M	F	M
50:A62-63	Were there any [other] unusual circumstances or conditions connected with the birth? If so, what were they?[7]								
	1. None	39	37	20	22	132	113	127	125
51:A64-65	What defects in the child were noted at birth or shortly after?[8]								
	1. None	4	0	6	0	134	128	127	121
	2. Birthmarks					3	1	4	4
	3. ?					0	0	2	2
	†4. Yes	5	9	6	11				
	†5. No	41	41	38	39				
52:A66	Does the parent attribute any weakness, ailment, or speech defect of the child to the circumstances of birth of the child?								
	1. Strongly believes or suspects direct or indirect causal relationship					3	3	2	4
	2. Believes no relationship, direct or indirect					133	137	137	137
	3. ?					0	1	6	3
53:A67	What does the other parent believe?								
	1. Strongly believes or suspects direct or indirect causal relationship					2	2	2	1

[7] There were 73 circumstances or conditions reported in both Studies II and III, each by fewer than three of the informants represented in any one column of the table; 44 of these 73 were reported by the control and 42 by the experimental group respondents. The word "other" was used only in Study III.

[8] In Study III there were 61 additional defects reported, each by fewer than three of the informants represented in any column in the table; 31 of these were reported by the control and 38 by the experimental group respondents. In Study II the wording of the question was "Were there any defects noted at birth or shortly thereafter?"

	(1)	(2)	(3)	(4)	(5)	(6)	(7)	(8)
2. Believes no relationship, direct or indirect					134	137	134	136
3. ?					0	2	9	7
54:A68 Was the child planned?								
1. Yes	27	30	34	30	85	78	82	77
2. No	21	17	14	18	63	69	63	67
3. ?	1	2	0	0	2	3	5	6
† 4. Adopted	1	1	2	2				
55:A69 Was the child wanted by both of you?[9]								
1. By both	48	48	47	45	145	140	142	136
2. By father only	1	0	1	1	3	2	1	2
3. By mother only	0	0	0	2	0	1	1	1
4. By neither	0	0	0	1	2	2	1	2
5. When born, but not before	0	1	1	0	0	4	2	4
6. When born, but not before by father								
7. ?	0	1			0	1		1
8. Not wanted when it was first learned wife was pregnant; when felt inevitable, dreaded not so much			1		0			
† 9. Would rather have had the child when younger				1			1	0
† 10. Wanted by both, but mother wanted a girl				1			0	0
56:A70-71 How long (in weeks) was the baby breast fed?								
a. Minimum[10]			1.5	-1			-1	-1
b. Maximum			42	46			42	34
c. Mean (excluding "never")			16.7	9.5			11.5	6.9
d. Median (excluding "never")							6.4	2.8
e. 90th percentile (excluding "never")							29.3	20.5
f. Never			13	19			54	60
g. N			48	50			150	147

[9] The words "by both of you" were not included in Study II.

[10] "_" indicates "less than."

Item No.: IBM Card and Column No.	Item; or Question and Response Codings; or Computed Values	Study II Control Group (N = 50)		Study II Experimental Group (N = 50)		Study III Control Group (N = 150)		Study III Experimental Group (N = 150)	
		F	M	F	M	F	M	F	M
57:A72-73	Why was bottle feeding adopted (most important reason)?[11]								
	1. ?					19	1	15	1
	2. Mother had insufficient milk		24		20	67	67	57	57
	3. Didn't want to be bothered		0		2	2	6	6	6
	4. Doctor's recommendation		5		6	15	15	14	12
	5. Mother ill		2		9	6	7	9	10
	6. Mother preferred it		1		1	12	10	7	6
	7. Child never bottle fed					10	11	4	4
	8. Milk not right; quality poor					4	4	3	4
	9. Milk supply diminished					4	2	7	11
	10. Sucking was painful to the mother					0	4	1	4
	11. Mother had difficulty breast feeding first child so preferred not to feed this child		0		4	1	1	4	5
	12. Mother too nervous					1	3	2	4
	13. Mother not able to (inverted nipples)		0		1	3	3	3	3
58:A74	Did you or the other parent hold the child during bottle feeding?								
	1. Yes		21		21	108	107	108	113
	2. No		3		20	9	11	14	10
	3. Sometimes held, sometimes did not					27	21	21	22
	4. ?		0			4	1	1	0
	5. Child held by someone other than parent				2	1	1	0	0
	6. Child not on bottle					1	1	0	0

[11] In both Study II and Study III there were 30 additional reasons reported, each by fewer than three of the informants represented in any one column of the table; 17 of these 30 were reported by the control and 20 by the experimental group respondents. Some respondents in Study II gave more than one response.

Item		C1	C2	C3	C4	C5	C6
	† 7. Some of both	14				4	3
	† 8. Nursed	0					3
59:A75-76	How old was the child (in months) when bottle feeding was replaced by cup feeding?[12]						
	a. Minimum	3	3	6			3
	b. Maximum	24	36	36			36
	c. Mean	10.7	10.5	11.3			10.3
	d. Median		9.4	11.8			10.6
	e. 90th percentile		14.5	18.7			14.5
	f. N	36	46	148			143
60:A77-78	What sorts of feeding problems did you meet at first?[13]						
	1. None	32	31	116	105	115	110
	2. Many changes of formula required	7	4	6	2	5	6
	3. Child refused milk	0	1	0	3	0	0
	4. Much throwing up	3	6	4	6	2	5
	5. Allergic to certain foods	1	3	0	3	1	2
	6. Didn't take as much as he should have			2	1	3	5
	7. Colic			1	3	8	2
	8. Some changes in formula required			5	4	3	0
	9. Difficult to satisfy in terms of amount	1	3	0	1	2	3
61:A79	In comparison with other babies, how much did the child cry during the first few weeks or months of its life?						
	1. Much more than average	6	2	4	7	3	11
	2. Somewhat more than average	9	11	12	18	17	22

12For purposes of computing the maximum and minimum values, means, medians, and 90th percentiles, the response "not replaced as yet," which was given for 3 control and 5 experimental group subjects, was excluded, as were the responses designated as "uncertain."

13In both Study II and Study III there were 49 additional problems reported, each by fewer than three of the informants represented in any one column of the table; 26 of these 49 were reported by the control and 28 by the experimental groups. Some respondents in Study II gave more than one response.

Item No.: IBM Card and Column No.	Item; or Question and Response Codings; or Computed Values	Study II Control Group (N = 50)		Study II Experimental Group (N = 50)		Study III Control Group (N = 150)		Study III Experimental Group (N = 150)	
		F	M	F	M	F	M	F	M
	3. About average		12		20	88	69	86	74
	4. Somewhat less than average		19		8	38	34	27	26
	5. Much less than average		3		8	6	22	10	15
	6. Uncertain		1		1	2	0	7	2
62:A80	What was the probable cause of the crying (main cause)?[14]								
	1. Uncertain		3		1	4	5	4	8
	2. Formula didn't agree		0		1	1	2	0	4
	3. Hungry, not fed often enough					1	8	2	2
	4. Colic		9		4	6	8	7	13
	5. Baby hungry; insufficient nourishment					1		1	3
	6. Very hot weather and the child developed diaper rash								
	†7. Hungry		15		9	1	0	3	1
	X. Unasked (crying not a significant problem)								
63-79 (odd)	Give age to nearest month of the following:		24		32	134	124	130	117
63:B6-7	First tooth								
	a. Minimum		3		2		2		1
	b. Maximum		10		10		13		18
	c. Mean		6.4		6.4		6.6		6.7
	d. Median				6.4		6.3		6.2
	e. 90th percentile						9.0		9.2
	f. N		46		46		143		147

[14] In both Studies II and III there were 29 additional causes reported, each by fewer than three of the informants represented in any one column of the table; 16 of these 29 were reported by the control and 13 by the experimental group respondents. Some respondents in Study II gave more than one response. Question No. 62 was asked only of the informants who gave a rating higher than "about average" in response to No. 61.

64:B8 Did you consider this to be:[15]				
1. Average			84	71
2. Early, precocious, advanced			26	40
3. Slow, retarded			37	36
4. ?			2	2
65:B9-10 Full set of 20 baby teeth				
a. Minimum	13	12	8	6
b. Maximum	36	54	42	48
c. Mean	16.1	27.4	22.5	22.4
d. Median			22.8	23.7
e. 90th percentile			33.0	28.9
f. N	34	19	80	92
66:B11 Did you consider this to be:				
1. Average			87	94
2. Early, precocious, advanced			26	29
3. Slow, retarded			23	20
4. ?			3	2
67:B12-13 Creeping (and, in Study II, or crawling)				
a. Minimum	5	5.5	5	4
b. Maximum	12	13	15	17
c. Mean	7.8	8.7	7.5	7.6
d. Median		9.0	7.8	7.8
e. 90th percentile			10.3	11.2
f. N	42	42	140	144
68:B14 Did you consider this to be:				
1. Average			87	83
2. Early, precocious, advanced			27	25
3. Slow, retarded			24	31
4. ?			4	1

[15] For all even-numbered items from 64 through 80 the number of informants responding was not limited, in any case, to the number who responded to the preceding item; if an informant did not give an exact age in response to any odd-numbered item, she was asked to indicate nevertheless whether she considered her child to be average, advanced, or retarded with reference to the aspect of development in question.

Item No.: IBM Card and Column No.	Item; or Question and Response Codings; or Computed Values	Study II Control Group (N = 50)		Study II Experimental Group (N = 50)		Study III Control Group (N = 150)		Study III Experimental Group (N = 150)	
		F	M	F	M	F	M	F	M
69:B15-16	Sitting up unsupported[16]								
	a. Minimum		4		4		3		3
	b. Maximum		10		10.5		15		12
	c. Mean		6.7		6.6		6.6		6.4
	d. Median				6.8		6.2		6.3
	e. 90th percentile						8.4		8.5
	f. N		44		46		137		137
70:B17	Did you consider this to be:								
	1. Average						98		93
	2. Early, precocious, advanced						23		35
	3. Slow, retarded						27		22
	4. ?						2		0
71:B18-19	First steps alone								
	a. Minimum		8		8		8		7
	b. Maximum		18		22		23		18
	c. Mean		11.9		12.9		12.0		12.3
	d. Median				13.3		11.7		12.0
	e. 90th percentile						14.4		15.1
	f. N		47		50		149		149
72:B20	Did you consider this to be:								
	1. Average						77		84
	2. Early, precocious, advanced						33		33
	3. Slow, retarded						39		33
	4. ?						1		0
73:B21-22	Voluntary control of bowels								
	a. Minimum		10		6		6		6
	b. Maximum		30		36		36		48
	c. Mean		17.6		18.4		20.4		20.0
	d. Median				18.3		20.1		18.1
	e. 90th percentile						30.3		30.5
	f. N		47		44		134		141

[16] In Study II this item was worded "Sitting alone."

74:B23	Did you consider this to be:				
	1. Average			71	63
	2. Early, precocious, advanced			24	37
	3. Slow, retarded			52	48
	4. ?			2	1
75:B24-25	Voluntary control of bladder, day				
	a. Minimum	11	9.5	6	6
	b. Maximum	36	48	42	54
	c. Mean	20.7	20.2	21.4	21.6
	d. Median		18.5	22.5	20.5
	e. 90th percentile			30.0	30.4
	f. N	47	47	142	140
76:B26	Did you consider this to be:				
	1. Average			75	60
	2. Early, precocious, advanced			31	42
	3. Slow, retarded			43	46
	4. ?			0	1
77:B27-28	Voluntary control of bladder, night				
	a. Minimum	9	6	3	8
	b. Maximum	36	108	66	72
	c. Mean	25.2	30.4	25.9	26.7
	d. Median		22.4	24.1	24.1
	e. 90th percentile			39.5	40.7
	f. N	46	42	124	119
78:B29	Did you consider this to be:				
	1. Average			60	54
	2. Early, precocious, advanced			43	46
	3. Slow, retarded			42	43
	4. ?			4	1
79:B30-31	Using spoon in feeding self				
	a. Minimum	5	6	5	7
	b. Maximum	30	24	36	36
	c. Mean	13.5	12.8	15.4	14.8
	d. Median		11.8	14.2	13.6
	e. 90th percentile			20.5	22.8
	f. N	42	43	130	129

Item No.: IBM Card and Column No.	Item; or Question and Response Codings; or Computed Values	Study II Control Group (N = 50) F	M	Study II Experimental Group (N = 50) F	M	Study III Control Group (N = 150) F	M	Study III Experimental Group (N = 150) F	M
80:B32	Did you consider this to be:								
	1. Average						99		93
	2. Early, precocious, advanced						27		27
	3. Slow, retarded						19		27
	4. ?						4		1
81-88	In each of the following activities rate your child's coordination (at present and as you have watched him developing, provided he engages in the activity):								
81:B33	Throwing								
	1. Superior	5	9	7	8	40	47	36	32
	2. Inferior	5	6	4	5	5	1	10	7
	3. Average	40	35	39	37	104	102	103	108
	4. ?					1	0	1	2
82:B34	Catching								
	1. Superior	3	9	4	4	23	15	16	17
	2. Inferior	6	8	8	12	18	9	23	27
	3. Average	40	33	38	34	104	122	106	98
	4. ?					3	3	3	3
83:B35	Drawing and coloring								
	1. Superior	14	18	13	13	50	46	50	48
	2. Inferior	4	8	7	8	7	14	6	15
	3. Average	32	24	29	29	88	85	89	86
	4. ?	0	0	1	0	5	0	5	1
84:B36	Writing								
	1. Superior	10	10	7	9	26	24	32	35
	2. Inferior	6	8	6	10	6	6	6	9
	3. Average	30	30	28	22	52	45	97	86
	4. ?					6	5	8	7
85:B37	Jumping								
	1. Superior	5	8	6	7	68	59	44	43

	1	2	3	4	5	6	7	8
2. Inferior	5	3	2	3	4	4	8	6
3. Average	40	39	40	40	78	86	97	96
4. ?	0	0	2	0	0	1	1	4
86:B38 Cutting, using scissors								
1. Superior	8	8	9	6	50	47	40	46
2. Inferior	5	6	2	6	3	6	5	6
3. Average	35	34	35	36	87	91	95	84
4. ?	0	0	1	0	5	3	2	4
87:B39 Running								
1. Superior	11	13	14	12	72	52	51	56
2. Inferior	3	3	3	4	7	3	8	7
3. Average	36	34	33	34	71	95	90	86
4. ?					0	0	1	1
88:B40 Manipulating blocks, tinker toys, beads, and other tasks requiring manual dexterity								
1. Superior	17	16	13	16	62	69	58	63
2. Inferior	2	4	3	1	3	2	0	1
3. Average	31	29	34	33	84	77	90	85
4. ?					1	2	2	1
89:B41-42 How old was the child (in months) when you began to train him in voluntary bladder control?								
a. Minimum	6		3				4	4
b. Maximum	24		24				32	30
c. Mean			12.5				15.1	13.5
d. Median	13.6		11.6				14.6	11.9
e. 90th percentile							23.8	18.4
f. N	49		46				144	148
90:B43-44 How old was the child (in months) when you began to train him in voluntary bowel control?								
a. Minimum	3		3				3	3
b. Maximum	24		24				36	24
c. Mean	12.6		11.1				13.0	11.8
d. Median			11.3				11.9	11.7
e. 90th percentile							23.0	18.2
f. N	49		46				148	144

Item No.: IBM Card and Column No.	Item; or Question and Response Codings; or Computed Values	Study II				Study III			
		Control Group (N = 50)		Experimental Group (N = 50)		Control Group (N = 150)		Experimental Group (N = 150)	
		F	M	F	M	F	M	F	M
91:B45-46	What did you do in trying to train the child for bowel control, to put the idea across to the child that you desired him to be trained?[17]								
	1. Nothing		2		1		3		4
	2. Set on when believed ready		3		5		50		29
	3. Praised for proper performance		17		33		7		1
	4. Took regularly at certain time						49		82
	5. Explained what was expected		2		11		2		0
	6. Put on chair; used suppositories						4		1
	7. Put on at certain time; used suppositories								
	8. Set on when believed ready; explained what was expected; praised for proper performance						4		1
	9. Set on when believed ready; made noise--"grunted"						3		2
	10. Took regularly; showed displeasure at accidents						6		10
	11. Took regularly; praised for proper performance						2		4
	12. Child watched sib--imitated sib								
	†13. Showed displeasure at accidents		6		25		5		2
	†14. Took regularly		36		32		4		0
	†15. Made noises		1		5				
	†16. Punished for accidents		5		7				
	†17. Shamed him		3		3				

[17] For both Studies II and III there were 23 other responses given, each by fewer than three of the informants represented in any one column of the table; 14 of these 23 were given by the control and 12 by the experimental group respondents. Some respondents in Study II gave more than one response. The phrase "in trying to train the child for bowel control" was omitted in Study II.

92:B47-48 — What did you do in trying to train the child for bladder control, to put the idea across to the child that you desired him to be trained?[18]

1. Nothing	1	1	7	5
2. Praised him for proper performance	13	29	5	2
3. Punished him for accidents	0	10	3	1
4. Took him regularly at certain time	38	30	63	85
5. Put him on when believed ready			21	19
6. Took him regularly; ran water			8	6
7. Took him regularly; placed small can under sink for him				
8. Praised for proper performance; showed displeasure for accidents; took him regularly			4	0
9. Showed him how (parent demonstrated)			3	1
10. Took him regularly; punished for accidents			1	3
11. Encouraged imitation of older sibling			0	3
12. Took him regularly; praised for proper performance			2	3
13. Watched sibling; imitated sibling			4	2
14. Showed displeasure at accidents	3	25	3	0
† 15. Showed him	3	5	1	1
† 16. Put him on at anticipated time	2	3		
† 17. Explained	1	8		

93:B49 — As compared with other children what was the child's reaction to toilet training?

1. Much more than average	7	4	5	9

[18] For both Studies II and III there were 58 other responses given, each by fewer than three of the informants represented in any one column of the table; 33 of these were given by the control and 29 by the experimental group respondents. Some respondents in Study II gave more than one response. The phrase "in trying to train the child for bladder control" was omitted in Study II.

Item No.: IBM Card and Column No.	Item; or Question and Response Codings; or Computed Values	Study II Control Group (N=50) F	M	Study II Experimental Group (N=50) F	M	Study III Control Group (N=150) F	M	Study III Experimental Group (N=150) F	M
	2. Somewhat more than average					23	23	17	18
	3. About average					65	70	89	76
	4. Somewhat less than average					37	39	22	26
	5. Much less than average					16	13	13	20
	6. ?					2	0	3	0
94:B50	How did you teach the child to use a crayon or pencil?								
	1. ?								
	2. Did nothing; child learned by himself					12	0	29	4
	3. Adult placed it in right hand					16	11	21	21
	4. Adult offered it toward right hand					12	19	38	34
	5. Adult placed it in center and let him choose hand to be used; offered child a choice					3	1	6	8
	6. Adult showed him, using the right hand (child to imitate parent's movements)					39	43	31	39
	7. Child imitated older sibling; learned from older sibling, older children					11	9	4	5
	8. Placed it in left hand					53	60	19	30
	9. Parent placed it on child's right side					0	1	0	0
	10. Parent placed pencil in right hand and moved hand					4	5	1	1
	11. Offered it toward left hand					0	1	1	4
	12. Told child to put it in right hand					0	0	0	1
	13. Learned in Sunday school					0	0	0	1
	14. Placed it on left side					0	0	0	1

95:B51 How did child react to this?

1. ?	15	5	35	11
2. No reaction; child followed adult's or sib's cues	20	29	50	63
3. Child shifted it to other hand immediately	1	4	1	1
4. Child had to be reminded several times to use hand the adult suggested	0	1	2	2
5. Child had to be reminded many times to use hand the adult suggested	1	0	3	0
6. Child followed adult's or sib's cues but occasionally shifted to other hand	9	4	9	7
7. Child took it with right hand	51	56	18	26
8. Child followed adult's or sib's cues but quite often shifted it to other hand	3	2	1	4
9. Child followed adult's or sib's cues but about half the time shifted it to other hand	6	3	1	2
10. Child picked it up with left hand	9	11	9	11
11. Child usually picked it up with right but occasionally with left hand	1	0	5	5
12. Child picked it up with right hand	18	18	6	6
13. Child usually picked it up with left but occasionally with right hand	0	0	0	1

96:B52 Child's original preference (crayon or pencil)

1. Very much right	36	52	59	73
2. Mostly right	59	48	22	18
3. Significantly mixed	16	8	14	13

Item No.: IBM Card and Column No. / Item; or Question and Response Codings; or Computed Values	Study II Control Group (N = 50) F	M	Study II Experimental Group (N = 50) F	M	Study III Control Group (N = 150) F	M	Study III Experimental Group (N = 150) F	M
4. Mostly left					13	10	9	10
5. Very much left					3	11	9	10
6. Not reasonably certain but think preferred right					12	6	30	21
7. Not reasonably certain but think preferred left					2	4	3	2
8. Not reasonably certain but think had no preference; significantly mixed					8	10	2	2
9. ?	1	1	0	0	0	0	2	1
†10. Right	38	38	32	37				
†11. Left	11	11	14	13				
97:B53 Which hand does he use now in handling a pencil or crayon?								
1. Very much right					93	109	113	106
2. Mostly right					36	19	18	23
3. Significantly mixed					4	3	3	3
4. Mostly left					4	5	6	4
5. Very much left					10	12	9	12
6. Not reasonably certain but think prefers right					2	1	0	0
7. Not reasonably certain but think has no preference; significantly mixed					0	1	0	1
8. ?					1	0	1	1
98:B54 How did you teach the child to use a spoon?[19]								
1. ?					13	0	24	3
2. Did nothing; child learned by himself					6	4	7	7

[19] There were 6 additional responses given, each by fewer than three of the informants represented in any one column of the table; all 6 were given by the control respondents and one by an experimental group respondent.

3. Adult placed spoon in right hand	44	59	66	62
4. Adult offered spoon toward right hand	17	6	10	10
5. Adult placed spoon in center and let him choose hand to be used; offered child a choice	37	48	29	42
6. Adult showed him, using the right hand (child to imitate parent's movements)	4	2	1	3
7. Child imitated older sibling; learned from older sibling, older children	18	11	4	4
8. Parent placed spoon on child's right side	2	6	2	2
9. Parent placed spoon in right hand and moved child's hand to mouth	7	7	6	15

99:B55 How did child react to this?

1. ?	15	2	26	2
2. No reaction; child followed adult's or sib's cues	22	20	50	59
3. Child shifted spoon to other hand immediately	2	8	6	8
4. Child had to be reminded several times to use hand the adult suggested	4	6	4	1
5. Child had to be reminded many times to use hand the adult suggested	2	3	1	3
6. Child followed adult's or sib's cues but occasionally shifted to other hand	11	6	12	13
7. Child took spoon with right hand	36	46	14	18
8. Child followed adult's or sib's cues but quite often shifted to other hand	3	3	3	4

Item No.: IBM Card and Column No.	Item; or Question and Response Codings; or Computed Values	Study II				Study III			
		Control Group (N = 50)		Experimental Group (N = 50)		Control Group (N = 150)		Experimental Group (N = 150)	
		F	M	F	M	F	M	F	M
	9. Child followed adult's or sib's cues but about half the time shifted to other hand					8	8	6	3
	10. Child picked up spoon with left hand					10	8	6	11
	11. Child usually picked up spoon with right hand but occasionally with left hand					2	2	15	13
	12. Child picked up spoon with right hand					18	20	7	14
	13. Child usually picked up spoon with left hand but occasionally with right hand					0	0	0	1
100:B56	Child's original preference (spoon)								
	1. Very much right					23	48	52	58
	2. Mostly right					58	47	18	24
	3. Significantly mixed					18	15	22	20
	4. Mostly left					13	12	8	11
	5. Very much left					4	9	8	11
	6. Not reasonably certain but think preferred right					16	4	30	17
	7. Not reasonably certain but think preferred left					3	2	4	5
	8. Not reasonably certain but think had no preference; significantly mixed					9	13	4	3
	9. ?					6	0	4	1
101:B57	Which hand does he use now in eating with a spoon?								
	1. Very much right					101	115	109	109
	2. Mostly right					30	15	23	22
	3. Significantly mixed					3	5	2	2

4. Mostly left	3	4	6	3
5. Very much left	12	11	10	13
6. Not reasonably certain but think prefers right	1	0	0	0
7. Not reasonably certain but think has no preference; significantly mixed	0	0	0	1
102:B58 If left-handed preference was shown at first, in either of above usages, what did you do when he showed this preference?				
1. ?	1	1	1	0
2. Acceptance; no attempt to change	16	11	18	24
3. Some unsuccessful efforts to change	5	7	4	1
4. Tried hard but without success to change	0	1	0	2
5. Forced child to change over, with ease	3	2	2	0
6. Nothing	0	3	2	3
7. Parent effected change-over by changing position at table favoring right hand	0	2	0	1
103:B59 What did the other parent do?				
1. ?	2	3	1	1
2. Acceptance; no attempt to change	12	10	17	21
3. Some unsuccessful efforts to change	6	4	4	0
4. Tried hard but without success to change	0	2	0	2
5. Forced child to change over, with ease	4	1	3	1
6. Forced child to change over, with difficulty	0	0	1	1
7. Nothing	1	6	1	5
8. Parent effected change-over by changing position at table favoring right hand	0	1	0	0

Item No.: IBM Card and Column No.	Item; or Question and Response Codings; or Computed Values	Study II Control Group (N = 50)		Study II Experimental Group (N = 50)		Study III Control Group (N = 150)		Study III Experimental Group (N = 150)	
		F	M	F	M	F	M	F	M
104:B60	Has child's handedness ever been changed in other respects at that time or since? If yes, why?								
	1. No	42	42	40	41	149	149	150	148
	2. Yes, reason not given	1	0	2	0	0	0	0	1
	3. Purposeful change made because parents thought it best	0	0	3	3	0	0	0	1
	4. Yes, because arm or collarbone broken	0	1	0	1	1	0	0	0
	5. ?	7	5	1	1	0	1	0	0
	†6. Voluntary change	0	2	4	4				
105:B63	Have the child's hands (either or both) ever been bandaged, tied up, or restrained in any way? If yes, why?[20]								
	1. No	44	45	39	39	129	120	128	132
	2. Injury to arm or hand	2	3	3	5	9	11	4	3
	3. Done purposely to discourage existing handedness	0	0	0	0	1	1	0	0
	4. For sucking fingers or thumb	3	2	0	2	7	11	8	7
	5. Burned right or left hand			2	5	2	4	6	4
	6. Impetigo, infections, infectious diarrhea, eczema, to prevent child from touching bandages					1	3	3	4
	7. ?	0	0	0	1	1	3	3	4
	†8. Yes	6	5	11	10	0	0	1	0

[20] In Study II this item was administered as two questions, the first of which could be answered by yes, no, or ?, and the total for these responses is 50 in each column; the other question in Study II was concerned with the purposes of bandaging and was asked only of those who gave a yes answer to the first question.

106:B64-65 For how long was this done? (in weeks)[21]							
a. Mean	3.0	3.0	3.9	3.1	2.3	2.4	2.7
b. Median				2.3	2.3	2.0	2.5
c. N	4	4	10	21	29	21	17
107:B66 Has the child ever written backwards (not backhand) to any significant degree (so writing would have to be held up to a mirror to be read)?							
1. Yes	6	6	3	5	8	3	8
2. No	42	42	41	41	40	43	43
3. ?	2	2	0	0	0	3	0
4. Child has not learned to write				103	101	101	99
108:B67 What is your opinion of left-handedness? Should it be discouraged?[22]							
1. Should be discouraged absolutely	0	0	0	3	0	5	3
2. Should probably be discouraged	0	2	0	13	11	10	6
3. Probably a handicap, but shouldn't be discouraged	11	7	13	16	15	22	26
4. Doesn't make any difference	35	35	37	48	44	86	77
5. Should be encouraged or trained if child prefers it	4	6	0	68	76	25	35
6. No opinion	0	0	0	1	2	0	1
7. ?				0	1	1	
8. Useless to discourage because won't succeed in changing handedness			1	1	1	0	0
9. Child should be significantly mixed			0	0	0	1	0
109:B68 What is the other parent's opinion of it?							
1. Should be discouraged absolutely	0	1	1	3	2	6	5
2. Should probably be discouraged	2	0	1	12	13	14	8

[21]One mother in each group in Study III stated that her child had had his hand bandaged for one year--off and on; these responses were not included in the tabulation.

[22]"Should it be discouraged?" was not included in Study II.

31

Item No.: IBM Card and Column No.	Item; or Question and Response Codings; or Computed Values	Study II Control Group (N = 50) F	M	Study II Experimental Group (N = 50) F	M	Study III Control Group (N = 150) F	M	Study III Experimental Group (N = 150) F	M
	3. Probably a handicap, but shouldn't be discouraged	4	2	9	5	11	12	21	14
	4. Doesn't make any difference	34	34	29	30	50	46	79	76
	5. Should be encouraged or trained if child prefers it	5	5	1	0	58	63	21	28
	6. No opinion	3	6	8	13	4	2	0	2
	7. ?					10	11	9	17
	8. Useless to discourage because won't succeed in changing handedness					2	1	0	0
	9. Child should be significantly mixed					0	0	0	0
110:B69	Do you believe there is any relation between the child's handedness and his developing (or failure to develop) stuttering?								
	1. Strongly believes direct causal relationship			0	0	5	6	2	2
	2. Suspects there may be direct causal relationship			1	1	16	17	6	8
	3. Strongly believes indirect causal relationship			1	0	5	12	2	6
	4. Suspects there may be indirect causal relationship			2	2	42	41	15	20
	5. Believes no relationship, direct or indirect			44	42	62	51	86	90
	6. ?			2	5	20	23	39	24
111:B70	What does the other parent believe?								
	1. Strongly believes direct causal relationship			0	0	4	4	1	3
	2. Suspects there may be direct causal relationship			1	1	15	14	9	4

	Col1	Col2	Col3	Col4	Col5	Col6
3. Strongly believes indirect causal relationship	4	1	7	3	0	0
4. Suspects there may be indirect casual relationship	18	14	31	32	2	0
5. Believes no relationship, direct or indirect	83	81	43	54	40	39
6. ?	38	44	51	42	6	10

112-119 Beyond what age, in months, would you be alarmed if a child did not:

112:B71-72 Walk alone?

	Col1	Col2	Col3	Col4
a. Minimum	12	9	12	9
b. Maximum	30	36	28	60
c. Mean	17.5	17.2	18.0	18.4
d. Median	17.7	17.7	17.8	17.6
e. 90th percentile	23.3	23.3	23.0	23.9
f. N	150	148	150	148

113:B73-74 Have bowel control?

	Col1	Col2	Col3	Col4
a. Minimum	8	9	9	12
b. Maximum	60	72	60	72
c. Mean	25.9	25.4	28.6	28.1
d. Median	23.0	22.9	26.9	24.2
e. 90th percentile	35.3	35.9	36.2	36.3
f. N	148	142	149	141

114:B75-76 Have daytime bladder control?

	Col1	Col2	Col3	Col4
a. Minimum	12	9	9	12
b. Maximum	60	72	60	60
c. Mean	27.3	25.7	30.2	29.4
d. Median	24.1	22.9	29.5	23.0
e. 90th percentile	35.9	35.9	36.5	39.5
f. N	148	144	149	143

115:B77-78 Have nighttime bladder control?

	Col1	Col2	Col3	Col4
a. Minimum	12	9	12	12
b. Maximum	120	132	120	144
c. Mean	37.6	37.7	43.2	43.4
d. Median	34.7	34.1	35.9	35.2
e. 90th percentile	54.5	58.1	67.5	69.5
f. N	146	144	148	140

33

Item No.: IBM Card and Column No.	Item; or Question and Response Codings; or Computed Values	Study II				Study III			
		Control Group (N = 50)		Experimental Group (N = 50)		Control Group (N = 150)		Experimental Group (N = 150)	
		F	M	F	M	F	M	F	M
116:B79-80	Speak words?								
	a. Minimum					6	6	6	8
	b. Maximum					48	48	60	48
	c. Mean					22.2	22.8	20.3	18.7
	d. Median					23.6	23.8	18.3	18.0
	e. 90th percentile					28.7	24.2	31.7	33.5
	f. N					147	149	146	150
117:C6-7	Speak sentences?								
	a. Minimum					10	12	10	12
	b. Maximum					84	60	60	60
	c. Mean					30.8	30.2	30.7	28.4
	d. Median					28	28	28	27.5
	e. 90th percentile					41.6	36.3	43	35.5
	f. N					147	148	145	150
118:C8-9	Speak intelligibly, so he can be clearly understood?								
	a. Minimum					10	15	14	18
	b. Maximum					78	72	72	90
	c. Mean					38.3	40.5	41.4	38.7
	d. Median					36	36	41	36
	e. 90th percentile					52.5	56.8	57	54.5
	f. N					149	149	146	150
119:C10-11	Speak fluently, without hesitation or repetition?								
	a. Minimum					16	18	18	24
	b. Maximum					144	120	120	120
	c. Mean					53.1	52.2	54.9	48.9
	d. Median					48	48	60	48
	e. 90th percentile					68.9	68.9	79.4	69.5
	f. N					142	143	149	138

120:C12 How carefully have you studied the age norms for these activities?

1. Very carefully studied	11	22	3	12	3	12
2. Read repeatedly	6	7	14	38	4	36
3. Read them once or twice or heard them	22	14	62	75	51	79
4. Never read them or heard them presented systematically	11	6	71	25	92	23

121:C13 What do you believe these norms represent? What do they mean?

1. Age at which a normal child must do it	1	4	5	2	11	6
2. Average age, allowing some variation	34	23	87	97	88	113
3. A rough indication, at best	14	17	14	17	6	6
4. ?	1	6	10	5	22	8
5. Age at which average or normal child should do it			30	27	21	15
6. Other responses			4	2	2	2

122:C14 How helpful were these norms to you in rearing the child?

1. Essential	7	9	9	16	8	16
2. Rather helpful	17	24	45	73	28	54
3. Could have done without them; not helpful	25	9	34	29	31	53
4. Disturbing; source of worry or befuddlement	1	2	2	2	1	4
5. No connection, unaware of norms, never thought about them	0	6	60	30	80	23
6. ?			0	0	2	0

123:C15 How consistently did you compare your child's development with these norms?

1. Often	4	9	34	45	16	44
2. Seldom or occasionally	38	28	55	80	57	78
3. Never	8	9	61	25	77	28

Item No.: IBM Card and Column No.	Item; or Question and Response Codings; or Computed Values	Study II				Study III			
		Control Group (N = 50)		Experimental Group (N = 50)		Control Group (N = 150)		Experimental Group (N = 150)	
		F	M	F	M	F	M	F	M
124:C16	How did the child usually compare with the norms?								
	1. Consistently advanced		8		6	45	36	31	24
	2. About average most of the time		35		28	65	84	50	95
	3. Consistently retarded		2		7	11	17	15	14
	4. ?		5		9	17	13	54	17
125*	What illnesses did the child have before (more than one month before) the onset of stuttering?23								
	1. None					45	45	33	33
	2. Measles						35		50
	3. Chicken pox						32		35
	4. Mumps						11		12
	5. Whooping cough						1		7
	6. Pneumonia						9		.6
	7. Tonsillitis						8		23

23In reporting the findings of Study II, Darley stated: "No significant differences were found between the groups of children with regard to incidence of the five most commonly reported infectious childhood diseases; [or with regard to] incidence of tonsillectomies, adenoidectomies, or total operations . ." (11, p. 88). In Study III questions 125 through 148 were addressed to both parents in each case, but approximately 5 to 25 per cent of the fathers were unable to give reasonably clear answers, particularly with reference to the time of specific illnesses in relation to the onset of stuttering, and so the presumably more trustworthy responses of the mothers are given in the table. See Chapter 3 for further explanation of items 125-148. For all odd-numbered items from 125 through 155 only those responses are listed which were reported by three or more of the mothers in one or both groups; for the odd-numbered items 149-155 the additional responses are summarized in footnotes. For all even-numbered items from 126 through 148 the responses of informants who could specify the number of illnesses, their children had, but could not state definitely that they had had them within the period in question, are classified as "Undetermined"; the numbers of informants giving indicated frequencies of such responses are shown under 148A. Informants who could not specify the number of illnesses or the dates of them, but who did assert that their children had had illnesses, are represented under 148B, and these indefinite and undated responses are not included in the other tabulations found in 126 through 148C. For each control group child the age used as the point of reference is that corresponding to the age of onset of stuttering for the matched experimental group child. See also Table 6 in text.

8. Influenza	9	5
9. Convulsions	2	4
10. Ear infection	17	13
11. Asthma	3	4
12. Bronchitis	12	9
13. Diarrhea (infectious)	4	8
14. Colic	2	4
15. Croup	4	2
16. Throat infection	10	5
17. German measles	11	3
18. Virus infection	3	1
19. Roseola	2	3

126:C17 Total number of illnesses before (more than one month before) onset of stuttering

1. None	39	33
2. One	53	42
3. Two	20	35
4. Three	17	21
5. Four	8	6
6. Five	2	4
7. Six	4	6
8. Seven	0	1
9. Eight	0	1
10. Nine	1	0
11. Undetermined	6	1

127* What illnesses did the child have just before (one month before or less) or at onset of stuttering?

1. None	133	133
2. Measles	0	5
3. Influenza	3	1

128:C18 Total number of illnesses just before (one month before or less) or at onset of stuttering

1. None	133	133
2. One	8	13

37

Item No.: IBM Card and Column No.	Item; or Question and Response Codings; or Computed Values	Study II Control Group (N = 50) F	M	Experimental Group (N = 50) F	M	Study III Control Group (N = 150) F	M	Experimental Group (N = 150) F	M
	3. Two						1		1
	4. Three						0		2
	5. Undetermined						8		1
129*	What illnesses did the child have within one month after onset of stuttering?								
130:C19	Total number of illnesses within one month after onset of stuttering								
	1. None					133		139	
	(2. One)						8		8
	(3. Two)						1		1
	(4. Three)						0		1
	(5. Undetermined)						8		1
131*	What other illnesses has the child had since one month after onset of stuttering?								
	1. None						68		69
	2. Measles						34		21
	3. Chicken pox						24		26
	4. Mumps						8		8
	5. Scarlet fever						5		1
	6. Pneumonia						3		4
	7. Tonsillitis						10		10
	8. Influenza						10		6
	9. Ear infection						10		14
	10. Asthma						6		2
	11. Throat infection						6		5
	12. German measles						5		0
132:C20	Total number of illnesses since one month after onset of stuttering								
	1. None					68		69	

2. One	37	46
3. Two	26	13
4. Three	5	11
5. Four	5	5
6. Five	3	0
7. Six	2	4
8. Seven	1	1
9. Undetermined	3	1

133* Did he have any severe illnesses before (more than one month before) the onset of stuttering? Which ones?

1. None	116	109
2. Measles	6	9
3. Chicken pox	3	4
4. Pneumonia	3	5
5. Tonsillitis	2	6
6. Ear infection	2	4
7. Bronchitis	1	4
8. Diarrhea (infectious)	2	4
9. Virus infection	3	0

134:C21 Total number of severe illnesses before (more than one month before) onset of stuttering

1. None	116	109
2. One	31	27
3. Two	2	9
4. Three	1	0
5. Four	0	4
6. Undetermined	0	1

135* Did he have any severe illnesses just before (one month before or less) or at the onset of stuttering? Which ones?

1. None	147	143
2. Tonsillitis	0	3

136:C22 Total number of severe illnesses just before (one month before or less) or at the onset of stuttering

1. None	147	143

Item No.: IBM Card and Column No.	Item; or Question and Response Codings; or Computed Values	Study II Control Group (N = 50) F	M	Study II Experimental Group (N = 50) F	M	Study III Control Group (N = 150) F	M	Study III Experimental Group (N = 150) F	M
	2. One						3		5
	3. Two						0		1
	4. Undetermined						0		1
137*	Did the child have any severe illnesses within one month after onset of stuttering? Which ones?								
	1. None						147		147
138:C23	Total number of severe illnesses within one month after onset of stuttering								
	1. None						147		147
	2. One						3		1
	3. Two						0		1
	4. Undetermined						0		1
139*	Has the child had any severe illnesses since one month after onset? Which ones?								
	1. None						137		121
	2. Measles						5		7
	3. Tonsillitis						2		4
	4. Ear infection						0		5
140:C24	Total number of severe illnesses since one month after onset of stuttering								
	1. None						137		121
	2. One						10		23
	3. Two						2		2
	4. Three						1		1
	5. Four						0		2
	6. Undetermined						0		1

141*   Did the child have unusually high fever (103° and over) in connection with any illness before (more than one month before) the onset of stuttering? Which illnesses?

1. None	82	81
2. Measles	18	14
3. Chicken pox	5	2
4. Pneumonia	7	5
5. Tonsillitis	5	14
6. Influenza	5	3
7. Ear infection	7	9
8. Bronchitis	6	4
9. Diarrhea (infectious)	1	3
10. Throat infection	7	2
11. Cold	3	6
12. German measles	4	1
13. Strep throat	1	3

142:C25 Total number of illnesses with unusually high fever (103° and over) before (more than one month before) onset of stuttering

1. None	82	81
2. One	50	46
3. Two	8	9
4. Three	4	5
5. Four	1	4
6. Five	0	4
7. Seven	1	0
8. Eight	2	0
9. Undetermined	2	1
	146	142

143*   Did the child have unusually high fever (103° and over) in connection with any illness just before (one month before or less) or at onset of stuttering? Which illnesses?

1. None

41

Item No.: IBM Card and Column No.	Item; or Question and Response Codings; or Computed Values	Study II Control Group (N = 50)		Study II Experimental Group (N = 50)		Study III Control Group (N = 150)		Study III Experimental Group (N = 150)	
		F	M	F	M	F	M	F	M
144:C26	Total number of illnesses with high fever (103° and over) just before (one month before or less) or at onset of stuttering								
	1. None						146		142
	2. One						1		6
	3. Two						0		1
	4. Undetermined						3		1
145*	Did the child have unusually high fever (103° and over) in connection with any illness within one month after onset of stuttering? Which illnesses?								
	1. None						143		145
146:C27	Total number of illnesses with high fever (103° and over) within one month after onset of stuttering								
	1. None						143		145
	2. One						4		3
	3. Two						0		1
	4. Undetermined						3		1
147*	Has the child had unusually high fever (103° and over) in connection with any illness since one month after onset of stuttering? Which illnesses?								
	1. None						108		106
	2. Measles						13		10
	3. Chicken pox						6		2
	4. Scarlet fever						3		2
	5. Pneumonia						1		3
	6. Tonsillitis						4		7

7. Influenza	5	3
8. Ear infection	8	8
9. Throat infection	3	4
10. Cold	0	4

148:C28 Total number of illnesses with high fever (103° and over) since one month after onset of stuttering

1. None	108	106
2. One	28	29
3. Two	5	5
4. Three	3	5
5. Four	2	1
6. Five	1	1
7. Six	0	1
8. Eight	0	1
9. Undetermined	3	1

148A Number of undated illnesses (each informant reporting could give the number of illnesses the child had had but could not date them)

1. None	137	148
2. One	5	1
3. Two	0	2
4. Three	1	1
5. Eight	1	0
6. Nine	1	0
7. More than nine	3	0

148B Number of informants who stated that the child had been ill but could not give the number of illnesses or their dates

1. Yes	11	1
2. No	139	149

148C Total number of illnesses and recurrences of illnesses that were dated or coded "U" (informant could give number

43

Item No.: IBM Card and Column No.	Item; or Question and Response Codings; or Computed Values	Study II				Study III			
		Control Group (N = 50)		Experimental Group (N = 50)		Control Group (N = 150)		Experimental Group (N = 150)	
		F	M	F	M	F	M	F	M
	of illnesses but could not date them); this tabulation does not include responses summarized in 148B								
	1. None						12		13
	2. One						37		25
	3. Two						28		31
	4. Three						23		30
	5. Four						20		20
	6. Five						13		11
	7. Six						4		5
	8. Seven						2		4
	9. Eight						3		5
	10. Nine						3		3
	11. Eleven						1		1
	12. Fifteen or more						4		2
149:C29	What operations did the child have before (more than one month before) onset of stuttering?[24]								
	1. None					132	132	129	130
	2. Adenoidectomy					3	0	2	2
	3. Tonsillectomy and adenoidectomy					4	5	8	9
150:C30	What operations did the child have just before (one month before or less) or at onset of stuttering?[25]								
	1. None					150	150	148	149

[24] There were 20 additional responses given, each by fewer than three of the informants represented in any one column of the table; 14 of these 20 were reported by the control and 9 by the experimental group respondents. Also, one control mother and one control father reported the operation "medotomy," for which we have no definition.
[25] One operation was reported by each of three experimental group respondents.

151:C31	What operations did the child have within one month after onset of stuttering?[26]				
	1. None	150	150	148	148
152:C32	What operations has the child had since one month after onset of stuttering?[27]				
	1. None	139	137	128	128
	2. Tonsillectomy	1	0	4	5
	3. Tonsillectomy and adenoidectomy	8	9	16	14
153:C33-34	What injuries did the child have before (more than one month before) onset of stuttering?[28]				
	1. None	114	108	127	123
	2. Injury to head	8	12	4	6
	3. Fell on chin	3	1	0	0
	4. Cut lip	1	3	2	1
	5. Cut finger	1	3	2	2
	6. Child burned	3	2	2	0
154:C35-36	What injuries did the child have just before (one month before or less) or at onset of stuttering?[29]				
	1. None	145	147	149	148
155:C37-38	What injuries did the child have within one month after onset of stuttering?[30]				
	1. None	146	148	148	150

[26] Two operations were reported by experimental group respondents.

[27] There were 8 additional operations reported, each by fewer than three of the informants represented in any one of the columns of the table; 4 of these 8 operations were reported by the control and 5 by the experimental group respondents.

[28] There were 41 additional injuries reported, each by fewer than three of the informants represented in any one column of the table; 28 of these 41 were reported by the control and 19 by the experimental group respondents.

[29] There were 8 additional injuries reported, each by fewer than three of the informants represented in any one column of the table; 5 of these 8 were reported by the control and 3 by the experimental group respondents.

[30] There were 4 additional injuries reported, each by fewer than three of the informants represented in any one column of the table; 3 of these 4 were reported by the control and 2 by the experimental group respondents.

Item No.: IBM Card and Column No.	Item; or Question and Response Codings; or Computed Values	Study II				Study III			
		Control Group (N = 50) F	M	Experimental Group (N = 50) F	M	Control Group (N = 150) F	M	Experimental Group (N = 150) F	M
156:C39-40	What injuries has the child had since one month after onset of stuttering?[31]								
	1. None					129	120	135	132
	2. Injury to head (banged head)					3	6	2	2
	3. Severe cut over eye					3	2	0	1
	4. Cut forehead					3	1	0	0
157:C41	How often does the child have colds?								
	1. Less often than once a year						0		7
	2. Once or twice a year						63		67
	3. Three to five times a year						69		62
	4. Six to ten times a year						15		14
	5. More than ten times a year						3		0
158:C42-43	Present height (in inches)								
	a. Minimum	36			34		33		34
	b. Maximum	65			68		52		54
	c. Mean	52.3			52.0		42.9		43.3
	d. Median						43.9		43.2
	e. 90th percentile						48.4		49.7
	f. N	44			45		149		129
159:C44	Evaluation of present height (based on charts prepared by Department of Pedi- atrics, University of Iowa, from data compiled by the Iowa Child Welfare Research Station, 1943)								
	1. More than 1 S.D. above mean						30		43
	2. Between 1 S.D. above mean and mean						35		28
	3. At mean						7		7
	4. Between 1 S.D. below mean and mean						44		24
	5. More than 1 S.D. below mean						32		27

31There were 41 additional injuries reported, each by fewer than three of the informants represented in any one column of the table; 25 of these 41 were reported by the control and 21 by the experimental group respondents.

Item	Category	1	2	3	4	5	6	7	8
160:C45-46	**Present weight (in pounds)**								
	a. Minimum					36	25	27	25
	b. Maximum					125	130	72	76
	c. Mean					70.1	69.8	42.6	43.9
	d. Median							39.6	42.3
	e. 90th percentile							55.1	59.3
	f. N							144	143
161:C47	**Evaluation of present weight (based on charts referred to under Item 159)**					47	49		
	1. More than 1 S.D. above mean							25	36
	2. Between 1 S.D. above mean and mean							50	48
	3. At mean							5	6
	4. Between 1 S.D. below mean and mean							38	33
	5. More than 1 S.D. below mean							26	20
162:C48	**In your opinion, how well developed physically is the child now?**								
	1. Very rugged; well developed	12	7	11	12	69	64	61	54
	2. Normal physique	23	33	26	25	53	57	69	69
	3. Tall and thin	8	3	2	2	4	2	8	6
	4. Obese, overweight	2	1	1	4	1	1	2	4
	5. Frail; retarded development	1	3	7	4	0	0	1	3
	6. Small and/or thin					23	26	9	14
	†7. A little small; rather thin, or tall	3	2	2	3				
163:C49	**At times when the child has been ill, how much attention did he get?**								
	1. Casually attended to			5	1	2	9	3	1
	2. Good care but not constant			27	20	111	103	78	82
	3. Waited on constantly			7	17	29	25	38	36
	4. Spoiled and indulged excessively			11	9	5	8	25	23
	5. No need for attention, never sick in bed					3	5	6	7
164:C50	**After such care, how quickly did the child readjust?**								
	1. Immediately			4	1	80	79	111	103
	2. Gradually			7	6	27	27	22	25
	3. No readjustment necessary			39	40	36	38	14	21

Item No.: IBM Card and Column No.	Item; or Question and Response Codings; or Computed Values	Study II Control Group (N=50) F	M	Study II Experimental Group (N=50) F	M	Study III Control Group (N=150) F	M	Study III Experimental Group (N=150) F	M
	4. Sometimes immediately, sometimes gradually					4	2	1	0
	5. ?		0		3	3	4	2	1
165:C51-52	Does the child now have any physical defect?[32]								
	1. None		48		44	132	128	122	123
	2. Flat-footed		1		2	6	7	4	2
	3. Eye condition					2	3	2	6
	4. One eye slightly crossed					0	0	3	3
166:C53	Does he wear glasses? Or has he ever worn them?								
	1. Yes		9		12	2	2	6	6
	2. No		40		37	0	0	4	4
	3. Has worn them		1		1	0	0	1	1
	4. Has never worn them					148	148	139	139
167:C54-55	If yes, for what cause?[33]								
	1. Astigmatism		5		3				
	2. Mildly nearsighted		2		1				
168:C56	Does the child have any hearing difficulty?								
	1. No		47		49	146	146	144	142
	2. Suspected but not confirmed		0		1	2	2	2	6
	3. Yes, mild		1		0	1	2	3	0

[32] For both Studies II and III there were 40 additional defects reported, each by fewer than three of the informants represented in any one column of the table; 17 of these 40 were reported by the control and 26 by the experimental group respondents. Some respondents in Study III gave more than one response. Four experimental group fathers gave "stuttering" as a response to this question.

[33] For both Studies II and III there were 9 additional causes reported, each by fewer than three of the informants represented in any one column of the table; 6 of these 9 were reported by the control and 3 by the experimental group respondents. Some respondents in Study II gave more than one response.

	C1	C2	C3	C4	C5	C6
4. Yes, severe without aid	0	0	0	0	1	1
5. Yes, when he has a cold						
†6. Uncertain	2	0	1	0	0	0
169:C57 How is the child's appetite now?						
1. Good	38	32	94	94	86	82
2. Fair	9	14	32	36	34	38
3. Poor	2	2	11	9	18	21
4. Variable	1	2	13	11	12	9
170:C58 How well does the child sleep?						
1. Very well	41	35	125	119	93	80
2. Average, fair	9	11	22	25	45	52
3. Poorly	0	4	2	4	11	13
4. Variable			1	2	1	5
171:C59 How many hours' sleep does the child get per night on the average?						
a. Minimum	7	8			8	7
b. Maximum	12	12			14	14
c. Mean	9.5	10.3			10.9	10.9
d. Median	10	10			11	11
e. 90th percentile	12	11			12	12
f. N	49	50			150	150
172:C60 Does the child sleep alone or not?						
1. Yes	43	40	127			122
2. With one other child	4	8	17			13
3. With two other children	2	0	0			0
4. With one parent	0	1	4			4
5. With someone else	0	0	0			1
6. With one parent and one child			0			1
7. Indefinite	0	0	2			
†8. Starts each night alone, but mother spends part of almost every night (2:00–6:00 a.m.) in child's bed	0	1				
†9. Yes, but ends up in parents' bed	1	0				9

Item No.: IBM Card and Column No.	Item; or Question and Response Codings; or Computed Values	Study II Control Group (N = 50)		Study II Experimental Group (N = 50)		Study III Control Group (N = 150)		Study III Experimental Group (N = 150)	
		F	M	F	M	F	M	F	M
173:C63	How particular is the child about his food?[34]								
	1. Eats everything		15		13	24	23	16	19
	2. Eats practically everything, one or two dislikes		22		14	92	90	96	94
	3. Many dislikes		12		20	28	32	34	30
	4. Extremely hard to please, likes only one or two things		1		3	6	5	4	7
174:C64	In comparison with other children, how much energy does the child have?								
	1. Much more than average	2	5	11	10	28	21	34	26
	2. Somewhat more than average	22	24	24	22	73	61	57	49
	3. About average	22	17	12	17	47	66	50	64
	4. Somewhat less than average	4	4	3	1	2	1	7	11
	5. Much less than average	0	0	0	0	0	1	2	0
175:C65	In comparison with other children, how much energy did the child have just before (within one month before) or at the onset of stuttering?								
	1. Much more than average					24	22	32	27
	2. Somewhat more than average					66	50	54	45
	3. About average					55	70	51	65
	4. Somewhat less than average					2	7	10	12
	5. Much less than average					1	1	2	1
	6. ?					2	0	1	0

34 A related question--"What kinds of feeding problems do you have with him now?"--was included in the interview, but, presented in relation to item 173, no response to it was obtained from approximately four fifths of the control and half of the experimental group parents. The responses obtained from the other informants do not warrant detailed presentation.

176* What is the usual mood of the child?[35]								
1. Usually happy, affectionate, good-natured, jolly, pleasant, cheerful, contented, easygoing, jovial, sunny, placid, etc.	36	36	44	39	132	134	115	128
2. Cranky, sensitive, impatient, moody, quick-tempered, teasing, devilish, irritable, etc.	4	5	21	17	11	16	12	17
3. Very excitable, nervous, tense, energetic	5	5	37	40	6	2	6	3
4. Neutral, even-keeled, quiet, reserved, daydreamy, serious	17	23	11	17	11	15	11	9
177:C66 How much do you worry about the child's health?								
1. A great deal; practically all the time	0	0	3	1	10	8	3	10
2. Quite a lot	3	6	2	8	12	13	17	24
3. Not much	7	13	3	7	45	45	41	31
4. Only when the child is sick	39	31	42	34	83	84	89	85
178:C67 How much does your wife (husband) worry about the child's health?								
1. A great deal; practically all the time	0	1	5	1	13	6	6	10
2. Quite a lot	7	1	3	4	19	18	33	20
3. Not much	12	11	5	4	51	42	39	32
4. Only when the child is sick	30	37	37	39	65	84	69	84
5. ?	1	0	0	2	2	0	3	4
179:C68 As compared with other children, how much did your child babble during infancy?								
1. Much more than average	1	1	0	1	5	8	3	6
2. Somewhat more than average	9	7	1	4	18	26	18	20
3. About average	34	36	38	37	105	99	106	107

[35] For both Studies II and III there were 60 additional moods reported, each by fewer than three of the informants represented in any one column of the table; 40 of these 60 were reported by the control and 34 by the experimental group respondents. Some respondents in Study II gave more than one response.

Item No.: IBM Card and Column No.	Item; or Question and Response Codings; or Computed Values	Study II				Study III			
		Control Group (N = 50)		Experimental Group (N = 50)		Control Group (N = 150)		Experimental Group (N = 150)	
		F	M	F	M	F	M	F	M
	4. Somewhat less than average	4	6	7	5	9	11	11	12
	5. Much less than average	0	0	0	2	4	4	1	4
	6. ?	2	0	4	1	9	2	11	1
180:C69-70	When did the child speak his first words (in months)?								
	a. Minimum		6		6		5		4
	b. Maximum		24		18		30		30
	c. Mean		9.9		10.9		10.8		10.9
	d. Median				11		10.7		11.4
	e. 90th percentile						16.7		17.1
	f. N		3		11		131		137
181:C71-72	When did the child begin to use sentences (in months)?								
	a. Minimum		12		14		8		8
	b. Maximum		48		72		48		44
	c. Mean		24.6		26.7		21.0		21.8
	d. Median				22.8		21.1		21.7
	e. 90th percentile						30		30.4
	f. N		5		9		131		136
182:C73	Do you consider the child to have been slow in beginning to talk in comparison with other children?								
	1. Much faster than average	2	2	1	1	10	15	17	17
	2. Somewhat faster than average	12	13	6	8	37	32	24	26
	3. About average	28	24	23	23	77	73	74	65
	4. Somewhat slower than average	5	9	13	11	23	26	24	22
	5. Much slower than average	3	2	6	6	2	3	10	20
	6. ?	0	0	1	1	1	1	1	0
183:C74	How much did the child talk from ages 1 to 5 (or 1 to age at time of								

interview if less than 5 years old)
as compared with other children?36

1. Much more than average	20	19	22	21	6	2	1	3
2. Somewhat more than average	48	42	43	55	10	13	19	12
3. About average	61	69	73	59	21	26	25	27
4. Somewhat less than average	18	13	9	14	10	5	3	6
5. Much less than average	3	4	1	1	2	3	0	0
6. ?	0	3	2	0	1	1	2	2

184*

What method was used in teaching
the child to talk?37

1. None	30	41	23	27	0	4	1	0
2. ?	0	7	1	2	1	2	1	0
3. Much conscious and directed stimulation38	3	2	2	0	32	4	12	20
4. Use of pictures to identify	8	4	3	2	37	2	2	17
5. Reading and letting the child fill in words	2	1	0	0	13	2	1	9
6. Getting the child to name what he sees	1	2	1	3	33	3	2	17
7. Talked to the child	26	14	34	32	45	6	30	39
8. Brother told the child words	0	1	4	4	1	1	0	2
9. Playing with sibling	5	4	12	10	1	1	0	0
10. Associating objects with words	15	12	17	17	1	0	0	0
11. Some stimulation	8	9	1	3	1	0	0	0
12. Helped the child to correct way of saying words	2	8	2	6	1	0	0	0
13. Pronounced words for the child (saying word, having the child repeat it)	36	33	36	21	3	3	0	0
14. Read to the child	11	16	12	8	35	0	11	32

---

36 The phrase "or 1 to age at time of interview if less than 5 years old" was not included in the question in Study II.
37 For both Studies II and III there were 14 additional methods reported, each by fewer than three of the informants represented in any one column of the table; 10 of these 14 were reported by the control and 7 by the experimental group respondents. Some respondents in Study II gave more than one response.
38 In Study II this code was "Much stimulation."

Item No.: IBM Card and Column No.	Item; or Question and Response Codings; or Computed Values	Study II Control Group (N = 50) F	M	Study II Experimental Group (N = 50) F	M	Study III Control Group (N = 150) F	M	Study III Experimental Group (N = 150) F	M
	15. Pronounced words clearly for the child; never talked baby talk					2	4	2	3
	16. Heard others talk					10	9	4	6
	17. Never talked baby talk to the child					2	4	0	4
	18. No conscious effort					11	14	9	12
185:C75	How frequently did the child get what he wanted without talking, in comparison with other children?								
	1. Much more than average					4	6	4	9
	2. Somewhat more than average					19	16	21	21
	3. About average					96	85	101	96
	4. Somewhat less than average					24	28	12	17
	5. Much less than average					3	15	2	7
	6. ?					4	0	10	0
186:C76-77	Did someone else do most of the child's talking for him? Who?39								
	1. No one	34	31	41	40	130	126	118	112
	2. ?	0	0	1	0	3	1	3	2
	3. Mother	7	8	1	1	10	7	9	17
	4. Older sibling	7	10	2	2	10	8	13	10
	5. Yes (person not identified)	0	0	0	3	0	0	0	0
	6. All siblings (older)					2	4	0	1
	7. Mother and father					1	2	4	4

39For both Studies II and III there were 14 additional responses given, each by fewer than three of the informants represented in any one column of the table; 7 of these 14 were reported by the control and 7 by the experimental group respondents. Some respondents in Study II gave more than one response.

187:C78-79 Who in your immediate family is quite talkative?[40]

1. No one	10	8	22	20	21	21	31	33
2. Mother	27	26	12	19	33	48	34	38
3. Father	6	6	6	7	9	15	10	10
4. Older sibling	10	8	6	7	21	18	11	9
5. Younger sibling	5	8	5	3	1	1	3	3
6. Grandparent	6	4	7	5	14	11	17	19
7. Sibling of parent	0	1	1	1	14	2	15	10
8. Father and older sib					2	0	3	0
9. Mother and father					3	3	1	7
10. The child in question					8	5	4	2
11. Whole family	0	1	0	0	13	11	5	2
12. Mother; maternal grandparent	1	1	2	2	2	2	0	6
13. Grandparent; sibling at present					1	0	4	3
14. Mother; older sibling					3	3	0	1

188:C80 As a child learning to talk, did your child have chances to talk as much as he wanted to?

1. Much more than average					3	12	7	7
2. Somewhat more than average					40	30	22	24
3. About average					99	98	104	99
4. Somewhat less than average					5	9	15	16
5. Much less than average					1	1	2	2
6. ?	2	4	1	1	2	0	0	2
†7. Yes	36	35	35	37				
†8. No	12	11	14	12				

189:D6 Did you ever talk baby talk to the child?

1. Yes					35	29	53	38
2. No					113	121	97	112
3. ?					2	0	0	0

[40]For both Studies II and III there were 21 additional responses given, each by fewer than three of the informants represented in any one column of the table; 12 of these 21 were reported by the control and 16 by the experimental group respondents. Some respondents in Study II gave more than one response.

Item No.: IBM Card and Column No.	Item; or Question and Response Codings; or Computed Values	Study II				Study III			
		Control Group (N = 50)		Experimental Group (N = 50)		Control Group (N = 150)		Experimental Group (N = 150)	
		F	M	F	M	F	M	F	M
190:D7	Have you ever been concerned about the child's speech?[41]								
	1. Yes	6	10	45	49	4	5	132	142
	2. No	44	39	5	1	146	145	18	8
191:D8	Has your wife (husband) ever been concerned about the child's speech?								
	1. Yes	7	6	46	45	3	5	140	137
	2. No	43	43	3	5	146	144	10	11
	3. ?	0	0	0	0	1	1	0	2
192:D9	Has any other relative ever been concerned about the child's speech?								
	1. Yes	3	4	28	38	2	5	83	93
	2. No	47	45	22	12	147	145	62	56
	3. ?	0	0	0	0	1	0	5	1
193:D10-11	Has the child ever had any trouble with the mouth, teeth, throat, or nose, or is there anything unusual about them?[42]								
	1. No	29	24	21	22	100	103	98	98
	2. Tongue-tied	1	4	1	0	0	1	1	0
	3. Nosebleeds	0	1	1	1	0	0	3	4
	4. "Bad" tonsils	9	11	16	17	11	9	11	9
	5. "Bad" adenoids	5	5	5	9	6	5	2	3
	6. "Bad" baby teeth	0	0	1	3	5	4	0	0
	7. Asthma	0	0	1	0	2	1	3	1
	8. Many sore throats	0	0	0	2	2	1	1	3
	9. "Bad" tonsils and adenoids					3	5	6	6
	10. Overbite					0	0	3	2

[41] In Study II the word "worried" was used in place of "concerned" in this and the following two items.

[42] For both Studies II and III there were 66 additional troubles reported, each by fewer than three of the informants represented in any one column of the table; 31 of these 66 were reported by the control and 49 by the experimental group respondents. Some respondents in Study II gave more than one response.

194:D12 Has the child ever had a speech defect? What defect?[43]

1. None	38	41	0	0	140	139	11	5
2. Baby talk	6	6	0	0	5	4	0	0
3. Stuttering	0	0	43	49	0	0	109	118
4. Repetition, not called stuttering	1	0	0	0	1	0	0	0
5. Don't know	2	2	0	0	1	0	6	3
6. Lisping	0	0	5	0	0	0	3	1
7. Other articulatory defect	0	0	1	7	4	1	0	0
8. Speech retardation	0	0	0	2	0	3	2	1
9. Refused to talk, ages 1-2	0	0	0	1	0	0	1	0
10. Stuttering and articulatory defect	0	0	0	0	0	0	0	0
11. Inability to find right word					0	0	13	21
12. Hesitation, not called stuttering; child not called stutterer					0	1	2	1
13. Articulatory problem; "speech block," not called stuttering					0	0	2	0
14. Nasal speech					0	1	1	0
† 15. Couldn't talk plain	0	0	1	1				
† 16. Occasional halting	1	0	0	0				
† 17. Stuttering noted	0	1	0	0				
† 18. Seven-month period of stammering	1	0	0	0				

195:D13 Has the child ever stuttered? (Control: Does the child now show or has he, or she, ever shown any nonfluencies--repetitions, hesitations, etc.--in speech?)

1. Yes	63	66	136	144
2. No	72	63	9	4
3. ?	4	2	3	0
4. Yes, but not at present time	11	19	2	2

[43] All the experimental group parents responding to this question and to the one following qualified as such according to the criteria set forth in Chapter 1. Some respondents in Study II gave more than one response to question 194.

Item No.: IBM Card and Column No.	Item; or Question and Response Codings; or Computed Values	Study II				Study III			
		Control Group (N = 50)		Experimental Group (N = 50)		Control Group (N = 150)		Experimental Group (N = 150)	
		F	M	F	M	F	M	F	M
196:D14-15	How old was the child (in months) when he first began to stutter? (Control: How old was the child (in months) when you began to notice his speech in these respects?)[44]								
	a. Minimum			18	16.5	10	20	8	18
	b. Maximum			132	108	72	86	85	84
	c. Mean			53	46.2	34.4	39.2	41.2	42.4
	d. Median					36	36	37	40
	e. 90th percentile					48	57	63	64
	f. Can't recall; did not regard child as stutterer (nonfluent)			1	1	94	79	9	0
	g. N			49	49	56	71	140	150
197*	Describe the situation in which the child stuttered the very first time. (To interviewer in Study III: If "can't recall" is response, ask for description of first situation the parent can recall in which he or she observed the child stuttering.)[45]								
	1. ?			11	0	142	143	30	24

[44]In Study II the question was worded "At what age (to the nearest month) was the speech difficulty first noticed?" In Study III the wording "his speech in these respects" refers to the nonfluencies mentioned in 195.

[45]The symbol "?" in this and subsequent items through 213 means that the respondent could not recall the "very first" situation; when it precedes a response, as in "?: Telling parent something," the interpretation to be made is that the respondent answered with reference to an early, but not the first, situation in which the child stuttered. For both Studies II and III there were 54 additional situations reported, each by fewer than three of the informants represented by any one column in the table; 6 of these 54 were reported by the control and 50 by the experimental group respondents. Of these 50, 45 were reported by experimental group respondents in Study III, and of these 45, there were 28, reported by 15 fathers and 24 mothers, which were not the first situations and 17, reported by 11 fathers and 18 mothers, which were, according to the

2.	?: Telling parent something	3		31	27
3.	?: Telling something at the table	1	3	15	9
4.	?: Asking parent for something		2	14	3
5.	?: When he came in to tell parent something				
6.	?: Talking to parents			7	8
7.	?: Asking parent question at home			6	4
8.	?: Competing with sib for the privilege of speaking			2	7
9.	?: Telling playmates something			5	2
10.	?: Calling parent's attention to something			2	5
11.	?: Telling parent about TV program			3	0
12.	?: Explaining something to parent			3	3
13.	?: Telling parent something			3	4
14.	When he came in to tell something			6	5
†15.	Playing outside	3		0	3
†16.	Spontaneous speaking in home	0		31	8
198:D18	Was the child competing with someone else for the privilege of speaking?	31			39

informants, the first situations in which the children were thought to stutter. Thus, in Study III there were only 18 fathers and 26 mothers who claimed to be able to recall the "very first situations." The 17 presumably "very first" situations were reciting a piece at home, asking for something at the table, trying to get the mother's attention, talking about what had happened while riding in a car after a slight accident and while competing with others for the privilege of speaking, asking the parent for something, telling something at the table, explaining something to the parent, competing with a sibling for the privilege of speaking, after a fall from a table, competing with adults for the privilege of speaking, upon meeting the father at the station after the father's two-week absence and with the mother present, talking to the parents, telling relatives something, when on a drive with parents and friends, asking the parent a question in the car, after a scolding, and calling to the mother after witnessing a parental "fight." The 28 other situations which were not "the very first" were essentially similar to these; the ones which, while possibly or probably experienced at least occasionally by most children, might have been more or less upsetting were "talking after being hit by another child" and "arguing with parent over something," each of which was reported for one child, but only by one of the parents in each case. In Study II more than one response was given for some children. In Study II the question was worded "In what situation was it first noticed and commented upon?"

Item No.: IBM Card and Column No.	Item; or Question and Response Codings; or Computed Values	Study II				Study III			
		Control Group (N = 50)		Experimental Group (N = 50)		Control Group (N = 150)		Experimental Group (N = 150)	
		F	M	F	M	F	M	F	M
	(That is, was the child trying to interrupt someone else, or was someone else trying to interrupt him?)[46]								
	1. Yes					1	3	5	11
	2. No					3	9	18	17
	3. ?					2	2	5	7
	4. ?; yes					19	13	22	22
	5. ?; no					24	21	75	77
	6. ?; ?					26	37	25	16
199:D19	Did the child seem to be having difficulty in thinking of the right words to express something he wanted to tell about?								
	1. Yes					1	5	10	14
	2. No					2	7	11	14
	3. ?					3	1	6	7
	4. ?; yes					18	25	28	28
	5. ?; no					24	10	67	67
	6. ?; ?					27	37	28	20
200:D20	Was the child in a condition of frustration or bewilderment?								
	1. Yes					1	5	8	7
	2. No					3	7	14	19
	3. ?					2	1	5	9

[46]See footnote 45 for an explanation of the "?" code. In this and other items through 213 the responses as coded may be read in order as meaning yes, no (both of these, and only these, refer, according to the respondent in each case, to the very first instance of stuttering), "first instance not recalled," "yes, but with reference to early instances, not the first one," "no, but with reference to early instances, not the first one," and, ?; ?, "can remember early instances of stuttering, though not the first one, but cannot definitely recall anything specific of the sort to which the question refers."

4. ?; yes	14	7	13	16
5. ?; no	28	29	84	84
6. ?; ?	27	36	26	15

201:D21 Was the child speaking to someone who was not listening to him? (To father who was reading the paper, for example, or to mother who was busy getting dinner?)

1. Yes	1	4	5	6
2. No	3	5	15	19
3. ?	2	4	7	10
4. ?; yes	10	11	21	12
5. ?; no	33	24	76	87
6. ?; ?	26	37	26	16

202:D22 Had the child just received punishment or scolding?

1. Yes	0	2	1	3
2. No	4	10	20	25
3. ?	2	1	6	7
4. ?; yes	2	1	4	4
5. ?; no	40	36	92	96
6. ?; ?	27	35	27	15

203:D23 Had the child just received a severe fright (e.g., being bitten by a dog, unpleasant experiences in the dark)?

1. Yes	0	0	3	4
2. No	4	12	19	25
3. ?	2	1	7	6
4. ?; yes	3	1	0	2
5. ?; no	39	35	95	98
6. ?; ?	27	36	26	15

204:D24 Did the time when the child began to stutter coincide with the arrival of a new baby in the home?

1. No	70	75	137	140
2. Yes, within preceding month	1	1	0	3

Item No.: IBM Card and Column No.	Item; or Question and Response Codings; or Computed Values	Study II				Study III			
		Control Group (N = 50)		Experimental Group (N = 50)		Control Group (N = 150)		Experimental Group (N = 150)	
		F	M	F	M	F	M	F	M
	3. Yes, within preceding week					0	0	1	0
	4. Yes, within following week					0	2	0	0
	5. Yes, within following month					1	2	1	5
	6. Yes, within following two to three months					1	1	4	2
	three months					2	4	4	0
	7. ?								
	8. Yes, within preceding two to three months					0	0	1	0
	three months					0	0	2	0
	9. Yes, four months afterward								
205:D25	Did the time when stuttering was first noticed coincide with the child's realization of the mother's pregnancy?								
	1. No					72	79	142	147
	2. Yes, within preceding month					0	0	0	0
	3. Yes, within preceding week					0	0	2	0
	4. Yes, within following week					0	2	0	0
	5. Yes, within following month					0	1	1	2
	6. ?					3	3	5	2
	7. Four months before onset					0	0	0	1
206:D26	At the time when stuttering was first noticed, had the child been asking to do something not ordinarily allowed?								
	1. Yes					0	1	1	0
	2. No					4	11	21	25
	3. ?					2	1	5	10
	4. ?; yes					4	2	3	1
	5. ?; no					37	31	95	99
	6. ?; ?					28	39	25	15

207:D27 — At the time when stuttering was first noticed, had there been changes in the child's physical environment (moving of furniture or actual changing of houses)?

1. Yes	1	4	2	10
2. No	3	8	20	21
3. ?	2	1	5	5
4. ?; yes	4	5	5	7
5. ?; no	39	32	93	93
6. ?; ?	26	35	25	14

208:D28 — When stuttering was first noticed, was the child trying unsuccessfully to say something in a certain length of time before someone else took over the conversation?

1. Yes	1	3	5	10
2. No	3	9	16	16
3. ?	2	1	6	9
4. ?; yes	11	9	22	22
5. ?; no	32	26	68	76
6. ?; ?	26	37	33	17

209:D29 — At this time was the child in a state of excitement due to a vigorous game or a trip?

1. Yes	3	2	9	10
2. No	1	9	13	17
3. ?	2	2	5	8
4. ?; yes	10	11	34	25
5. ?; no	30	25	60	70
6. ?; ?	29	36	29	20

210:D30 — At the time when stuttering was first noticed, was the child failing to make himself understood?

1. Yes	2	6	8	9
2. No	2	5	14	16
3. ?	2	2	5	10

Item No.: IBM Card and Column No.	Item; or Question and Response Codings; or Computed Values	Study II				Study III			
		Control Group (N = 50)		Experimental Group (N = 50)		Control Group (N = 150)		Experimental Group (N = 150)	
		F	M	F	M	F	M	F	M
	4. ?; yes					10	9	13	12
	5. ?; no					32	27	84	88
	6. ?; ?					27	36	26	15
211:D31	At the time when you first noticed his stuttering, was the child ill or unusually fatigued?								
	1. Yes					0	3	4	4
	2. No					3	9	17	21
	3. ?					3	1	6	10
	4. ?; yes					2	4	10	13
	5. ?; no					41	32	85	86
	6. ?; ?					26	36	28	16
212:D32	At the time when stuttering was first noticed, was the child seemingly in a great hurry to tell about something?								
	1. Yes					4	8	12	17
	2. No					0	4	10	10
	3. ?					2	1	5	8
	4. ?; yes					26	23	70	75
	5. ?; no					16	10	26	23
	6. ?; ?					27	39	27	17
213:D33	Had you just caught the child doing something of which he was made to feel ashamed?								
	1. Yes					0	2	0	2
	2. No					4	10	22	25
	3. ?					2	1	5	9
	4. ?; yes					1	1	2	2
	5. ?; no					41	35	96	98
	6. ?; ?					27	36	25	14
214:D34-35	Who first decided that the child was stuttering (or the equivalent, for								

example, stammering, hesitating in his speech, impediment, "something wrong")? (Study II: Who first noticed the speech difficulty?)

1. ?	3	1	30	17	12	8
2. Mother	27	28	15	55	79	92
3. Father	3	2	11	2	17	12
4. Mother and father	16	15	18	8	38	27
5. Mother; other relative	0	0	0	1	0	0
6. Sibling	1	0	1	0	1	1
7. Whole family	0	(2)[47]	0	0	1	0
8. Grandparent	0	(1)	0	1	1	6
9. Other relative	0	3	0	1	1	0
10. Teacher	0	0	0	0	1	2
11. Doctor	0	(1)	0	0	0	1
12. School nurse			0	0	0	1
13. Hired help			0	0	0	0

215:D36 Did you accept this decision or diagnosis then?

1. Yes	40	48			130	140
2. No	5	1			16	3
3. ?	5	1			4	7

216:D37 Did your wife (husband) accept this decision or diagnosis then?

1. Yes	42	43			135	129
2. No	2	1			6	15
3. ?	6	6			9	5
4. Parent not in home at this time					0	1

217:D38-39 Imitate and describe what the child was doing in his speech when he first stuttered--the very first time you noticed the child stuttering, or during the period when the stuttering still was the same as it had been

---

[47] Numbers in parentheses refer to children who were also reported as having been "first diagnosed by mother and father," code No. 4.

Item No.: IBM Card and Column No. — Item; or Question and Response Codings; or Computed Values	Study II Control Group (N = 50)		Study II Experimental Group (N = 50)		Study III Control Group (N = 150)		Study III Experimental Group (N = 150)	
	F	M	F	M	F	M	F	M
the very first time it was noticed by anyone.[48]								
1. ?			2	1	5	4	7	4
2. Repetition of whole word			38	43	12	14	25	25
3. Repetition of first sound			26	26	0	0	6	7
4. Repetition of first syllable			4	14	0	2	34	38
5. Complete blocks on first sound of word					0	0	0	1
6. Prolongations of vowel			3	5	0	0	1	1
7. Prolonged vocalization before production of word			2	3	0	0	1	0
8. Prolonged initial sound			3	1	0	0	3	0
9. Cleared throat					8	9	0	0
10. Silent interval			1	0			2	1
11. Couldn't finish sentences--said, "ah, ah, ah"			0	2	0	0	0	1
12. Repetition of whole word and syllable					1	2	21	26
13. Repetition of whole word and use of "ah" (interjected)					8	3	3	3
14. Extraneous sound (ah, ah) at beginning of sentence					5	3	2	0
15. Repetition of first syllable; prolongation of initial sound					0	1	5	3
16. Repetition of word, syllable; prolongation of initial sound					0	0	2	0
17. Prolongations of vowels and consonants					0	0	1	2

[48]In Study II the question read: "Describe and imitate the very first symptoms noticed. How did it sound at the outset?" See Tables 38-43 (Chapter 6) and the accompanying text for detailed analysis of the responses to this question and to items 218, 221, 227, and 236.

18. Repetition of word, first syllable and initial sound	0	0	0	1
19. Repetition of whole word; silent interval	3	2	0	1
20. Repetition of whole words and phrases	8	5	4	3
21. Repetition of first syllable; repetition of first sound	0	0	0	1
22. Prolongation of sounds; pauses in speech	0	0	3	1
23. Use of "ah"; pauses between words and in middle of word	1	1	1	0
24. Says "ah" and pauses between words (silent interval)	4	10	1	1
25. Repetition of whole words and prolongations of words and consonants	0	1	0	3
26. Repetition of word, syllable, phrase	0	0	2	2
27. Repetition of word; prolongations of vowels	0	0	1	0
28. Repetition of word, first syllable, first sound; complete blocks on first sound	0	0	0	1
29. Repetition of syllables and phrases	0	0	0	1
30. Repetition of words; blocks on initial sound	0	0	0	1
31. Repetition of words, syllables, interjections	0	1	1	2
32. Repetition of words; pauses in middle of sentence	0	0	1	0
33. Block before word (gutteral sounds emitted)	0	0	1	0
34. Repetition of syllables; blocks on initial sounds	0	0	0	1
35. Couldn't finish sentence; said "ah, ah, ah"; repetition of word, first syllable, and initial sound	0	0	0	1

Item No.: IBM Card and Column No.	Item; or Question and Response Codings; or Computed Values	Study II Control Group (N = 50) F	M	Study II Experimental Group (N = 50) F	M	Study III Control Group (N = 150) F	M	Study III Experimental Group (N = 150) F	M
36.	Repetition of first sound; repetition of first syllable; complete blocks on first sound; prolongation of vowels, initial consonant					0	0	0	1
37.	Repetition of whole word, syllable sound; complete blocks on first sound; prolongation of initial consonant; interjections (uh)					0	0	1	0
38.	Repetition of word, first syllable, initial letter; prolongation of vowels and consonants					0	0	0	1
39.	Repetition of word, syllable, phrase; prolongation of sounds; interjections					0	0	0	1
40.	Repetition of word, syllables, phrases; prolongations					0	0	2	1
41.	Repetition of words, first syllables; silent interval					1	0	1	0
42.	Use of interjections					4	7	5	5
43.	Repetition of words, first syllables; initial letter and phrases; interjections					0	0	1	0
44.	Prolongations of sounds; interjections					0	1	0	1
45.	Repetition of syllables; prolongations of sounds; interjections					0	0	1	0
46.	Prolongations of vowels; repetitions of words					1	0	0	0
47.	Repetition of words and phrases; interjections					0	2	0	1
48.	Repetition of words; interjections; silent interval					0	1	0	0

49. Repetition of whole words; interjections; silent intervals (pauses)	4	1	0	0
50. Repetition of phrases	4	3	1	2
51. Repeated gasps	0	0	1	0
52. Repetition of words, phrases; prolongation of vowels	0	0	1	1
53. Repetiton of words, syllables; prolongations	0	0	1	1
54. Repetition of syllables; interjections	0	0	0	1
55. Repetition of initial consonant; prolongation	0	0	0	1
56. Repetition of words, syllables; interjections; silent intervals	0	0	0	1
57. Repetition of syllables; silent intervals	0	1	0	0
58. Repetition of whole word; use of "ah" (interjection); repetition of whole sentence	1	0	0	0
59. Repetition of words; interjected extraneous sounds	0	1	1	1
60. Repetition of words, phrases; interjections; pauses between words	1	0	0	0
61. Repetition of phrases; pauses between words	2	6	0	0
62. Repetition of syllables and words; prolongations of sounds; pauses in speech; extraneous sounds at beginning of sentence	1	0	0	0
63. Repetition of syllable and prolongations of syllable at same time	0	0	0	0
64. Repetition of words; accented words	0	0	1	1
65. Repetition of phrases, syllables; interjections	0	1	0	0
66. Repetition of phrases; interjections; pauses between words (silent interval)	0	2	1	0

Item No.: IBM Card and Column No.	Item; or Question and Response Codings; or Computed Values	Study II				Study III			
		Control Group (N = 50)		Experimental Group (N = 50)		Control Group (N = 150)		Experimental Group (N = 150)	
		F	M	F	M	F	M	F	M
	67. Block before a word			0	1	0	0	1	0
	68. Repetition of words; prolongations; interjections					0	0	0	1
	†69. Prolonged initial consonant			3	1				
	†70. Repeated vocalization before word			1	1				
	†71. Repetition of several syllables successively								
	†72. Open mouth			0	1				
	†73. Whisper			0	1				
	†74. Preceded by "hey"			1	1				
	†75. Repetition of phonation ("sw" words)			1	0				
	†76. Hesitated			4	1				
	†77. Unable to explain it			1	0				
	†78. Unable to form sounds, start words			1	0				
	†79. Panting before word			1	0				
	†80. Repetition of several sounds			0	2				
	†81. Very rapid speech			1	1				
	†82. Stumbling over words			0	0				
	†83. Slight hesitation after first syllable			0	1				
	†84. Hesitation between words			0	1				
218:D40	When you first noticed that the child was stuttering was he repeating a whole word (boy-boy-boy)?								
	1. Yes					43	40	89	95
	2. No					27	41	53	47
	3. ?					5	4	8	8

Item		Col 1	Col 2	Col 3	Col 4
219:D41	If yes, how many times did he repeat it?				
	1. ?	6	3	3	2
	2. Once	2	1	2	1
	3. Twice	9	7	6	6
	4. Three times	5	3	23	25
	5. Four times	0	1	7	16
	6. Five times	1	1	2	7
	7. More than five times	2	3	6	2
	8. Two to three times	13	11	15	15
	9. Three to four times	4	7	20	18
	10. Four to five times	1	0	6	3
220*	What word was it?[49]				
	1. ?	6	7	35	37
	2. "I"	6	3	9	10
	3. Daddy-daddy	5	0	0	0
	4. Mama	0	4	0	0
221:D42	When you first noticed that the child was stuttering was he repeating a syllable (e.g., ca-ca-cat)?				
	1. Yes	4	10	97	103
	2. No	65	69	43	42
	3. ?	6	5	10	5
222:D43	If yes, how many times did he repeat it?				
	1. ?	0	1	3	7
	2. Once	0	0	3	0
	3. Twice	1	3	6	6
	4. Three times	2	1	19	28
	5. Four times	0	3	9	6
	6. Five times	0	0	5	8
	7. More than five times	0	1	7	10

[49] There were 66 additional words reported, each by fewer than three of the informants represented in any one column of the table; 35 of these 66 were reported by the control and 31 by the experimental group respondents. These were mostly common words, such as "my-a, my-a," "and, and, and," "did, did, did."

Item No.: IBM Card and Column No.	Item; or Question and Response Codings; or Computed Values	Study II Control Group (N = 50) F	M	Study II Experimental Group (N = 50) F	M	Study III Control Group (N = 150) F	M	Study III Experimental Group (N = 150) F	M
	8. Two to three times					0	1	23	15
	9. Three to four times					1	0	14	13
	10. Four to five times					0	0	8	10
223*	What word was he saying?50								
224:D44	Was he prolonging a sound (e.g., wh...at or s...ay)?								
	1. Yes					7	8	42	42
	2. No					66	74	98	103
	3. ?					2	3	10	5
225:D45	If yes, how long did he prolong it? (in seconds)								
	1. ?					1	0	2	2
	2. One second					2	6	9	7
	3. Two seconds					4	2	19	23
	4. Three seconds					0	0	7	6
	5. One to two seconds					0	0	1	1
	6. Four to five seconds					0	0	4	3
226*	What sound? What word?51								
227:D46	Was he making extraneous sounds such as "ah," "er," "well," "and"?								
	1. Yes					42	40	57	63
	2. No					28	37	87	81
	3. ?					6	8	6	6
228:D47	Were there conspicuous silent periods within speech?								
	1. Yes					26	21	24	15
	2. No					47	60	117	127
	3. ?					2	3	9	8

50The small number of respondents able to answer this question unequivocally precludes meaningful treatment of the responses obtained.

51See footnote 50.

229:D48	Was he doing what you describe on the first word of a sentence?				
	1. Yes	42	36	110	119
	2. No	26	45	33	24
	3. ?	7	4	7	6
	4. Not using a sentence at this time	0	0	0	1
230*	What word in what sentence?[52]				
231:D49	Was he doing it on words scattered throughout the sentence?				
	1. Yes	40	62	103	99
	2. No	30	17	42	45
	3. ?	5	6	5	5
	4. Not using a sentence at this time	0	0	0	1
232*	What words in what sentence?[53]				
233:D50	Had anyone, prior to the time stated in question 196, thought that the child was stuttering?				
	1. Yes			14	6
	2. No			133	143
	3. ?			3	1
234:D51	Have you ever noticed other children doing such things in their speech-- that is, doing the sorts of things you have described and imitated as the things your child was doing when you first noticed he was stuttering?				
	1. Yes	64	75	72	76
	2. No	5	7	76	74
	3. ?	6	2	2	0
235:D51A	Describe the first situation in which your child did something which you felt at that time indicated he had a				

[52]See footnote 50.
[53]See footnote 50.

Item No.: IBM Card and Column No.	Item; or Question and Response Codings; or Computed Values	Study II Control Group (N = 50) F	M	Study II Experimental Group (N = 50) F	M	Study III Control Group (N = 150) F	M	Study III Experimental Group (N = 150) F	M
	speech problem (you may or may not have called it stuttering).[54]								
	1. ?							107	104
	2. ?: Telling parent something							9	7
	3. ?: Teacher told parent the child had a problem							2	6
	4. Telling parent something							3	1
236:D51B	Describe what the child did in that situation (or what the child was doing at about that time).[55]								
	1. ?							5	2
	2. Repetition of whole word							10	10
	3. Repetition of first sound							4	2
	4. Repetition of first syllable							24	23
	5. Complete blocks on first sound							0	1
	6. Prolongations of vowel							0	1
	7. Prolonged initial sound							5	2
	8. Silent interval							1	1
	9. Repetition of whole word and syllable							17	31
	10. Repetition of whole word and "ah" (interjected)							1	4

[54] There were 32 additional situations or circumstances each reported by one or two cases in the experimental group. Of these, 10 referred to the first situation, according to the informant in each instance, and 22 referred to an early but not the first situation. The ? code ("can't recall first situation") in this case means primarily that the informant did not associate the feeling that the child had a speech problem with a specific speaking situation, but rather with the fact that the age of entering school was approaching, or with the judgment that the child was "getting worse" or that the child "should have been over it by now," and the like. The ? before a response means that the response does not refer to the first situation but to the first one the informant could remember.

[55] See Tables 38-43 (Chapter 6) and the accompanying text for a detailed analysis of responses to this question and to items 217, 218, 221, and 227.

11. Extraneous sound (ah, ah) at beginning of sentence	2	0
12. Repetition of first syllable; prolongation of initial sound	5	2
13. Repetition of word, syllable; prolongation of initial sound	1	0
14. Prolongations of vowels and consonants	3	3
15. Repetition of word, first syllable, and initial sound	1	0
16. Repetition of whole word and phrases	2	1
17. Said "ah" and paused between words (silent interval)	0	1
18. Repetition of whole words and prolongations of vowels and consonants	0	1
19. Repetition of word, syllable, phrase	2	3
20. Repetition of word; prolongation of vowels	1	0
21. Repetition of word, first syllable, first sound; complete blocks on first sound	0	1
22. Repetition of syllables and phrases	0	2
23. Repetition of words; blocks on initial sound	0	1
24. Repetition of words, syllables; interjections	3	6
25. Repetition of words; pauses in middle of sentence	1	0
26. Repetition of syllables; blocks on initial sounds	1	1
27. Couldn't finish sentence--said, "ah, ah"; repetition of word, first syllable, and initial sound	0	1

Item No.: IBM Card and Column No.	Item; or Question and Response Codings; or Computed Values	Study II Control Group (N = 50)		Study II Experimental Group (N = 50)		Study III Control Group (N = 150)		Study III Experimental Group (N = 150)	
		F	M	F	M	F	M	F	M
28.	Repetition of first sound; repetition of first syllable; complete blocks on first sound; prolongation of vowels, initial consonant							0	1
29.	Repetition of whole word, syllable sound; complete blocks on first sound; prolongation of initial consonant; interjections (uh)							1	0
30.	Repetition of word, first syllable, initial sound; prolongation of vowels and consonants							0	1
31.	Repetition of word, syllable, phrase; prolongation of sounds; interjections							1	1
32.	Repetition of word, syllables, phrases; prolongations							2	1
33.	Repetition of words, first syllables; silent interval							1	1
34.	Interjections							1	1
35.	Repetition of words, first syllables; initial sound and phrases; interjections							1	2
36.	Repetition of syllables; prolongations of sounds; interjections							1	0
37.	Repetition of words and phrases; interjections							4	2
38.	Repetition of phrases							0	1
39.	Repeated gasps							1	1
								1	0
40.	Repetition of words, phrases; prolongation of vowels							2	0

41.	Repetition of words, syllables; prolongations	2	3
42.	Repetition of syllables; interjections	3	2
43.	Repetition of initial consonant; prolongation	0	1
44.	Repetition of words; prolongation of sounds	0	1
45.	Repetition of words, syllables; interjections; silent intervals	0	1
46.	Repetitions; prolongations; hesitations	1	1
47.	Repetition of syllables; silent intervals	1	0
48.	Repetition of words; eye blink	1	0
49.	Repetition of words; phrases; interjections; pauses between words	0	1
50.	Repetition of syllables and words; prolongations of sounds; pauses in speech; extraneous sounds at beginning of sentence		
51.	Repetition of words; accented words	1	0
52.	Repetition of words; repetition of syllables; prolongation; complete blocks	1	0
53.	Block before a word		
54.	Blocked on first sound; cheeks puffed out and air came through teeth sounding like a whistle on word production		
55.	Repetition of words, syllables; prolongations; interjections	0	1
56.	Repetition of words; interjections; squinted eyes and veins in neck protruded	3	1
57.	Complete block on first sound; face got red; "dringed" up his face; tension in neck musculature	0	1

Item No.: IBM Card and Column No.	Item; or Question and Response Codings; or Computed Values	Study II				Study III			
		Control Group (N = 50)		Experimental Group (N = 50)		Control Group (N = 150)		Experimental Group (N = 150)	
		F	M	F	M	F	M	F	M
	58. Complete block on first sound; put hand over mouth							0	1
	59. Repetition of first syllables; eye blink; "stare"							0	1
	60. Prolongations of sounds; interjections; pauses in speech							1	0
237:D51C	How old was the child at that time (in months)?[56]								
	a. Minimum							22	24
	b. Maximum							85	89
	c. Mean							44.3	47.3
	d. Median							42	45
	e. 90th percentile							72	73
	f. N (uncertain responses excluded)							119	130
238:D52-53	How soon after it was first noticed did someone say something to the child about his stuttering? (Does not refer necessarily to telling him outright that he had defect.)								
	1. Nothing ever said					57	58	32	28
	2. ?					3	8	18	8
	3. Immediately					8	8	39	35
	4. Next time it occurred; next day					0	8	0	4
	5. After it occurred several times					4	8	25	31
	6. Within one week					0	1	4	5
	7. Within one to four weeks					3	1	12	12
	8. Within two to six months					0	1	9	9
	9. Within six months to one year					0	0	2	10
	10. After one year or more					0	0	9	8

[56]The age values shown here may be compared with those obtained in response to question 196; the means here are approximately three to five months higher and the medians are both five months higher than those for 196. See Chapter 6 for relevant discussion.

239:D54-55 Who first said something about it?[57]

1. No one	3	0	56	56	32	28
2. ?	27	21	8	1	12	7
3. Mother	19	18	5	17	37	69
4. Father	16	16	3	3	35	12
5. Mother and father			2	4	19	5
6. Sibling	1	2	0	2	1	4
7. Grandparent			0	1	10	17
8. Maternal grandparent	0	1	0	1	0	0
9. Other relative	0	3	0	0	4	3
10. Teacher			0	0	0	1
11. Doctor			0	0	0	1
12. Neighbor			0	0	0	1
13. Friend of parents			0	0	0	1
14. Someone in child's school	0		0	0	0	1
15. Hired help		1	0	0	0	0

240:D56-57 What was first said to the child?[58]

1. Nothing	25	21	56	56	32	28
2. ?	4	0	0	0	11	8
3. Slow down	4	8	6	6	47	41
4. Stop and take it easy	1	0	0	0	8	5
5. Stop and start over	6	7	1	2	10	11
6. Slow down; stop and start over			3	4	4	10
7. Slow down and take it easy			0	0	3	3
8. Stop and think what you're going to say and then say it			0	2		5
9. Stop and take it easy; think of what you're saying			0		1	2
10. Think of what you're saying	3	4	1	1	2	3
11. Take it easy	3	1	1	3	1	1
12. Helped him say word	0	3	4	2	8	4

[57] Some respondents in Study II gave more than one response.
[58] For both Studies II and III there were 61 additional comments reported, each by fewer than three of the informants represented in any one column of the table; 7 of these 61 were reported by the control and 55 by the experimental group respondents. Some respondents in Study II gave more than one response.

Item No.: IBM Card and Column No.	Item; or Question and Response Codings; or Computed Values	Study II Control Group (N = 50) F	M	Study II Experimental Group (N = 50) F	M	Study III Control Group (N = 150) F	M	Study III Experimental Group (N = 150) F	M
241:D58	How frequently were such comments made?								
	1. 5 to 25 times a day					1	2	13	15
	2. 5 to 25 times a week					2	1	37	31
	3. 5 to 20 times a month (now and then)					10	5	29	30
	4. Some, but less often than 3 above					6	15	20	31
	5. Never					56	58	29	27
	6. ?					0	3	22	15
	7. One time					0	1	0	1
242:D59	Did the child at first stutter only on (specify words):								
	1. One particular word			0	0	7	3	3	0
	2. Two or three particular words			4	1	3	0	7	9
	3. No particular words			46	45	60	78	134	135
	4. ?			0	4	5	3	6	6
243:D60	When stuttering was first noticed was it accompanied by any grimaces or bodily contortions?								
	1. Yes							19	23
	2. No							127	126
	3. ?							4	1
244:D61	Did he seem indifferent to his very first stoppages?								
	1. Yes					71	76	132	131
	2. No					4	8	13	18
	3. ?					0	0	5	1
245:D62	When the stuttering was first noticed, did the child seem to be aware of the fact that he was speaking in a different manner or doing something wrong?								
	1. Yes					9	12	10	17

		(1)	(2)	(3)	(4)
	2. No	133	134	69	64
	3. ?	0	6	3	2
246:D63	Did the child show surprise or bewilderment after having had trouble on a word				
	1. Yes	8	6	3	3
	2. No	139	139	80	72
	3. ?	3	5	1	0
247:D64	Did the very first stoppages seem to be unpleasant to the child?				
	1. Yes	19	8	7	3
	2. No	130	137	77	72
	3. ?	1	5	0	0
248:D65	Do you think the child felt irritated when the very first stoppages occurred?				
	1. Yes	17	10	9	7
	2. No	131	131	72	68
	3. ?	2	9	3	0
249:D66	Did the very first stoppages seem to be done chiefly by or in the:				
	1. ?	73	71		
	2. Tongue	14	19		
	3. Chest	0	2		
	4. Diaphragm	0	0		
	5. Throat	9	5		
	6. In mind, forming sentences, ideas	3	3		
	7. Mouth	31	28		
	8. Voice box	0	0		
	9. No place	18	19		
	10. Mouth or lips	0	1		
	11. Lips	1	2		
250:D67	At the time when stuttering was first noticed, was the child using force or more effort than usual "to get his words out"? Was there more than usual muscular tension?				
	1. No force or tension	95	94	59	63

Item No.: IBM Card and Column No.	Item; or Question and Response Codings; or Computed Values	Study II Control Group (N = 50)		Study II Experimental Group (N = 50)		Study III Control Group (N = 150)		Study III Experimental Group (N = 150)	
		F	M	F	M	F	M	F	M
	2. Some, but slight, force or tension					7	9	30	33
	3. Moderate force or tension					3	4	14	11
	4. Excessive force or tension					0	1	7	10
	5. ?					2	1	5	1
251:D68-69	What was the child's own first reaction to the trouble he was having saying words?59								
	1. ?			0	16			5	9
	2. No reaction			17	12			121	110
	3. Cried			1	3			1	0
	4. Laughed							3	4
	5. Kept on trying								
	†6. Embarrassed			3	3			6	8
	†7. Didn't want to talk			3	1				
	†8. Worried			0	3				
	†9. Not informed			14	15				
252:D70	When was the child told he was thought to have a speech defect?								
	1. Not told							115	89
	2. ?							8	6
	3. Immediately after it was noticed							3	6
	4. After it was noticed several times							5	9
	5. Two to four weeks after onset							2	6
	6. Three months after onset							0	5
	7. Six months after onset							5	10
	8. One year after onset							7	9
	9. Two years after onset							2	8
	10. Three or four years after onset							3	2

59For both Studies II and III there were 38 additional reactions, each reported by one or both parents in only one or two cases in the experimental groups. There was more than one response by some respondents in Study II. In Study II the question was "What was the child's own first reaction to his speech difference?"

253:D71-72 Who told him?

1. No one	114	91
2. ?	9	6
3. Mother	11	28
4. Father	3	1
5. Mother and father	4	2
6. Mother, father, teacher	1	0
7. Sibling	1	3
8. Grandparent	2	4
9. Other relative	1	3
10. Teacher	1	0
11. Doctor	0	1
12. Speech correctionist	0	1
13. Neighbor	0	1
14. Friend of parent	1	0
15. Playmate	1	5
16. Children he associated with	1	1
17. No one, but he heard others talking about him	0	3

254* How was the child told, under what circumstances, and precisely what was he told?60

1. The child was told directly by parents that he stuttered	6	8
2. The child was told by parents that he stuttered and given some advice	2	10
3. The child overheard parents, relatives, or physician talking about his stuttering	1	7
4. Parents told the child he would be taken to speech therapist or clinic; stuttering not mentioned	1	5

60The categories listed are made up of the specific responses reported. Examples of the unclassified ("other") responses are "Told him to take it easy. He thought it was a big joke." "Interrupted him and asked if that was the only way he could talk." "Child reported that children were making fun of him."

Item No.: IBM Card and Column No.	Item; or Question and Response Codings; or Computed Values	Study II Control Group (N = 50) F	M	Study II Experimental Group (N = 50) F	M	Study III Control Group (N = 150) F	M	Study III Experimental Group (N = 150) F	M
	5. ?							3	1
	6. Other							22	29
255:D73-74	What was the child's own first reaction to being informed that he was thought to have a speech defect?[61]								
	1. Was not informed			14	15			115	91
	2. ?			1	6			10	10
	3. Didn't appear to bother him; no reaction[62]			17	12			19	30
	4. Worried			0	3			0	1
	5. Cried			1	3			0	0
	6. Embarrassed			3	3			0	0
	7. Didn't want to talk			3	1			0	1
256:D75	How soon after you noticed that he was stuttering did the child begin to avoid speech situations?								
	1. Has never avoided them							141	123
	2. ?							1	1
	3. Immediately							1	2
	4. One month, three months							1	13
	5. About one year							0	3
	6. About two years							1	2
	7. Three years								
	8. Immediately after stuttering was called to the child's attention							0	1
	9. A month after it was called to his attention							0	1
	10. About 3 months after it was called to his attention							3	3

61 For both Studies II and III there were 35 additional reactions, each reported by one or both parents in only one or two cases in the experimental group. Some respondents in Study II gave more than one response.

62 The words "no reaction" were included in the code only in Study II.

257:D76-77 What did the child do to make speaking easier for himself during the first few days after you noticed he was stuttering?[63]

1. Nothing	31	32	130	125
2. Substituted words	1	2	3	1
3. Decreased rate	1	3	2	1
4. Increased loudness	1	2	2	4
5. Twisted mouth; made facial movement	0	3	1	1
6. Stopped and started over	3	0	3	3
†7. Some bodily movement	5	5		

258* In what situations did the child have the most trouble speaking at first?[64]

1. None	9	6	8	0
2. ?	5	4	11	4
3. When excited	24	22	44	35
4. Speaking in competition with others			13	9
5. When telling parents something			21	10
6. When tired	7	8	4	16
7. Just after the child came in from outdoors and told of experience			3	4
8. When child was in a hurry to tell something				
9. When he was not feeling well			0	3
10. When scolded			0	3
†11. When many were listening	4	1	0	4
†12. When there was a pressing need for communication	10	17		
†13. At school	0	3		
†14. When relating new experiences	4	2		

[63] For both Studies II and III there were 26 additional things, each reported by one or both parents in only one or two cases in the experimental groups. Some respondents in Study II gave more than one response.

[64] For both Studies II and III there were 207 additional situations, each reported by one or both parents in only one or two cases in the experimental groups. Some respondents in both studies gave more than one response.

Item No.: IBM Card and Column No.	Item; or Question and Response Codings; or Computed Values	Study II Control Group (N = 50)		Study II Experimental Group (N = 50)		Study III Control Group (N = 150)		Study III Experimental Group (N = 150)	
		F	M	F	M	F	M	F	M
259*	In what situations did the child have the least trouble speaking at first?65								
	1. None			13	9			31	21
	2. ?			8	8			13	19
	3. When not excited; calm and relaxed			16	14			35	26
	4. When talking alone with one parent or adult								
	5. When rested			4	7			11	10
	6. When playing with other children							5	5
	7. When alone; talking to self							13	11
	8. Reading							8	9
	9. Singing							3	9
	10. Prayers							2	7
	†11. At home			1	5			0	3
	†12. When there was no urgency to communicate			7	12				
	†13. When one or few were listening			4	1				
260:D78-79	To what specific persons did the child stutter more often at first?66								
	1. None			36	36	54	60	105	98
	2. ?			2	1	2	0	11	9
	3. Mother			0	2	1	6	4	5
	4. Father			1	1	2	5	8	5

65For both Studies II and III there were 97 additional situations, each reported by one or both parents in only one or two cases in the experimental groups. In both studies some respondents gave more than one response.

66For both Studies II and III there were 25 additional persons reported, each by fewer than three of the informants represented in any one column of the table; 7 of these 25 were reported by the control and 21 by the experimental respondents. Some respondents in Study II gave more than one response.

5. Older sibling	5	0	4	0	1	0
6. Strangers	4	5	2	2	6	4
7. Grownups		0	0	1	3	3
8. Mother and father			5	5	6	7
261:E6-7 To what specific persons did the child stutter less often at first?[67]						
1. None	36	41	52	64	103	104
2. ?	3	1	3	2	11	6
3. Mother	2	3	1	2	2	7
4. Father	1	2	1	2	5	0
5. Older sibling	1	1	0	2	5	0
6. Younger sibling	1	1	0	0	4	2
7. Grandparent	0	0	3	1	2	3
8. Strangers	2	0	0	0	0	5
9. Children	5	0	4	4	4	4
10. Playmates			4	0	4	7
11. Mother and father			0	0	3	3
12. Neighbor					0	
262:E8 How did you feel when you first felt your child had a speech problem? How concerned were you? (Refers to the time when child first did something that the parent felt indicated the presence of speech problem.)						
1. Very much concerned	9	25	0	2	31	46
2. Quite concerned			3	1	27	41
3. Slightly concerned			8	11	72	54
4. No concern, or practically none	16	6	64	70	19	9
5. ?			0	0	1	0
†6. Somewhat concerned	13	9				
†7. Not very concerned	12	9				
263:E9 How did your husband (wife) feel?						
1. Very much concerned			0	2	36	38

[67]For both Studies II and III there were 21 additional persons reported, each by fewer than three of the informants represented in any one column of the table; 9 of these 21 were reported by the control and 14 by the experimental group respondents. Some respondents in Study II gave more than one response.

Item No.: IBM Card and Column No.	Item; or Question and Response Codings; or Computed Values	Study II Control Group (N = 50)		Study II Experimental Group (N = 50)		Study III Control Group (N = 150)		Study III Experimental Group (N = 150)	
		F	M	F	M	F	M	F	M
	2. Quite concerned					4	1	41	32
	3. Slightly concerned					5	5	62	51
	4. No concern, or practically none					64	74	9	23
	5. ?					1	1	2	6
	6. ?; not sure he (or she) noticed anything					1	1	0	0
264:E10	How often did you or a member of the immediate family ask the child to talk slowly, slow down?								
	1. 5 to 25 times a day					0	1	17	17
	2. 5 to 25 times a week					2	0	42	34
	3. Now and then (from 5 to 20 times a month)					7	7	35	29
	4. Some but less often than 3 above					12	13	21	36
	5. Never					54	63	32	32
	6. ? (unable to recall number of times)					0	1	3	2
	7. Once (one time)					0	1	0	0
265:E11	How often did you tell him to think about what he was going to say?								
	1. 5 to 25 times a day					0	1	10	15
	2. 5 to 25 times a week					1	1	21	15
	3. Now and then (from 5 to 20 times a month)					2	5	23	22
	4. Some but less often than 3 above					9	13	15	23
	5. Never					63	64	75	73
	6. ? (unable to recall number of times)					0	1	5	2
	7. Once (one time)					0	1	1	0
266:E12	How often did you suggest that he hold his tongue or lips a certain way?								
	1. 5 to 25 times a day					0	0	1	2

(Counts are shown in four columns, left to right; no column headers are printed.)

	1	2	3	4
[previous question, continued]				
2. 5 to 25 times a week	0	0	2	1
3. Now and then (from 5 to 20 times a month)	0	0	1	1
4. Some but less often than 3 above	0	0	3	2
5. Never	75	86	141	144
6. ? (unable to recall number of times)	0	0	2	0
267:E13 How often did you suggest that he take a deep breath?				
1. 5 to 25 times a day	0	0	0	0
2. 5 to 25 times a week	1	0	5	7
3. Now and then (from 5 to 20 times a month)	1	1	1	2
4. Some but less often than 3 above	1	3	4	5
5. Never	72	82	137	136
6. ? (unable to recall number of times)	0	0	3	0
268:E14 How often did you tell him to stop and start over?				
1. 5 to 25 times a day	0	0	9	10
2. 5 to 25 times a week	1	1	24	28
3. Now and then (from 5 to 20 times a month)	4	6	31	21
4. Some but less often than 3 above	9	11	23	27
5. Never	61	65	62	62
6. ? (unable to recall number of times)	0	2	1	2
7. Once (one time)	0	1	0	0
269:E15 How often did you tell him to relax or take it easy?				
1. 5 to 25 times a day	0	0	11	11
2. 5 to 25 times a week	1	0	29	26
3. Now and then (5 to 20 times a month)	4	5	30	22
4. Some but less often than 3 above	10	12	20	15
5. Never	60	65	56	76

Item No.: IBM Card and Column No.	Item; or Question and Response Codings; or Computed Values	Study II Control Group (N = 50) F	M	Study II Experimental Group (N = 50) F	M	Study III Control Group (N = 150) F	M	Study III Experimental Group (N = 150) F	M
	6. ? (unable to recall number of times)					0	3	4	0
	7. Once (one time)					0	1	0	0
270:E16	How often did you say the difficult words for him?								
	1. 5 to 25 times a day					0	0	8	5
	2. 5 to 25 times a week					2	1	13	29
	3. Now and then (5 to 20 times a month)					4	1	23	21
	4. Some but less often than 3 above					4	10	25	23
	5. Never					62	73	74	71
	6. ? (unable to recall number of times)					2	1	7	1
271:E17	How often did you have the child practice reading aloud?								
	1. 5 to 25 times a day					0	0	0	0
	2. 5 to 25 times a week					0	0	4	1
	3. Now and then (5 to 20 times a month)					0	0	2	3
	4. Some but less often than 3 above					0	0	0	2
	5. Never					19	22	89	87
	6. ? (unable to recall number of times)					0	0	2	0
272:E18	How often did you suggest that he say some other word?								
	1. 5 to 25 times a day					0	0	1	0
	2. 5 to 25 times a week					0	0	0	5
	3. Now and then (5 to 20 times a month)					0	1	2	0
	4. Some but less often than 3 above					1	3	2	8
	5. Never					73	82	142	137
	6. ? (unable to recall number of times)					0	0	2	0

273:E19 — How often did you tell him to be careful of his speech, to try to keep from stuttering?

Response	(1)	(2)	(3)	(4)
1. 5 to 25 times a day	0	1	2	1
2. 5 to 25 times a week	0	0	2	9
3. Now and then (5 to 20 times a month)	1	0	13	4
4. Some but less often than 3 above	1	1	3	9
5. Never	73	84	127	127
6. ? (can't recall how often)	0	0	3	0

274:E20-21 — What other suggestions have you made to help the child speak well; what other things have you done?[68]

Breakdown (two columns):

Response	(1)	(2)
1. Nothing	3	0
2. Repeated after him	2	8
† 3. Suggested he talk slowly	34	38
† 4. Think about what he's going to say	20	27
† 5. Relax	2	5
† 6. Take a deep breath	1	6
† 7. Stop and start over	25	28
† 8. Mostly let him finish at own rate	3	2
† 9. Take it easy	17	20
†10. Be quiet when excited	0	4

Additional columns (rows 1–2 only):

Response	(1)	(2)	(3)	(4)
1. Nothing	67	80	121	109
2. Repeated after him	0	1	0	1

275:E22 — How often have these helps been offered to him?

Response	(1)	(2)	(3)	(4)
1. 5 to 25 times a day	8	15	1	6
2. 5 to 25 times a week	16	17	8	11
3. Now and then (from 5 to 20 times a month)	11	8	10	13
4. Some but less often than 3 above	5	6	8	8
5. ? (unable to recall number of times)	1	0	0	1

[68] For both Studies II and III there were 105 additional suggestions reported, each by fewer than three of the informants represented in any one column of the table; 15 of these 105 were reported by the control and 99 by the experimental group respondents. Some respondents in Study II gave more than one response. In Study II the question read: "What have you done to help him speak well?"

Item No.: IBM Card and Column No.	Item; or Question and Response Codings; or Computed Values	Study II Control Group (N = 50) F	M	Study II Experimental Group (N = 50) F	M	Study III Control Group (N = 150) F	M	Study III Experimental Group (N = 150) F	M
	†6. Never			3	0				
	†7. Lately			3	2				
276:E22A	Did you or anyone else listening to the child react in any way to the fact that he seemed to be having difficulty?69								
	1. Yes					7	7	63	85
	2. No					58	65	64	44
	3. ?					0	0	3	3
277:E22B	Did you avert your gaze?								
	1. Yes					1	3	19	34
	2. No					64	69	108	96
	3. ?					0	0	3	2
278:E22C	Did you try to change the subject?								
	1. Yes					0	1	11	16
	2. No					64	70	119	116
	3. ?					0	1	0	0
279:E22D	Did you register surprise?								
	1. Yes					1	2	12	19
	2. No					64	70	116	111
	3. ?					0	0	2	2
280:E22E	Did you "shush" him?								
	1. Yes					2	0	8	18
	2. No					63	72	122	113
	3. ?					0	0	0	1
281:E22F	Did you try to get him not to talk so much?								
	1. Yes					3	1	10	16

69Questions 276 through 284 were asked with reference to the time when the parent first felt that the child had a speech problem (item 235); 20 fathers and 18 mothers in the experimental group felt unable to recall their reactions even vaguely for the purpose of answering these questions.

2. No			62	71	120	115
3. ?			0	0	0	1
282:E22G Did you laugh?						
1. Yes			2	1	11	16
2. No			63	71	117	115
3. ?			0	0	3	1
283:E22H Did you look worried?						
1. Yes			1	3	26	44
2. No			64	69	97	82
3. ?			0	0	7	6
284:E22I Did you do anything else?[70]						
1. Nothing			63	69	113	110
2. ?			0	0	3	1
3. Tensed up when he stuttered			0	0	3	8
285:E23 What has been the general course of the problem since you first noticed it?[71]						
1. Becoming rapidly worse	1	4	0	0	3	1
2. Becoming gradually worse	20	20	3	2	38	45
3. Stayed about the same	15	12	25	30	36	36
4. Becoming gradually better	12	10	30	26	41	33
5. Becoming rapidly better	2	3	5	6	3	6
6. ?			1	3	2	2
7. Became rapidly worse, then gradually better			0	1	7	10
8. Became gradually better, then disappeared			11	15	1	1
9. Became gradually better, then gradually worse			0	0	1	4
10. Became gradually worse, then gradually better			0	0	8	3
11. Became gradually worse, then rapidly better			0	0	4	2

[70]There were 20 additional things reported, each by fewer than three of the informants represented in any one column of the table; 3 of these 20 were reported by the control and 19 by the experimental group respondents. Some respondents gave more than one response.

[71]For both Studies II and III there were 9 additional descriptions reported, each by fewer than three of the informants represented in any one column of the table; 1 of these 9 was reported by the control and 8 by the experimental respondents.

Item No.: IBM Card and Column No.	Item; or Question and Response Codings; or Computed Values	Study II				Study III			
		Control Group (N = 50)		Experimental Group (N = 50)		Control Group (N = 150)		Experimental Group (N = 150)	
		F	M	F	M	F	M	F	M
286:E24	After you first noticed that the child was stuttering was there ever a time when the speech improved greatly?								
	1. Yes					7	18	89	109
	2. No					58	58	55	40
	3. ?					9	8	6	1
287*	If yes, what was the probable cause of the change?72								
288:E27	After you first noticed that the child was stuttering was there ever a time when you felt the stuttering had completely disappeared?								
	1. Yes					13	21	37	52
	2. No					55	54	108	98
	3. ?					6	9	5	0
289*	If yes, what was the probable cause?73								
290:E30	After you first noticed that the child was stuttering was there ever a time when you felt the stuttering became more severe?								
	1. Yes					4	9	78	97

72Only 29 causes were reported, each by fewer than three of the informants represented in any one column of the table; 2 of these 29 were reported by the control and 28 by the experimental group respondents. Some of these factors might be grouped as follows: (a) reduced "tension" in the home, 6; (b) child less nervous, calmer, interested in other things, occupied, more relaxed, "not so tired," less excited, healthier, 9; (c) changed environment, entered school, getting along better at school, no longer influenced by or in conflict with certain former playmates, 7. In addition, these responses were obtained: "Getting older, growing out of it," "Parents desensitized," "Don't talk to her about it now, just let her talk and hear her stuttering out," "Absence of grandmother," "Bribed him--told him that if he would stop he would get certain things for Christmas," "Child now has large vocabulary."

73Only 18 causes were reported, each by fewer than three of the informants represented in any one column of the table; 3 of these 18 was reported by the control and 15 by the experimental group respondents.

2. No	53	68	72	66
3. ?	0	4	3	4

291*   If yes, what was the probable cause of the change?[74]

292:E33   How severe do you feel the stuttering is now? (Study II: How severe is the stuttering now?)

1. No stuttering; speech normal	2	3	2	0
2. Very mild	20	22	5	7
3. Mild	55	64	14	20
4. Average	37	26	12	17
5. Moderately severe	22	21	11	6
6. Severe	6	6	5	0
7. Very severe	4	4	1	0
8. Mild at times; average at other times	1	2		
9. ?	1	0		
10. Average at times; severe at other times	1	0		

293:E34-35   Describe and imitate the present pattern of stuttering.[75]

1. Repetition of whole word	17	15	14	12
2. Repetition of first letter or sound	5	4	26	25
3. Repetition of first syllable	20	31	11	6
4. Complete block on first letter	0	0	9	7
5. Prolongation of vowel	1	0	2	3
6. Prolonged vocalization before production of word	0	0	1	7
7. Block before word	1	1	7	4
8. Prolongation of consonant	0	0	3	3

---

[74] Only 27 causes were reported, each, with the exception of "excitement," which was mentioned by three experimental group mothers and fathers, by fewer than three of the informants represented in any one column of the table; 1 of these 26 was reported by the control and 25 by the experimental group respondents.

[75] In Study II, the 50 experimental group fathers gave 86 different responses and the 50 mothers gave 90 different responses; in Study III there was only one response per informant.

Item No.: IBM Card and Column No.	Item; or Question and Response Codings; or Computed Values	Study II				Study III			
		Control Group (N = 50)		Experimental Group (N = 50)		Control Group (N = 150)		Experimental Group (N = 150)	
		F	M	F	M	F	M	F	M
9.	Repeated vocalization before word								
10.	Block after starting word			3	6			1	0
11.	Repetition of phrases			1	0			1	1
12.	Silent interval between words			1	0			0	1
13.	Repetition of syllables and words			0	2			1	1
14.	Repetition of first syllable; prolongation of sounds							25	30
15.	Extraneous sound (ah); repetition of syllable							7	7
16.	?							3	4
17.	"Unable to express thoughts"							4	4
18.	Prolongation of initial sound in word							1	0
19.	Repeated vocalization (ah); repetition of short words and syllables							2	2
20.	Prolongation of vowels and consonants							4	1
21.	Repetition of whole word; prolongation of vowel							0	3
22.	Repetition of word and first syllable; prolongation of vowels, consonants							1	1
23.	Repetition of whole word, first syllable, first letter							7	8
24.	Repetition of whole word; repeated vocalization before word							4	3
25.	Repetition of first syllable; block before a word							0	1
26.	Repetition of whole word; repetition of phrases							3	2

27. Repetition of word; interjections of sounds			2	1
28. Repetition of word and first syllable; prolongation of vowels			1	0
29. Does not complete his sentences; incomplete sentences			0	0
30. Extraneous sound before word; repetition of syllables; prolongation of sounds	1	0	0	2
31. Repetition of first syllable; short interval between words			1	1
32. Repetition of syllables and words; interjections			1	4
33. Complete block on first letter; repetition of words and syllables			1	1
34. Repeats words, syllables, phrases			2	2
35. Blocks on initial letter; repetition of words			0	1
36. Blocks on initial sound; repetition of syllables			0	1
37. Repeated vocal pattern after first syllable of the word			0	1
38. "Unable to express thoughts"; repetition of word, first syllable, first letter			0	1
39. Blocks on initial syllable; prolongation of consonant			1	0
40. Repetition of words, syllables, phrases; prolongations; interjections (uh)			2	2
41. Block before word; repetition of first syllable; interjection of "uh"			1	0
42. Repetition of first letter, first syllable; complete block on first letter; prolongation of vowels and consonants; interjections			1	1

| Item No.: IBM Card and Column No. | Item; or Question and Response Codings; or Computed Values | Study II | | | | Study III | | | |
| | | Control Group (N = 50) | | Experimental Group (N = 50) | | Control Group (N = 150) | | Experimental Group (N = 150) | |
		F	M	F	M	F	M	F	M
43.	Repetition of words, syllables, phrases; prolongations							2	4
44.	Repetition of words, first syllables; silent intervals							2	1
45.	Repetition of words; prolongation of initial sound; block before initial sound							1	0
46.	Repetition of whole word, syllables, phrases; interjection of "well" at beginning; gasping							1	0
47.	Repetition of words, phrases; prolongation of consonants							2	0
48.	Repetition of words, initial syllables; prolongation of consonants							1	0
49.	Repeated vocalization of "uh"; repetition of short words, syllables, phrases							0	1
50.	Repetition of words, syllables; prolongations; complete blocks							1	1
51.	Repetition of syllables; prolongations; interjections							2	0
52.	Repetition of syllables; gasping during silent intervals							0	1
53.	Repetition of words, syllables; prolongations; interjections							1	5
54.	Repetition of words, phrases; interjections; pauses between words							0	1
55.	Repetition of syllables; pauses between words; interjections							1	0
56.	Repetition of words; prolongations of sounds							4	1

#	Item	1	2	3	4
57.	Takes a breath before a word ("like a gasp")			0	1
58.	Repetition of syllables; silent interval; repetition of interjections			1	0
59.	Repetition of words, syllables, phrases; interjections	0	1	1	0
60.	Slurring of words				
†61.	Precedes with "Say, Dad"	0	1		
†62.	Repetition of several consecutive syllables	0	1		
†63.	Precedes with "See"; repeats it	1	1		
†64.	Explodes sounds	1	0		
†65.	Stops and says, "I forgot"	2	1		
†66.	Jerky speech	1	0		
†67.	Repeats sentence	3	0		
†68.	Hesitation	1	0		
†69.	Blows breath out starting word	2	0		
†70.	Panting before starts	1	0		
†71.	Starts out loud				
†72.	Initiates word with gutteral sound	1	0		
†73.	Rapid repetition of several words	1	0		
†74.	Injects breathless noises	0	1		
†75.	Silent interval after starts word	0	1		
†76.	Hesitation after first syllable	0	1		
†77.	"Gropes" for words	0	1		

How many repetitions are there as a rule now before the word is finally spoken?

#		1	2	3	4
1.	None	6	3	6	9
2.	One	1	2	4	1
3.	Two	1	3	12	12
4.	Three	3	4	36	35
5.	Four	3	3	11	13
6.	Five	0	1	6	11

294:E36

Item No.: IBM Card and Column No.	Item; or Question and Response Codings; or Computed Values	Study II Control Group (N = 50) F	M	Study II Experimental Group (N = 50) F	M	Study III Control Group (N = 150) F	M	Study III Experimental Group (N = 150) F	M
	7. Five or more			9	6			12	12
	8. ?			0	0			3	0
	9. Two to three			9	10			28	27
	10. Three to four			7	13			24	22
	11. Four to five			7	4			8	8
295:E37	How much force or effort does the child use now in comparison to when stuttering was first noticed?								
	1. Much more			13	18			15	20
	2. Moderately more			19	16			39	43
	3. About the same			8	10			73	62
	4. Moderately less			7	1			13	9
	5. Much less			2	4			4	10
	6. None now							2	4
	7. ?			1	0			1	0
296:E38-39	How does he react now when he has a lot of trouble saying a word?[76]								
	1. ?								
	2. No reaction			1	2			3	1
	3. Stops trying			0	1			78	60
	4. Laughs			0				4	4
	5. Increases bodily activity for a moment				5			1	4
	6. Keeps trying			0				0	0
	7. Stops, begins again			30	26			18	26
	8. Substitutes another word			4	4			7	3
	9. Acts disgusted			3	5			1	1
	10. Acts embarrassed			1	3			5	3
	11. Acts angry			2	4			2	1

[76] For both Studies II and III there were 57 additional reactions each reported by one or both parents in only one or two cases in the experimental groups. Some respondents in Study II gave more than one response.

12. Stamps foot	1				0	1
13. Acts irritated, keeps trying		3			3	6
14. Acts frustrated					3	3
15. Says, "I can't say it."					0	5
†16. Speeds up	0	3				
297:E40 Does the child have especially difficult periods? (Study II: bad periods?)						
1. Yes	39	40			59	83
2. No	10	10			82	63
3. ?	1	0			7	2
298:E41 How frequently do they occur?						
1. At least once a day	5	6			25	30
2. 2 or 3 times a week	2	3			6	12
3. Once a week	1	3			1	6
4. 2 or 3 times a month	2	2			1	3
5. Less often than once a month	3	4			2	4
6. No regularity	25	23			23	28
299:E42-43 What seems to cause them?[77]						
1. ?	13	13			13	21
2. Fatigue	6	5			16	14
3. Excitement	10	9			16	22
300* During the past month in what situations have you personally observed the child stuttering more than usual?[78]						
1. None	5	2	1	4	26	20
2. ?	0	0	4	2	12	10
3. When excited	29	38	35	21	43	37
4. When speaking in competition	1	3	4	6	8	6
5. When talking fast; in a hurry to speak	2	0	7	6	13	8

[77] For both Studies II and III there were 62 reasons each reported by one or both parents in only one·or two cases in the experimental groups. Some mothers in Study II gave more than one response.

[78] For both Studies II and III there were 193 additional situations reported, each by fewer than three of the informants represented in any one column of the table; 47 of these 193 were reported by the control and 146 by the experimental group respondents. Some respondents gave more than one response. In Study II the question was worded "In what situations does he have the most trouble now?"

Item No.: IBM Card and Column No.	Item; or Question and Response Codings; or Computed Values	Study II Control Group (N = 50)		Study II Experimental Group (N = 50)		Study III Control Group (N = 150)		Study III Experimental Group (N = 150)	
		F	M	F	M	F	M	F	M
	6. When trying to gain a listener's attention			0	0	4	2	5	7
	7. When he doesn't know quite what to say; groping for words or ideas			5	3				
	8. When playing with other children			0	0	3	9	3	3
	9. When tired			9	14	4	2	1	3
	10. When he is being or fears he will be reprimanded			5	3	1	0	5	6
	11. Describing something; telling a story			4	4	1	3	6	9
	12. When asking for information			0	5	2	11	29	24
	13. Talking to adult strangers or to less familiar company			3	1	0	1	5	4
	14. When nervous, tense			0	1	0	0	3	9
	†15. When many listening			5	4	0	0	2	4
	†16. On telephone			1	5				
	†17. Oral reading			2	4				
	†18. At school			1	5				
	†19. At home			2	6				
	†20. When relating new experiences			2	7				
	†21. When mad, angry			3	0				
301*	During the past month in what situations have you personally observed that the child has had little or no trouble speaking?79								
	1. None			7	3	4	4	27	28
	2. ?			1	3	4	5	23	24

79For both Studies II and III there were 160 additional situations reported, each by fewer than three of the informants represented in any one column of the table; 41 of these 160 were reported by the control and 120 by the experimental group respondents. Some respondents gave more than one response. In Study II the question was worded "In what situations does he have the least trouble speaking now?"

	C1	C2	C3	C4	C5	C6
3. When not excited	3	13	9	5	0	0
4. Ordinary, normal conversation	3	3	20	13	18	14
5. All other times except situations described in preceding question (No. 300)						0
6. When calm, relaxed	1	0	10	15	0	20
7. Singing	12	14	4	3	19	3
8. During quiet play	5	9	0	0	3	0
9. When playing	1	4	2	9	0	7
10. When rested	5	4	2	0	10	0
11. When reading	5	6	0	0	4	3
12. When reciting	3	2	0	0	2	0
13. When story telling	2	3	0	0	0	1
14. When talking, playing with sibs	4	0	0	0	0	
15. When talking, playing with other children	6	4	2	0	0	
16. When alone with father or mother	9	9	2	2	0	3
17. When playing alone; talking to himself	10	4	2	0	0	0
18. With family only	8	10	1	0	1	1
19. When sure of what he wants to say	0	3	0	0	2	0
†20. When mad, angry	1	3	1	1	3	0
†21. At home					8	3
†22. When one or few listening					4	1

302:E44-45

During the past month to what specific persons have you observed the child stuttering more than usual (Study II: What people does he stutter to more often now?)80

	C1	C2	C5	C6
1. None	107	113	29	34
2. ?	4	2	1	1
3. Mother	7	2	2	2
4. Father	6	8	2	2
5. Grandparent	2	3		

80For both Studies II and III there were 11 additional persons each reported by one or both parents in only one or two cases. Some respondents in Study II gave more than one response.

Item No.: IBM Card and Column No.	Item; or Question and Response Codings; or Computed Values	Study II Control Group (N = 50) F	M	Study II Experimental Group (N = 50) F	M	Study III Control Group (N = 150) F	M	Study III Experimental Group (N = 150) F	M
	6. Strangers			6	7			3	2
	7. Grownups			3	1			2	2
	8. Playmates			0	1			3	2
	9. Mother and father							5	6
303:E46-47	During the past month to what specific persons have you observed that the child has had little or no trouble speaking? (Study II: What people does he stutter less often to now?)81								
	1. None			35	32			110	105
	2. ?			2	2			6	4
	3. Mother			0	6			2	9
	4. Father			0	3			4	1
	5. Younger sibling			1	3			5	4
	6. Grandparent			0	1			4	3
	7. Strangers			3	1			0	3
	8. Children			5	1			3	2
	9. Playmates							10	7
304:E48-49	During the past month what topics of conversation have given the child the most trouble? (Study II: What topics of conversation usually give him the most trouble?)82								
	1. None in particular			40	37	67	72	110	108
	2. ?			0	2	1	2	7	7
	3. His schoolwork			0	1	1	1	2	3

81For both Studies II and III there were 13 additional persons each reported by one or both parents in only one or two cases. Some respondents in Study II gave more than one response.

82For both Studies II and III there were 41 additional topics reported, each by fewer than three of the informants represented in any one column of the table; 8 of these 41 were reported by the control and 41 by the experimental group respondents. Some respondents in Study II gave more than one response.

4. Christmas gifts			0	0	3
5. Telling about things he'd never done before, new experiences			0	2	3
6. Asking questions			0	1	4
7. Telling about some event			0	6	3
8. School activities	0		1	3	2
9. Exciting topics	7		1	0	1

305:E50-51 When the child stutters does he make any grimaces or odd bodily movements, or does he seem to do anything else out of the ordinary?[83]

1. No	18	19	62	79	96	90
2. Lips compressed	3	3	0	0	1	1
3. Closes eyes	4	2	1	1	0	1
4. Tongue protrudes	1	4	0	0	0	0
5. Eyes enlarge	3	1	0	0	0	1
6. Mouth opens; is held open	10	14	0	0	9	2
7. Jerks head	2	2	0	0	3	1
8. Blinks eyes or bats eyes	5	4	1	1	3	6
9. Twists mouth to one side	6	4	0	0	3	1
†10. Twists face	4	6			2	
†11. Twists head to one side	3	1				
†12. Shows tension in face	4	1				

306:E52 How do you feel about this behavior? About these unusual things?

1. Strongly dislike	11	17	2	2	14	14
2. Moderately dislike	9	7	2	0	10	14
3. Mildly dislike			0	0	16	10
4. Generally tolerant or indifferent	11	7	9	2	12	15
5. Feel sorry for him			0	0	1	5
6. Don't dislike it but don't want him to do it (for his own sake)			0	0	0	1

[83] For both Studies II and III there were 107 additional things reported, each by fewer than three of the informants represented in any one column of the table; 10 of these 107 were reported by the control and 99 by the experimental group respondents. Some respondents in Study II gave more than one response.

Item No.: IBM Card and Column No.	Item; or Question and Response Codings; or Computed Values	Study II Control Group (N = 50)		Study II Experimental Group (N = 50)		Study III Control Group (N = 150)		Study III Experimental Group (N = 150)	
		F	M	F	M	F	M	F	M
307:E53	How does your wife (husband) feel about this behavior?								
	1. Strongly dislikes			10	10	3	1	14	8
	2. Moderately dislikes			6	8	2	0	12	10
	3. Mildly dislikes					0	0	13	7
	4. Generally tolerant or indifferent			13	8	8	2	10	16
	5. ?			2	5	0	0	4	12
	6. Feels sorry for him					0	0	0	4
	7. Hadn't noticed them							0	1
	8. Doesn't dislike it but doesn't want him to do it (for his own sake)					0	0	0	1
308:E54-55	What have you tried to do about this behavior?[84]								
	1. Suggested modification			5	3	0	0	0	2
	2. Nothing; overtly ignored it			20	26	1	0	41	39
	3. Nothing; no inner feelings about it			3	0	10	2	2	4
	4. Told him to slow down			0	1	2	0	2	4
309:E56	How much does the child talk now as compared with other children?								
	1. Much more than average	3	5	7	6	25	16	24	21
	2. Somewhat more than average	19	16	14	15	53	55	40	46
	3. About average	23	25	18	20	65	71	74	68
	4. Somewhat less than average	5	4	8	8	5	8	8	14
	5. Much less than average	0	0	0	1	2	0	2	1
	6. Can't say	0	0	2	0	0	0	2	0

[84] For both Studies II and III there were 18 additional things reported, each by fewer than three of the informants represented in any one column of the table; 1 of these 18 was reported by the control and 18 by the experimental group respondents.

310:E57 In comparison with other children, how much is the child permitted to talk at the dinner table? (Study II: Is the child permitted to talk at the dinner table?)

1. Much more than average	12	11	9	10
2. Somewhat more than average	48	33	41	36
3. About average	81	99	87	92
4. Somewhat less than average	7	5	8	7
5. Much less than average	1	2	0	1
6. Can't say	1	0	5	4
†7. Yes	49	48	48	46
†8. No	1	1	1	4

311:E58 Has he always been?

1. Yes	49	50	45	45
	139	145	138	134
2. No	1	0	4	5
	8	4	7	13
3. ?	0	0	0	0
	3	1	3	1

312:E59 In comparison with other children, how much is he permitted to when guests are present? (Study II: Is he permitted to when guests are present?)

1. Much more than average	7	4	4	7
2. Somewhat more than average	30	32	19	21
3. About average	103	102	109	104
4. Somewhat less than average	9	11	14	10
5. Much less than average	1	0	0	2
6. Can't say	0	1	4	6
†7. Yes	48	48	43	47
†8. No	2	2	5	2

313:E60 In comparison with other children, how much was the child taught to speak pieces? (Study II: Was the child taught to speak pieces?)

1. Much more than average	3	2	3	4
2. Somewhat more than average	17	15	14	11
3. About average	66	66	88	85

		Study II				Study III			
Item No.: IBM Card and Column No.	Item; or Question and Response Codings; or Computed Values	Control Group (N = 50)		Experimental Group (N = 50)		Control Group (N = 150)		Experimental Group (N = 150)	
		F	M	F	M	F	M	F	M
	4. Somewhat less than average	0	0	2	0	42	44	34	32
	5. Much less than average	36	31	35	44	19	21	6	15
	6. Can't say	14	18	7	6	2	2	5	3
314:E61	In comparison with other children, how much was he called on to perform before outsiders? (Study II: Was he sometimes called on to perform before outsiders?)								
	1. Much more than average					2	0	2	2
	2. Somewhat more than average					13	8	8	9
	3. About average					73	63	74	58
	4. Somewhat less than average					28	40	34	41
	5. Much less than average					30	34	29	38
	6. Can't say					2	4	3	2
	†7. Yes	30	26	30	37				
	†8. No	18	19	9	13				
315:E62	What was his usual attitude toward such requests? (Study II: demands?)								
	1. Cried	0	0	2	1	0	0	0	0
	2. Refused	0	1	2	4	10	11	13	20
	3. Asked not to	2	3	2	5	4	2	7	6
	4. Willing, though not eager	10	13	7	8	53	57	45	41
	5. Eager to	16	10	14	19	45	37	38	38
	6. ?	0	0	3	1	0	1	2	2
	7. Has never been called on					33	30	41	40
	8. Shy					5	11	2	1
	9. Half of time refused; half of time eager to					0	0	1	0
	10. Eager to around family; refused around strangers					0	1	0	0

316:E63 — What would you do today if the child should break into a conversation between you and a friend?85

Item	1	2	3	4	5	6	7	8
1. Reprimand him; ask him to be quiet; tell him to wait until you are through talking	22	26	22	28	100	88	99	99
2. Indicate disapproval, as by frown, but say nothing	10	1	2	2	3	2	6	7
3. Indicate no disapproval; let him continue	12	16	20	16	21	24	30	29
4. Sometimes reprimand him, sometimes indicate no disapproval, depends on situation					18	15	4	2
5. Try to distract him (by having child get something to show to the adult or by telling him what to play with); divert his attention								
6. Ask him to wait until you are through talking, but he won't so let him talk					0	3	0	1
7. Let child finish talking, then reprimand him for interrupting					2	3	1	4
8. ?; never happens					3	11	5	5
†9. Ask child to wait	7	7	2	1	1	1	4	0

317:E64 — How often do you suppose he is cut off each day without being allowed to finish what he has to say?

Item	1	2	3	4	5	6	7	8
1. Several times a day	6		15	57	47	60	67	
2. At least once a day	3		9	37	37	31	29	
3. Less than once a day	6		7	11	14	20	24	
4. Hardly ever	32		17	33	43	24	21	
5. Never	1		2	10	6	11	9	
6. ?				2	0	4	0	

85For both Studies II and III there were 10 additional actions reported, each by fewer than three of the informants represented in any one column of the table; 7 of these 10 were reported by the control and 6 by the experimental group respondents in Study II gave more than one response.

Item No.: IBM Card and Column No.	Item; or Question and Response Codings; or Computed Values	Study II Control Group (N = 50) F	M	Study II Experimental Group (N = 50) F	M	Study III Control Group (N = 150) F	M	Study III Experimental Group (N = 150) F	M
318:E65	How sensitive was (Study II: is) the child about his speech defect?								
	1. Very sensitive			10	15	0	1	7	7
	2. Moderately sensitive			4	11	0	0	4	14
	3. Mildly sensitive			15	13	2	2	21	25
	4. Not sensitive; apparently doesn't feel there is anything wrong with his speech			20	11	70	73	75	55
	5. Not sensitive; but probably feels there is something wrong with his speech			1	0	2	2	39	45
	6. ?					0	0	4	4
319:E67	If the child feels there is something wrong with his speech, whom does he blame for it? (Study II: Whom does the child blame for his stuttering?)								
	1. No one			50	48	2	2	62	84
	2. Himself			0	0	0	0	3	0
	3. ?							4	9
	4. Mother and father							1	0
	5. Once blamed uncle			0	1				
	6. Uncle "from whom he learned to stutter"[86]			0	1				
320:E68 321:E69	Why?[86] How concerned are you now about the child's stuttering?								
	1. Very much concerned					1	2	39	48
	2. Moderately concerned					1	0	41	47
	3. Mildly concerned					5	9	54	43
	4. Not at all					67	74	16	12

[86]Only six responses were obtained.

322:E70 How concerned is your wife (husband) now about the child's stuttering?

1. Very much concerned	1	0	50	39
2. Moderately concerned	1	1	45	44
3. Mildly concerned	3	4	46	48
4. Not at all	69	77	7	16
5. ?	0	3	2	3

323:E71 How ashamed are you of the child's speech now?

1. Very much	1		0	0	3	2
2. Moderately	2		0	0	1	5
3. Mildly			1	0	7	12
4. Not at all	41	40	86	96	139	131
5. ?			1	0	0	0
†6. Somewhat	7	9			0	0

324:E72 How ashamed is your wife (husband) of the child's speech now?

1. Very much	1		0	0	3	1
2. Moderately			0	0	2	3
3. Mildly	1		1	1	8	9
4. Not at all	40	40	85	94	132	128
5. ?	1		2	1	5	9
†6. Somewhat	8	5				

325:E73-74 Are there any other stutterers in your family? (Study II: Does any-one else in your family stutter?)[87]

1. None	36	34	30	26	142	141	115	115
2. Paternal grandmother	0	0	0	0	0	0	0	0
3. Paternal grandfather	0	0	0	0	0	0	0	0
4. Maternal grandmother	0	0	0	3	0	0	0	0
5. Maternal grandfather	0	0	3	1	0	0	3	0
6. Paternal uncle	0	0	1	0	0	0	0	0

[87]Some respondents in Study II gave more than one response, as coded. In Study II the total numbers of persons in the immediate families and among blood relatives reported as stutterers by the control group fathers and mothers and the experimental group fathers and mothers, respectively, were 7, 16, 27, and 30. In Study III the corresponding totals were 10, 9, 47, and 50.

Item No.: IBM Card and Column No.	Item; or Question and Response Codings; or Computed Values	Study II				Study III			
		Control Group (N = 50)		Experimental Group (N = 50)		Control Group (N = 150)		Experimental Group (N = 150)	
		F	M	F	M	F	M	F	M
7.	Paternal aunt					0	0	0	0
8.	Maternal uncle					0	0	0	0
9.	Maternal aunt					0	0	0	0
10.	Father of child	3			4	1	0	12	1
11.	Mother of child		1			0	0	0	0
12.	Brother of child					0	0	0	0
13.	Sister of child			3	3	1	0	0	5
14.	Sibling of child (unspecified)	0	1			0	0	5	7
15.	Maternal cousin					0	0	0	0
16.	Paternal cousin					0	0	1	0
17.	More distant relative	3	7	5	12		3	3	6
18.	Maternal uncle/aunt		5		4	2	6	3	4
19.	Paternal uncle/aunt	0	1	9	3	2		1	1
20.	Cousin (unspecified)	1	2	2	3	0	0	0	2
21.	Mother; maternal cousin					0	0	0	1
22.	Mother; maternal uncle					0	0	1	2
23.	Mother; maternal grandfather					0	0	4	1
24.	Father and sibling of child					0	0	1	1
25.	Father; paternal uncle/aunt					1	0	1	1
26.	Father; paternal uncle					0	0	1	1
27.	Father; paternal grandfather					1	0	1	0
28.	Father; sibling; paternal grandfather					0	0	0	0
29.	Maternal grandfather; maternal uncle; maternal cousin					0	0	1	0
30.	Maternal aunt; maternal uncle					0	0	0	1
31.	Maternal uncle; maternal cousin					0	0	1	1
32.	Maternal cousins (2)					0	0	1	1
33.	Paternal grandfather; paternal uncle					0	0	0	0
34.	Paternal uncle; cousin					0	0	0	1
35.	Paternal cousins (2)					0	0	1	0

326:E75-76 Which ones of these have you personally observed stuttering?[88]

	140	135	106	104
1. None	0	0	0	0
2. Maternal grandfather	0	3	0	3
3. Maternal aunt/uncle	1	0	12	6
4. Father	1	0	4	1
5. Father; paternal uncle/aunt	1	6	5	7
6. Sibling	0		3	4
7. Cousin				

327* Demonstrate or describe what the stuttering of each is or was like.[89]

328:E77-78 What other stutterers do you know by direct contact?[90]

	140	135	106	104
1. None	23	39	53	70
2. Neighborhood child	3	20	7	20
3. Neighborhood adult	2	4	3	3
4. Schoolmate of case	0	1	1	4
5. Employee	0	0	3	1
6. Business acquaintance; fellow workman	21	5	17	7
7. Schoolmate of parent	10	18	13	5
8. Business acquaintance; friends	2	0	3	0
9. Church friend	2	3	0	1
10. Business acquaintance; friend	4	0	1	0
11. ?	2	3	2	1
12. Relative by marriage	3	1	1	8
13. Close friend	1	13	3	3
14. Friend	6		9	5
15. Neighborhood boy; schoolmate of parent	0	3	0	1

[88] There were two single relatives and 15 combinations of two or more relatives, each reported by fewer than three of the informants represented in any one column of the table; 1 of these was reported by the control and 16 were reported by the experimental group respondents.

[89] The only responses obtained were from 8 mothers and 7 fathers in the experimental group.

[90] There were 101 additional persons reported, each by fewer than three of the informants represented in any one column of the table; 73 of these 101 were reported by the control and 43 by the experimental group respondents.

Item No.: IBM Card and Column No.	Item; or Question and Response Codings; or Computed Values	Study II				Study III			
		Control Group (N = 50)		Experimental Group (N = 50)		Control Group (N = 150)		Experimental Group (N = 150)	
		F	M	F	M	F	M	F	M
	16. Business acquaintance; schoolmate of parent					9	1	1	0
	17. Friend of parents; classmate of parents					4	1	0	0
	18. Schoolmates of parent					2	3	0	0
329*	How well do (did) you know each of these stutterers?91								
	1. Intimate acquaintance	9	3	8	5	23	17	33	38
	2. Knew quite well	11	11	25	13	56	40	42	30
	3. Casual acquaintance	14	12	17	21	70	68	50	57
330:E79	How do (did) you react to their stuttering?								
	1. Bothered very much					4	10	8	16
	2. Bothered moderately					19	22	14	17
	3. Bothered mildly					26	16	29	15
	4. Indifferent					54	38	51	49
	5. Mainly indifferent, but occasionally finds it sort of interesting and feels it makes the person a little more likable								
	6. ?					2	0	1	0
	7. Feels sorry for him					1	0	1	2
	8. Admiration					19	29	10	15
	9. Embarrassment					3	0	0	0
	10. Enjoyed it as a child					1	1	0	0
331:E80	How closely was the child in contact with any stutterer in the family or among acquaintances?								
	1. Intimate contact		5		9	4	8	34	39

91In addition to the responses reported, the following were reported by two experimental group fathers in Study III: "Frequent contact" and "Also in contact with a number of boys at camp who stutter."

	A	B	C	D	E	F
2. Frequent contact	7	6	15	20	11	13
3. Infrequent contact	3	4	17	28	27	27
4. Never in contact	33	31	108	90	73	68
5. ?	2	0	1	2	0	0
6. Intimate contact but has never stuttered in the child's presence						

332:F6 How closely does the child's stuttering resemble in detail that of any other stutterer with whom he was or is in frequent or intimate contact?

	A	B	C	D	E	F
			1	0	0	1
1. Very much	4	6			15	14
2. Moderately	1	0			9	11
3. Slightly	1	3			13	14
4. Not at all	10	11			9	15
5. ?	1	2			1	3

333:F7 How important do you think contact of the child with other stutterers might be?

	A	B	C	D	E	F
1. Strongly believes it is very important	10	15	7	14	15	16
2. Suspects it might be important	3	4	16	17	17	17
3. Strongly believes it has some importance	2	2	12	6	5	3
4. Suspects it might have some importance	13	7	31	39	14	16
5. Strongly believes it unimportant			34	27	40	44
6. Suspects it might be unimportant			44	38	22	18
7. ?			6	8	29	29
†8. Believes it unimportant	20	21				

334:F8 Did you try to prevent contact of the child with other stutterers?

	A	B	C	D	E	F
1. Tried very hard always			0	1	1	0
2. Tried usually			1	1	0	0
3. Tried occasionally			0	0	1	6
4. No	49	47	149	147	147	142
†5. Yes	0	1				

335:F9 Does the child know about their stuttering?

	A	B	C	D	E	F
1. Yes	19	19	25	18	13	17

115

Item No.: IBM Card and Column No.	Item; or Question and Response Codings; or Computed Values	Study II Control Group (N = 50) F	M	Study II Experimental Group (N = 50) F	M	Study III Control Group (N = 150) F	M	Study III Experimental Group (N = 150) F	M
336:F10	2. No			23	27	81	73	77	74
	3. ?			6	2	3	11	14	17
	If yes, how did he learn about it?								
	1. He heard them and asked about it			0	1	4	2	1	1
	2. He heard them and commented about it			11	8	3	6	1	2
	3. I told him about their speech			0	1	1	1	3	2
	4. He overheard us talking about their speech			4	2	2	4	0	5
	5. He overheard others talking about their speech			0	1	1	1	0	0
	6. ?			0	5	2	3	2	1
	7. Relative told him about it			0	0	0	0	1	1
	8. He heard the person talk (stutter)					6	8	6	4
	† 9. Stuttering jokes			1	0				
	†10. In speech class			1	0				
	†11. In speech clinic			0	1				
	†12. He heard			2	1				
337:F11	During the development of the child's speech (before he began to stutter) how much did you compare him with stutterers?								
	1. Almost constantly			1	2	0	0	0	1
	2. Moderately often					0	1	3	2
	3. Occasionally					10	8	7	4
	4. Never			46	42	139	141	136	142
	5. Compared child in general development with other stutterers					1	0	0	0
	† 6. Quite often			0	1				
	† 7. Hardly ever			3	2				
338:F12	Had you read about stuttering before your child began to stutter? (Controls: during the child's speech development?)								
	1. A great deal					1	1	3	2

		1	2	3	4	5	6
	2. Quite a bit	4	7	2	3		
	3. Slightly	33	43	31	32		
	4. None	112	99	114	113		
	†5. Yes					9	10
	†6. No					41	39
339:F13	Had you discussed stuttering before your child began to stutter? (Controls: during the child's speech development?)						
	1. A great deal	0	2	2	1		
	2. Quite a bit	2	2	4	6		
	3. Slightly	28	21	37	34		
	4. None	120	125	107	109		
	†5. Yes					8	12
	†6. No					42	38
340:F14	How much afraid were you that your child would stutter?						
	1. Very much afraid	0	2	2	0	1	0
	2. Moderately afraid	1	1	4	4		
	3. Slightly afraid	1	3	2	1		
	4. Not at all afraid, although had occasionally considered it	11	8	5	10		
	5. Not at all afraid; had never considered it	137	136	137	135	48	48
	†6. Rather afraid					0	4
	†7. Not very much afraid					2	3
341:F15	How afraid was your wife (husband) that your child would stutter?						
	1. Very much afraid	0	1	0	1	1	1
	2. Moderately afraid	0	1	3	1	0	0
	3. Slightly afraid	3	1	1	2	1	3
	4. Not at all afraid, although had occasionally considered it	10	7	6	6	2	2
	5. Not at all afraid; had never considered it	133	138	134	132	47	44
	6. ?	4	2	6	8	3	5
	†7. Rather afraid					0	0
	†8. Not very much afraid					0	0

117

Item No.: IBM Card and Column No.	Item; or Question and Response Codings; or Computed Values	Study II				Study III			
		Control Group (N = 50)		Experimental Group (N = 50)		Control Group (N = 150)		Experimental Group (N = 150)	
		F	M	F	M	F	M	F	M
342:F16	Did you look for resemblances between your child and any stutterers you knew or had read about?								
	1. Very often					0	1	0	2
	2. Quite often					0	1	3	2
	3. Occasionally					8	4	6	6
	4. No			43	40	140	144	138	140
	5. ?			0	0	2	0	2	0
	6. Yes			6	8				
343*	What do you think causes stuttering?[92]								
344*	What do you think caused your child's stuttering?[93]								
345*	How do you think stuttering can be overcome?[94]								
	1. Relax, relieve tension, keep calm	2	3	3	3	7	16	13	10
	2. Find out what the cause is					7	3	2	0
	3. Send to speech correctionist; speech therapy					19	16	7	6
	4. Get practice in speaking					9	2	1	0
	5. Encourage child to talk					2	5	1	1
	6. Talk more					8	2	1	0
	7. Slow down rate	2	9	6	5	21	13	16	9
	8. Speech exercises	7	1	1	3	4	6	3	2
	9. Psychotherapy; psychoanalysis					3	2	0	0

[92] see Table 54 (Chapter 6), for a tabulation of classified responses.
[93] see Table 54 (Chapter 6), for a tabulation of classified responses.
[94] For both Studies II and III 305 additional responses were made, each by fewer than three of the informants represented in any one column of the table; 123 of these 305 responses were made by the control and 182 by the experimental group respondents. Some respondents in both studies gave more than one response.

10. Build confidence				11	7	7	1
11. Person must overcome it himself; self-control				12	5	2	0
12. Think out words or ideas before speaking	0	0	3	9	4	6	3
13. Change environment; improve home conditions				5	7	2	9
14. Do not be concerned; "do nothing"; give child attention	0	4	0	3	3	1	0
15. Be patient with child				3	7	4	13
16. Do not rush child				0	4	0	0
17. Give child security, attention, and affection				2	17	2	0
18. Remove pressures; solve conflicts				3	10	1	1
19. Will outgrow stuttering				0	0	4	5
20. Parent should not react to stuttering				0	0	4	0
21. Rest more; get plenty of rest				0	0	3	1
22. Ignore it				7	21	9	7
23. Stuttering can't be overcome				3	0	0	2
24. ?	9	6	13	10	25	18	35	50
†25. Help self when child gets older	0	0	2	5			
†26. Training	0	0	3	0			
†27. Follow clinic instructions	0	0	3	1			
†28. Work with them	8	1	0	0			
346* How do you account for any improvement (you think there has been) in the child's speech?95							
1. More relaxed						8	7
2. Age, getting older; growing out of it						4	2
3. More confidence in self						0	3

95There were 18 additional reasons reported, by experimental group respondents only, each by fewer than three of the informants represented in any one column of the table. Some respondents gave more than one response.

Item No.: IBM Card and Column No.	Item; or Question and Response Codings; or Computed Values	Study II Control Group (N = 50) F	M	Study II Experimental Group (N = 50) F	M	Study III Control Group (N = 150) F	M	Study III Experimental Group (N = 150) F	M
	4. Growth of vocabulary; learning to express ideas							3	0
	5. Speech is being let alone; not correcting him; parents are disregarding it (e.g., repetitions, etc.)							2	3
	6. Parents more relaxed, assuring, attentive, patient; calmer home atmosphere							0	8
	7. ?							20	14
	8. No improvement, or not enough improvement							104	103
347:F19	How well do you feel you have handled the speech problem?								
	1. Very well; the best possible way			27	15			48	39
	2. Moderately (Study II: pretty well; an occasional mistake)			9	9			41	41
	3. Not very well; many mistakes			9	14			19	16
	4. Not at all well; all wrong			2	7			1	3
	5. ?			3	5			8	13
	6. Best way knew how							31	34
	7. Not done enough							0	3
348:F20	Would you handle it very differently if you were to meet the problem again?								
	1. Very differently			4	11			9	15
	2. Somewhat differently			17	16			46	50
	3. About the same			27	22			82	74
	4. ?			0	1			11	10

349:F21-22 What would you do differently?96

1. Would do nothing		46	37
2. Take the child to a "speech doctor" sooner		13	10
3. Have more patience		1	5
4. Would ignore it more at the start		0	9
5. Wouldn't tell him to take it easy, slow down, etc. (wouldn't correct him)		3	7
6. Find out more about it sooner		3	0

350:F23 What foreign language have you taught or tried to teach your child?

1. None	139	141	143	145
2. French	1	2	0	0
3. Spanish	1	1	0	1
4. German	0	2	1	1
5. Danish	0	0	1	0
6. Bohemian	1	0	1	0
7. Norwegian	2	1	0	0
8. Swedish	0	0	1	0
9. Hawaiian	0	1	0	0
10. Hebrew	3	1	2	2
11. French and German	2	1	0	0
12. English	0	0	1	1
13. Greek	0	0	1	1
14. Words in French, German, and Dutch	0	1	0	0
15. Hungarian, some Dutch	1	0	0	0

351:F24 Do you and your wife (husband) customarily correct each other's grammar at home?

1. Very often; as a regular thing	2	3	1	0
2. Moderately often	6	5	3	6

96There were 50 additional responses made, each by fewer than three of the informants represented in any one column of the table. Some respondents gave more than one response.

Item No.: IBM Card and Column No.	Item; or Question and Response Codings; or Computed Values	Study II Control Group (N = 50)		Study II Experimental Group (N = 50)		Study III Control Group (N = 150)		Study III Experimental Group (N = 150)	
		F	M	F	M	F	M	F	M
	3. Occasionally					80	71	64	55
	4. Never					62	71	82	89
352:F25	How often do you correct your child's grammar each day?								
	1. 5 to 25 times a day					3	2	4	0
	2. 5 to 25 times a week					22	19	17	11
	3. Now and then (5 to 20 times a month)					39	48	27	33
	4. Some but less often than 3 above					48	44	38	54
	5. Never					37	37	62	52
	6. ?					1	0	2	0
353:F26	Do you customarily correct one another's pronunciation at home?								
	1. Very often; as a regular thing					5	0	3	1
	2. Moderately often					3	7	7	4
	3. Occasionally					83	83	66	68
	4. No					59	60	74	77
354:F27	How often do you correct your child's pronunciation?								
	1. 5 to 25 times a day					3	0	6	3
	2. 5 to 25 times a week					26	24	31	23
	3. Now and then (5 to 20 times a month)					56	50	32	42
	4. Some but less often than 3 above					46	65	49	48
	5. Never					19	11	32	34
355:F28	Comparing your child's vocabulary with that of other children his age, do you think his vocabulary is:								
	1. Superior	29	17	13	15	69	63	61	51
	2. Average	15	29	33	33	69	75	76	86
	3. Inferior	4	1	2	2	12	11	12	12
	4. ?	0	0	1	0	0	1	1	1

356:F29	Comparing your child's grammar with that of other children his age, do you think his grammar is:				
	1. Superior	47	45	42	31
	2. Average	87	88	94	103
	3. Inferior	14	13	14	13
	4. ?	2	4	0	3
357:F30	Do you think about your child's stuttering (control group: speech) when you go to bed?				
	1. Very often; as a regular thing	1	0	4	10
	2. Moderately often	1	2	3	12
	3. Occasionally	2	4	28	35
	4. No	145	142	115	93
	† 5. Yes	39	37		
	No	11	13		
358:F31	Have you ever asked a doctor (Study II: "or speech expert") about your child's speech?				
	1. More than once or more than one doctor	0	0	39	47
	2. Once	2	3	49	45
	3. No	148	147	61	58
	4. ?			1	0
	† 5. Yes	11	13		
	† 6. No	39	37		
359:F32	Have you ever (before) consulted a speech expert about your child's speech?				
	1. More than once or more than one expert	0	0	17	18
	2. Once	1	2	38	43
	3. No	149	148	92	89
	4. ?	0	0	3	0
360:F33	Do you talk anxiously to your neighbors about his speech? (In Study II the word "anxiously" was not used)				
	1. Very often; as a regular thing	0	0	1	2

Item No.: IBM Card and Column No.	Item; or Question and Response Codings; or Computed Values	Study II				Study III			
		Control Group (N = 50)		Experimental Group (N = 50)		Control Group (N = 150)		Experimental Group (N = 150)	
		F	M	F	M	F	M	F	M
	2. Moderately often					1	0	2	11
	3. Occasionally					4	2	27	68
	4. No			33	25	145	148	120	69
	†5. Yes			16	25				
361:F34	Do you talk anxiously to your family and relatives about his speech?								
	1. Very often; as a regular thing					0	0	4	7
	2. Moderately often					0	0	10	22
	3. Occasionally					6	4	75	92
	4. No					144	146	61	29
362:F35	How much do you care about what outsiders know and think about your child's speech?								
	1. Very sensitive			0	0	3	3	8	12
	2. Moderately sensitive			1	3	12	6	9	11
	3. Slightly sensitive					13	15	33	36
	4. Not at all sensitive			45	41	122	126	100	91
	†5. Rather sensitive			1	4				
	†6. Not very sensitive			3	2				
363:F36	How much does your wife (husband) care?								
	1. Very sensitive			1	1	4	2	10	9
	2. Moderately sensitive			2	5	16	7	15	9
	3. Slightly sensitive					18	15	38	34
	4. Not at all sensitive			39	39	109	121	84	87
	5. ?			2	3	3	5	3	11
	†6. Rather sensitive			1	1				
	†7. Not very sensitive			5	1				

364* Describe your impression of what normal speech is like.[97]

1. Nonfluencies are normal if not excessive			64	73	17	25
2. Nonfluencies are permissible if they are occasional, or minimal; some are—some aren't			31	34	49	50
3. Nonfluencies are not permissible			28	25	55	37
4. Nonfluencies occur but are wrong			12	3	1	1
5. Nonfluencies occur only under pressure			5	2	2	6
6. No specific answer to this question			10	13	26	31

365:F37 Of what sex are most of the child's friends?

1. All same sex as child			18	16	12	16
2. Most same sex as child			56	53	64	66
3. All opposite sex			1	3	5	4
4. Most opposite sex			17	21	25	30
5. About half and half			56	56	44	34
6. ?			1	0	0	0
7. Adult females			1	0	0	0
8. Friends are adults			0	1	0	0
†9. Opposite sex as child	35	30				
†10. Same sex	3	2				
†11. Mixed	11	17				

366:F38 What is the average age of the child's companions as compared with the child's own age?[98]

1. Average more than 2 years older			10	11	15	22
2. Chiefly older, up to 2 years older	7	1	43	33	49	36

[97]More specific responses were reported than those listed; a very considerable variety of individual wordings have been grouped as here indicated for practical purposes of presentation.
[98]Some respondents in Study II gave more than one response.

Item No.; IBM Card and Column No.	Item; or Question and Response Codings; or Computed Values	Study II				Study III			
		Control Group (N = 50)		Experimental Group (N = 50)		Control Group (N = 150)		Experimental Group (N = 150)	
		F	M	F	M	F	M	F	M
	3. Chiefly younger, average more than 2 years younger		1		3	2	0	0	1
	4. Same age as subject (Study II: child)		38		39	85	91	77	76
	5. Chiefly younger, up to 2 years younger					4	9	7	10
	6. Several playmates about 2 years younger and several playmates about 2 years older					2	2	0	0
	7. About half more than 2 years older; about half up to 2 years younger					3	2	0	0
	8. Half up to 2 years older; half up to 2 years younger					0	1	2	2
	9. Half same age; half up to 2 years younger					0	0	0	1
	10. Half same age; half up to 2 years older					0	1	0	1
	†11. Adults		3		2				
	†12. Average more than 2 years' difference in age		2		4				
367:F39	How often does your child go to a friend's house to play?								
	1. Every day					69	59	62	49
	2. Every two or three days					51	51	33	43
	3. Once a week					15	19	22	18
	4. Two or three times a month					6	7	14	13
	5. Once a month					6	3	4	9
	6. Less than once a month					1	5	9	12
	7. ?					0	0	2	0
	8. Never					2	6	4	6
368:F40	How often do one or more of the child's friends come to the house to play?								

(Study II: How often do the child's friends come to the house?)

1. Every day	26	24	68	63	68	57
2. Every two or three days	12	7	54	52	40	44
3. Once a week	6	9	13	20	13	16
4. Two or three times a month	1	3	8	5	10	10
5. Once a month	2	3	5	5	3	8
6. Less than once a month	1	3	1	4	9	9
7. ?	0	0	0	0	2	0
8. Never			1	1	5	6

369:F41 Do you like to have them come to the house?

1. Very much like			70	84	68	86
2. Moderately like			60	57	57	47
3. Indifferent			13	3	16	6
4. Moderately dislike			4	4	7	10
5. Very much dislike			2	2	1	0
6. ?			1	0	0	0
†7. Yes	37	45				
†8. No	1	1				
†9. Qualified yes	12	4				

370:F42 Does your wife (husband) like to have them come to the house?

1. Very much like			61	61	75	62
2. Moderately like			75	67	58	37
3. Indifferent			7	10	6	30
4. Moderately dislike			5	6	9	13
5. Very much dislike			0	3	1	1
6. ?	0	1	2	2	0	4
†7. Yes	35	43				
†8. No	1	4				
†9. Qualified yes	14	2				

371:F43 How often does the child play with them?

1. Every day (Study II: daily)	37	41	130	122	116	112
2. Every two or three days			15	23	18	20
3. Once a week			2	2	9	7

Item No.: IBM Card and Column No.	Item; or Question and Response Codings; or Computed Values	Study II Control Group (N = 50) F	M	Experimental Group (N = 50) F	M	Study III Control Group (N = 150) F	M	Experimental Group (N = 150) F	M
	4. Two or three times a month					1	1	1	2
	5. Once a month					1	0	1	4
	6. Less than once a month					0	1	3	3
	7. ?					0	0	1	0
	8. Never		0		0	1	1	0	2
	9. Every four to five days					0	0	1	0
	†10. Quite often		8		3				
	†11. Only occasionally		5		5				
372:F44	Compared with other children, how well does your child play with other children?								
	1. Much better than average	1	4	2	4	10	8	9	8
	2. Somewhat better than average	18	16	11	8	39	38	29	14
	3. About average	26	27	30	30	92	97	90	108
	4. Somewhat less well than average	5	3	7	7	9	5	21	18
	5. Much less well than average	0	0	0	1	0	2	1	2
373:F45	As compared with other children, how mischievous is your child?								
	1. Much more than average	1	1	1	1	6	3	4	8
	2. Somewhat more than average	7	3	11	8	32	26	24	23
	3. About average	25	23	27	25	82	79	92	83
	4. Somewhat less than average	14	17	8	14	24	29	22	31
	5. Much less than average	3	6	3	2	5	13	8	5
	6. Can't say	0	0	0	0	1	0	0	0
374:F46	Do you wish he were more or less mischievous?								
	1. Less					22	30	24	29
	2. More					4	3	6	7
	3. Stay as is					124	117	118	114
	4. ?					0	0	2	0

375:F47

As compared with other children, how easily does your child get tired?

1. Much more than average	0	0	1	0	1	1	3	4
2. Somewhat more than average	7	8	6	4	17	13	13	26
3. About average	24	27	22	28	91	88	78	86
4. Somewhat less than average	18	15	14	11	27	35	32	22
5. Much less than average	1	0	7	7	13	12	21	12
6. ?	0	0	0	0	1	0	3	0

376:F48

As compared with other children, how good a sense of humor does your child have?

1. Much more than average	4	2	5	8	18	21	13	9
2. Somewhat more than average	24	25	15	16	55	36	49	55
3. About average	17	21	28	23	70	88	81	72
4. Somewhat less than average	4	2	2	3	7	4	7	11
5. Much less than average	0	0	0	0	0	0	0	2
6. ?	0	0	0	0	0	1	0	1
7. Unasked	1	0	0	0	0	0	0	0

377:F49

As compared with other children, how alert is your child?

1. Much more than average	7	6	3	2	22	18	26	18
2. Somewhat more than average	21	27	16	18	66	60	58	55
3. About average	18	14	28	25	61	71	62	72
4. Somewhat less than average	3	3	3	5	1	1	4	5
5. Much less than average	1	0	0	0	0	0	0	0

378:F50

Do you wish he were less or more alert?

1. Less	3	4	2	3	0
2. More	14	17	8	14	19
3. Stay as is	133	129	140	133	130
4. ?	0	0	0	0	1

379:F51

As compared with other children, how cooperative is your child?

1. Much more than average	6	9	2	3	6	6	8	8
2. Somewhat more than average	15	14	14	11	44	42	35	33
3. About average	23	21	26	24	89	86	84	83
4. Somewhat less than average	6	5	6	10	11	13	21	25

Item No.: IBM Card and Column No.	Item; or Question and Response Codings; or Computed Values	Study II Control Group (N = 50)		Study II Experimental Group (N = 50)		Study III Control Group (N = 150)		Study III Experimental Group (N = 150)	
		F	M	F	M	F	M	F	M
	5. Much less than average	0	0	2	2	0	2	0	1
	6. ?	0	0	0	0	0	1	2	0
380:F52	Do you wish he were more or less cooperative?								
	1. Less					1	2	1	1
	2. More					58	53	48	54
	3. Stay as is					91	94	99	95
	4. ?					0	1	2	0
381:F53	As compared with other children, how persistent (in getting a job done) is your child?								
	1. Much more than average	6	5	5	6	6	9	16	11
	2. Somewhat more than average	11	15	13	11	35	33	33	29
	3. About average	20	25	21	23	94	86	76	74
	4. Somewhat less than average	12	4	10	9	15	18	21	34
	5. Much less than average	1	1	1	1	0	3	1	1
	6. ?	0	0	0	0	0	1	3	1
382:F54	As compared with other children, how rebellious is your child?								
	1. Much more than average	0	0	0	2	7	6	7	6
	2. Somewhat more than average	4	7	10	12	22	27	37	28
	3. About average	30	26	34	26	99	93	92	97
	4. Somewhat less than average	16	14	4	8	17	19	8	16
	5. Much less than average	0	3	2	2	5	5	5	2
	6. ?	0	0	0	0	0	0	1	1
383:F55	As compared with other children, how friendly is your child toward his parents? (Study II: "toward his parents" not included)								
	1. Much more than average	5	4	9	11	12	16	14	10
	2. Somewhat more than average	19	25	20	11	53	56	34	47
	3. About average	22	16	19	23	85	75	97	86

	C1	C2	C3	C4	C5	C6	C7	C8
4. Somewhat less than average	4	4	2	0	4	2	4	4
5. Much less than average	0	0	0	0	1	0	1	0
6. ?	3	1	1	0	0	0	0	0

384:F56 As compared with other children, how able is your child to concentrate?

	C1	C2	C3	C4	C5	C6	C7	C8
1. Much more than average	10	15	10	6	0	3	5	3
2. Somewhat more than average	31	30	28	30	9	5	14	13
3. About average	87	91	99	100	29	30	26	26
4. Somewhat less than average	19	11	9	9	10	11	5	7
5. Much less than average	1	1	0	0	1	0	0	1
6. ?	3	2	4	5	0	0	0	0
7. Unasked	0	0	0	0	1	1	0	0

385:F57 As compared with other children, how aggressive is your child?

	C1	C2	C3	C4	C5	C6	C7	C8
1. Much more than average	7	17	8	10	3	3	3	1
2. Somewhat more than average	32	36	38	47	8	10	7	11
3. About average	83	73	76	65	25	21	27	18
4. Somewhat less than average	24	22	25	24	9	13	10	19
5. Much less than average	4	0	1	1	5	2	3	1
6. ?	0	2	2	3	0	1	0	0

386:F58 Do you wish he were less or more aggressive?

	C1	C2	C3	C4
1. Less	13	7	9	6
2. More	37	37	29	30
3. Stay as is	98	104	107	109
4. ?	2	2	5	3

387:F59 As compared with other children, how shy is your child?

	C1	C2	C3	C4
1. Much more than average	5	4	2	2
2. Somewhat more than average	29	25	24	12
3. About average	81	74	82	73
4. Somewhat less than average	27	36	33	47
5. Much less than average	8	10	8	16
6. ?	0	1	1	0

388:F60 As compared with other children, how cautious is your child about under-taking new things, going into

Item No.: IBM Card and Column No.	Item; or Question and Response Codings; or Computed Values	Study II				Study III			
		Control Group (N = 50)		Experimental Group (N = 50)		Control Group (N = 150)		Experimental Group (N = 150)	
		F	M	F	M	F	M	F	M
	different situations? (Study II: "How cautious is your child?")								
	1. Much more than average	4	2	7	4	1	5	8	8
	2. Somewhat more than average	18	22	13	17	25	21	29	40
	3. About average	19	15	20	23	75	79	70	75
	4. Somewhat less than average	9	11	8	5	38	32	37	22
	5. Much less than average	0	0	2	1	10	12	4	5
	6. ?	0	0	0	0	1	1	2	0
389:F61	Do you wish he were more or less cautious?								
	1. Less					15	11	23	23
	2. More					29	18	23	25
	3. Stay as is					105	120	104	99
	4. ?					1	1	0	3
390:F62	As compared with other children, how careless about his possessions is your child?								
	1. Much more than average	2	5	2	1	1	5	6	4
	2. Somewhat more than average	5	8	10	10	26	24	21	28
	3. About average	25	27	25	26	83	90	86	86
	4. Somewhat less than average	14	8	6	9	34	20	31	28
	5. Much less than average	4	2	7	4	4	11	6	4
	6. ?	0	0	0	0	2	0	0	0
391:F63	As compared with other children, how self-confident is your child? (Study II: "and free of shyness?")								
	1. Much more than average	4	2	3	2	9	5	8	5
	2. Somewhat more than average	11	13	8	7	53	36	31	28
	3. About average	21	21	27	21	72	95	93	92
	4. Somewhat less than average	13	13	10	17	13	12	17	22
	5. Much less than average	1	0	2	3	0	1	1	1
	6. ?	0	0	0	0	3	1	0	2

392:F64 Do you wish he were more or less self-confident?

1. Less	1	2	3	6
2. More	33	30	41	47
3. Stay as is	116	117	105	95
4. ?	0	0	1	2

393:F65 As compared with other children, how much picked on in school is your child?

1. Much more than average	0	1	0	0	0	2	2
2. Somewhat more than average	0	4	5	1	7	4	2
3. About average	13	26	27	48	47	30	39
4. Somewhat less than average	6	4	6	10	11	4	13
5. Much less than average	3	4	1	10	7	3	0
6. ?	1	3	3	16	12	27	14

394:F66 As compared with other children, how popular is your child?

1. Much more than average	4	5	4	8	5	6	5
2. Somewhat more than average	23	11	11	30	27	36	33
3. About average	18	31	26	102	110	96	97
4. Somewhat less than average	5	2	4	2	3	6	8
5. Much less than average	0	1	2	0	0	0	0
6. ?	0	0	2	8	5	6	7

395:F67-68 If your child is not very popular, why not? (Main reason)99

396:F69 Do you wish your child were more or less popular? (Study II: the phrase "or less" deleted)

1. Less	0	1	2	1
2. More	10	11	12	22
3. Stay as is	136	137	134	123
4. ?	3	0	2	4
†5. Yes	8	4	9	6
†6. No	42	45	40	43

99Responses were obtained from only 12 respondents in Study II and 17 in Study III, and in only 2 instances was the same response given by as many as 2 different informants. The reasons given were not remarkable, ranging from aggressiveness to shyness, with a few assorted ones such as "teases," "tattles," "possessive."

133

Item No.: IBM Card and Column No.	Item; or Question and Response Codings; or Computed Values	Study II Control Group (N = 50) F	M	Study II Experimental Group (N = 50) F	M	Study III Control Group (N = 150) F	M	Study III Experimental Group (N = 150) F	M
397:F70	As compared with other children, how much does your child fight?								
	1. Much more than average	0	1	0	0	2	0	1	4
	2. Somewhat more than average	5	5	4	4	12	14	12	15
	3. About average	15	21	25	27	94	85	100	97
	4. Somewhat less than average	29	16	14	11	30	40	29	28
	5. Much less than average	1	7	5	8	12	10	6	6
	6. ?	0	0	2	0	0	1	2	0
398:F71	As compared with other children, how much does your child show off?								
	1. Much more than average	2	1	1	1	2	3	2	1
	2. Somewhat more than average	11	5	13	7	37	25	22	17
	3. About average	24	34	27	28	95	91	104	104
	4. Somewhat less than average	11	6	6	11	13	30	21	26
	5. Much less than average	2	4	3	3	2	1	1	2
	6. ?	0	0	0	0	1	0	0	0
399:F72	As compared with other children, how much does your child daydream?								
	1. Much more than average	2	1	3	4	1	1	1	3
	2. Somewhat more than average	7	8	10	10	14	11	15	14
	3. About average	22	19	21	24	73	74	98	91
	4. Somewhat less than average	19	20	8	7	36	42	24	32
	5. Much less than average	0	2	2	1	10	14	3	5
	6. ?	0	0	6	3	15	8	9	5
400:F73	As compared with other children, how much does your child laugh?								
	1. Much more than average	4	1	4	1	13	13	7	10
	2. Somewhat more than average	22	19	18	11	60	39	48	36
	3. About average	23	28	27	35	76	94	92	95
	4. Somewhat less than average	1	2	1	3	1	4	3	7
	5. ?	0	0	0	0	0	0	0	2

401:F74 As compared with other children, how much does your child respect the rights of others?

1. Much more than average	1	3	3	1	3	5	4	3
2. Somewhat more than average	12	14	8	6	22	17	16	16
3. About average	32	20	30	32	103	108	106	106
4. Somewhat less than average	5	2	8	8	18	19	20	23
5. Much less than average	0	0	1	1	1	1	1	0
6. ?	0	1	0	0	3	0	3	1

402:F75 As compared with other children, how much does your child play alone?

1. Much more than average	2	2	1	7	1	5	11	10
2. Somewhat more than average	13	16	17	12	29	23	33	32
3. About average	14	12	19	21	71	73	81	76
4. Somewhat less than average	20	19	9	5	37	33	18	25
5. Much less than average	1	1	4	5	9	16	4	6
6. ?	0	0	0	0	3	0	3	1

403:F76 As compared with other children, how much does your child brag?

1. Much more than average	1	0	0	0	0	0	0	0
2. Somewhat more than average	3	9	8	4	9	7	9	9
3. About average	27	30	29	28	93	93	105	93
4. Somewhat less than average	16	7	4	12	28	26	26	29
5. Much less than average	2	4	6	3	12	15	3	11
6. ?	0	0	1	0	7	8	6	7

404:F77 As compared with other children, how much initiative does your child show?

1. Much more than average	3	1	2	2	8	8	9	4
2. Somewhat more than average	17	14	10	8	37	38	43	36
3. About average	20	26	29	24	97	84	92	100
4. Somewhat less than average	7	8	8	14	8	17	4	8
5. Much less than average	1	1	1	1	0	2	1	2
6. ?	0	0	0	0	0	1	0	0

405:F78 Do you wish your child had better manners or that his manners were not so good?

1. Better manners					69	64	50	58

Item No.: IBM Card and Column No.	Item; or Question and Response Codings; or Computed Values	Study II Control Group (N = 50) F	M	Study II Experimental Group (N = 50) F	M	Study III Control Group (N = 150) F	M	Study III Experimental Group (N = 150) F	M
	2. Not such good manners					7	3	0	0
	3. Stay as is					73	83	100	92
	4. Can't decide					1	0	0	0
406-462 (even)	How often has the following behavior occurred:100								
406:F79	Nervousness?								
	1. Very often (n)					1	5	11	17
	2. Quite often (n)					7	14	26	42
	3. Occasionally (n)					54	44	74	59
	4. Never		17		5	75	74	37	29
	5. ?					1	0	1	1
	6. Very often (p)					0	4	0	0
	7. Quite often (p)					2	3	0	1
	8. Occasionally					10	6	1	1
	†9. Often		15		32				
	†10. Seldom		17		13				
407:F80	If often, how do you feel about this behavior?								
	1. Very intolerant of it					0	9	7	21
	2. Moderately intolerant or disturbed					7	13	18	28
	3. Indifferent; no attitude apparent					2	1	3	2
	4. Moderately tolerant; not disturbed much					0	3	5	9
	5. Very tolerant; not disturbed at all					0	0	4	1
408:G6	Sleeplessness?								
	1. Very often (n)					3	2	6	4

100In coding, (n) means present time, during the past 30 days; (p) means prior to this, in the past, but not at the present time; Never means never in the past or at the present time.

2. Quite often (n)			3	2	11	8
3. Occasionally (n)			26	23	43	40
4. Never	25	29	100	103	87	92
5. ?			1	0	0	0
6. Very often (p)			2	5	0	0
7. Quite often (p)			2	2	0	1
8. Occasionally (p)			13	13	3	5
† 9. Often	3	7				
†10. Seldom	22	14				

409:G7 If often, how do you feel about this?

1. Very intolerant or disturbed			5	7	7	4
2. Moderately intolerant or disturbed			4	1	6	7
3. Indifferent; no attitude apparent			0	0	1	0
4. Moderately tolerant; not disturbed much			1	2	2	2
5. Very tolerant; not disturbed at all			1	1	1	0

410:G8 Nightmares?

1. Very often (n)			0	1	2	0
2. Quite often (n)			0	0	1	2
3. Occasionally (n)			30	28	59	54
4. Never	27	22	79	86	70	74
5. ?			2	1	0	0
6. Very often (p)			0	3	1	1
7. Quite often (p)			1	0	0	0
8. Occasionally (p)			38	31	17	19
† 9. Often	3	1				
†10. Seldom	20	27				

411:G9 If often, how do you feel about this?

1. Very intolerant or disturbed			1	2	1	1
2. Moderately intolerant or disturbed			0	2	3	1
3. Moderately tolerant; not disturbed much			0	0	0	0
4. Very tolerant; not disturbed at all			0	1	0	0

Item No.: IBM Card and Column No.	Item; or Question and Response Codings; or Computed Values	Study II Control Group (N = 50)		Experimental Group (N = 50)		Study III Control Group (N = 150)		Experimental Group (N = 150)	
		F	M	F	M	F	M	F	M
412:G10	Bed wetting?								
	1. Very often (n)					13	13	9	17
	2. Quite often (n)					3	9	12	6
	3. Occasionally (n)					28	20	37	28
	4. Never		34		35	79	79	80	84
	5. Very often (p)					2	1	2	2
	6. Quite often (p)					3	3	1	0
	7. Occasionally (p)					21	25	8	12
	†8. Often		1		5				
	†9. Seldom		14		9				
413:G11	If often, how do you feel about this?								
	1. Very intolerant or disturbed					3	3	3	3
	2. Moderately intolerant or disturbed					11	9	8	10
	3. Indifferent; no attitude apparent					4	3	1	2
	4. Moderately tolerant; not disturbed much					2	7	4	3
	5. Very tolerant; not disturbed at all					1	3	8	8
414:G12	Playing with sex organs?								
	1. Very often (n)					2	1	0	0
	2. Quite often (n)					3	2	5	8
	3. Occasionally (n)					27	31	38	32
	4. Never		0		39	99	97	101	96
	5. ?					3	1	4	1
	6. Very often (p)					0	1	0	0
	7. Quite often (p)					1	0	0	8
	8. Occasionally (p)					15	17	2	11
	†9. Often		9		2				
	†10. Seldom		41		9				
415:G13	If often, how do you feel about this?								
	1. Very intolerant or disturbed					0	0	0	1

		1	2	3	4	5	6
	2. Moderately intolerant or disturbed		0	0		3	2
	3. Indifferent; no attitude apparent		1	0		1	2
	4. Moderately tolerant; not disturbed much		0	2		0	2
	5. Very tolerant; not disturbed at all		5	2		1	3
416:G14	**Sleepwalking?**						
	1. Quite often (n)		0	1		0	0
	2. Occasionally (n)		6	6		4	3
	3. Never	18	143	142	44	144	146
	4. Occasionally (p)		1	1		2	1
	†5. Often	3			1		
	†6. Seldom	29			5		
417:G15	If often, how do you feel about this? 1. Moderately tolerant; not disturbed much						
418:G16	**Timidity?**						
	1. Very often (n)		0	1		1	0
	2. Quite often (n)		5	10		7	3
	3. Occasionally (n)	18	62	60	19	89	92
	4. Never		60	56		53	45
	5. ?		1	1		0	0
	6. Very often (p)		1	2		0	0
	7. Quite often (p)		1	5		0	1
	8. Occasionally (p)		21	15		0	3
	†9. Often	8			10		
	†10. Seldom	24			21		
419:G17	If often, how do you feel about this?						
	1. Very intolerant or disturbed		0	1		0	1
	2. Moderately intolerant or disturbed		3	9		5	3
	3. Indifferent; no attitude apparent		1	2		1	1
	4. Moderately tolerant; not disturbed much		0	5		0	0
	5. Very tolerant; not disturbed at all		3	2		2	3

139

Item No.: IBM Card and Column No.	Item; or Question and Response Codings; or Computed Values	Study II				Study III			
		Control Group (N = 50)		Experimental Group (N = 50)		Control Group (N = 150)		Experimental Group (N = 150)	
		F	M	F	M	F	M	F	M
420:G18	Showing off?								
	1. Very often (n)					6	5	5	4
	2. Quite often (n)					26	22	22	17
	3. Occasionally (n)					82	85	105	111
	4. Never		6		2	24	24	17	16
	5. Quite often (p)					0	0	1	0
	6. Occasionally (p)					12	14	0	2
	†7. Often		13		8				
	†8. Seldom		31		40				
421:G19	If often, how do you feel about this?								
	1. Very intolerant or disturbed					1	4	0	1
	2. Moderately intolerant or disturbed					5	6	8	8
	3. Indifferent; no attitude apparent					9	4	8	2
	4. Moderately tolerant; not disturbed much					4	7	5	4
	5. Very tolerant; not disturbed at all					9	5	7	6
	6. Thinks behavior is "funny, cute"					4	0	0	0
422:G20	Rudeness?								
	1. Very often (n)					2	5	2	2
	2. Quite often (n)					8	13	6	10
	3. Occasionally (n)					85	77	104	102
	4. Never		10		7	47	43	38	35
	5. ?					0	1	0	0
	6. Quite often (p)					0	1	0	0
	7. Occasionally (p)					8	10	0	1
	†8. Often		5		3				
	†9. Seldom		35		38				
423:G21	If often, how do you feel about this?								
	1. Very intolerant or disturbed					2	3	3	8
	2. Moderately intolerant or disturbed					5	10	5	3

	(R)	1	2	3	4
3. Indifferent; no attitude apparent		1			1
4. Moderately tolerant; not disturbed much		1	2	0	0
5. Very tolerant; not disturbed at all			1	0	0
424:G22 Quarreling?					
1. Very often (n)		7	11	4	10
2. Quite often (n)		44	40	27	37
3. Occasionally (n)	6	84	89	105	89
4. Never		9	9	14	14
5. ?		1	0	0	0
6. Occasionally (p)		5	1	0	0
†7. Often	15	19			
†8. Seldom	29	30			
425:G23 If often, how do you feel about this?					
1. Very intolerant or disturbed		7	6	3	20
2. Moderately intolerant or disturbed		20	24	12	17
3. Indifferent; no attitude apparent		5	6	1	4
4. Moderately tolerant; not disturbed much		11	10	7	3
5. Very tolerant; not disturbed at all		8	5	8	3
426:G24 Hitting other children?					
1. Very often (n)		1	4	2	4
2. Quite often (n)		13	16	14	25
3. Occasionally (n)	23	97	99	91	88
4. Never		26	18	40	30
5. ?		0	2	0	0
6. Very often (p)		1	0	0	0
7. Occasionally (p)		12	11	3	3
†8. Often	4	7			
†9. Seldom	23	39			
427:G25 If often, how do you feel about this?					
1. Very intolerant or disturbed		2	6	4	7
2. Moderately intolerant or disturbed		7	8	8	14

Item No.: IBM Card and Column No.	Item; or Question and Response Codings; or Computed Values	Study II Control Group (N = 50)		Study II Experimental Group (N = 50)		Study III Control Group (N = 150)		Study III Experimental Group (N = 150)	
		F	M	F	M	F	M	F	M
	3. Indifferent; no attitude apparent					1	2	0	3
	4. Moderately tolerant; not disturbed much					4	3	2	4
	5. Very tolerant; not disturbed at all					0	1	2	1
428:G26	Fighting?								
	1. Very often (n)					4	4	2	5
	2. Quite often (n)					9	18	15	23
	3. Occasionally (n)					88	83	103	95
	4. Never		19		5	38	34	30	27
	5. ?					0	2	0	0
	6. Quite often (p)					0	2	0	0
	7. Occasionally (p)					11	7	0	0
	†8. Often		8		9				
	†9. Seldom		23		36				
429:G27	If often, how do you feel about this?								
	1. Very intolerant or disturbed					3	6	2	8
	2. Moderately intolerant or disturbed					5	12	7	12
	3. Indifferent; no attitude apparent					0	1	1	4
	4. Moderately tolerant; not disturbed much					5	4	6	2
	5. Very tolerant; not disturbed at all		17		18	0	1	1	3
430:G28	Jealousy?								
	1. Very often (n)					4	3	2	5
	2. Quite often (n)					12	15	17	18
	3. Occasionally (n)					70	67	93	66
	4. Never		17		18	46	51	37	56
	5. ?					3	1	0	2
	6. Quite often (p)					1	1	0	0
	7. Occasionally (p)					14	12	1	2

431:G29

	e1	e2	(1)	(2)	(3)	(4)
†8. Often	7	1				
†9. Seldom	25	32				
If often, how do you feel about this?						
1. Very intolerant or disturbed			0	3	2	3
2. Moderately intolerant or disturbed			7	10	6	9
3. Indifferent; no attitude apparent			3	2	4	5
4. Moderately tolerant; not disturbed much			3	3	6	4
5. Very tolerant; not disturbed at all			2	1	1	3
6. Thinks behavior is "funny, cute"			1	0	0	0

432:G30

	e1	e2	(1)	(2)	(3)	(4)
Crying at home?						
1. Very often (n)			0	5	2	5
2. Quite often (n)			21	21	30	36
3. Occasionally (n)	17		119	120	111	98
4. Never			4	2	7	9
5. ?	2		1	0	0	0
6. Quite often (p)			0	0	0	1
7. Occasionally (p)			4	1	0	0
†8. Often	7	16				
†9. Seldom	26	32				

433:G31

	(1)	(2)	(3)	(4)
If often, how do you feel about this?				
1. Very intolerant or disturbed	5	6	7	9
2. Moderately intolerant or disturbed	7	11	10	18
3. Indifferent; no attitude apparent	2	2	4	4
4. Moderately tolerant; not disturbed much	4	3	8	7
5. Very tolerant; not disturbed at all	3	4	3	5

434:G32

	e1	e2	(1)	(2)	(3)	(4)
Crying at school?	42	28				
1. Very often (n)			0	1	0	0
2. Quite often (n)			0	2	0	0
3. Occasionally (n)			6	7	0	4
4. Never			47	62	40	56

Item No.: IBM Card and Column No.	Item; or Question and Response Codings; or Computed Values	Study II Control Group (N = 50)		Study II Experimental Group (N = 50)		Study III Control Group (N = 150)		Study III Experimental Group (N = 150)	
		F	M	F	M	F	M	F	M
	5. ?					27	9	27	7
	6. Very often (p)					1	0	1	0
	7. Quite often (p)					2	2	1	1
	8. Occasionally (p)					4	3	0	4
	†9. Often		1		1				
	†10. Seldom		3		13				
435:G33	If often, how do you feel about this?								
	1. Very intolerant or disturbed					0	3	0	0
	2. Moderately intolerant or disturbed					1	1	0	1
	3. Indifferent; no attitude apparent					0	0	0	1
	4. Moderately tolerant; not disturbed much					0	0	1	0
	5. Very tolerant; not disturbed at all					1	1	0	0
436:G34	Lying (deliberate)?								
	1. Very often (n)					2	0	1	0
	2. Quite often (n)					3	3	4	6
	3. Occasionally (n)					42	55	62	57
	4. Never		25		23	91	85	79	82
	5. ?					1	2	0	1
	6. Quite often (p)					0	0	1	1
	7. Occasionally (p)					11	5	2	2
	†8. Often		2		4				
	†9. Seldom		23		23				
437:G35	If often, how do you feel about this?								
	1. Very intolerant or disturbed					2	0	0	4
	2. Moderately intolerant or disturbed					2	2	0	1
	3. Indifferent; no attitude apparent					1	0	3	0

4. Moderately tolerant; not disturbed much	1	2	1	0		
5. Very tolerant; not disturbed at all	1	0	0	0		
438:G36 Thumb sucking?						
1. Very often (n)	19	12	12	10		
2. Quite often (n)	17	19	6	11		
3. Occasionally (n)	13	15	9	10		
4. Never	90	90	114	101	39	37
5. ?	0	1	0	0		
6. Very often (p)	2	3	3	6		
7. Quite often (p)	5	3	4	4		
8. Occasionally (p)	4	7	2	8		
†9. Often					6	11
†10. Seldom					5	2
439:G37 If often, how do you feel about this?						
1. Very intolerant or disturbed	10	9	7	8		
2. Moderately intolerant or disturbed	20	15	9	13		
3. Indifferent; no attitude apparent	2	4	1	4		
4. Moderately tolerant; not disturbed much	5	6	3	2		
5. Very tolerant; not disturbed at all	6	4	5	3		
440:G38 Hurting pets?						
1. Very often (n)	3	0	1	2		
2. Quite often (n)	1	5	0	1		
3. Occasionally (n)	15	11	19	18		
4. Never	130	133	123	122	48	43
5. Very often (p)	0	0	1	0		
6. Quite often (p)	0	0	0	1		
7. Occasionally (p)	1	1	6	6		
†8. Seldom					2	7
441:G39 If often, how do you feel about this?						
1. Very intolerant or disturbed	3	1	1	2		
2. Moderately intolerant or disturbed	1	2	1	0		

Item No.: IBM Card and Column No.	Item; or Question and Response Codings; or Computed Values	Study II Control Group (N=50) F	M	Study II Experimental Group (N=50) F	M	Study III Control Group (N=150) F	M	Study III Experimental Group (N=150) F	M
	3. Moderately tolerant; not disturbed much					0	0	1	0
	4. Very tolerant; not disturbed at all					2		0	0
442:G40	**Constipation?**								
	1. Very often (n)					1	0	3	5
	2. Quite often (n)					4	6	1	7
	3. Occasionally (n)					24	21	39	26
	4. Never		32		24	106	105	101	104
	5. ?					2	0	2	0
	6. Very often (p)					1	1	0	0
	7. Quite often (p)					0	2	2	0
	8. Occasionally (p)					12	15	2	1
	†9. Often		3		7				7
	†10. Seldom		13		19				
443:G41	**If often, how do you feel about this?**								
	1. Very intolerant or disturbed					0			
	2. Moderately intolerant or disturbed						2	2	4
	3. Moderately tolerant; not disturbed much					5	6	4	7
	4. Very tolerant; not disturbed at all					0	1	0	1
444:G42	**Nail biting?**								
	1. Very often (n)					2	6	5	7
	2. Quite often (n)					2	4	7	7
	3. Occasionally (n)					16	16	17	15
	4. Never		37		30	125	118	114	112
	5. ?					0	0	0	0
	6. Very often (p)					1	2	2	2
	7. Quite often (p)					2	1	4	5
	8. Occasionally (p)					2	3	1	2
	†9. Often		10		14				
	†10. Seldom		3		6				

445:G43	**If often, how do you feel about this?**				
	1. Very intolerant or disturbed	1	2	1	4
	2. Moderately intolerant or disturbed	3	6	6	7
	3. Indifferent; no attitude apparent	0	0	2	2
	4. Moderately tolerant; not disturbed much	1	5	4	3
	5. Very tolerant; not disturbed at all	2	0	2	3
446:G44	**Face twitching?**				
	1. Very often (n)	0	0	0	1
	2. Quite often (n)	0	1	3	1
	3. Occasionally (n)	4	3	6	3
	4. Never	146	146	141	145
	† 5. Often	45		36	
	† 6. Seldom	0 / 5		7 / 7	
447:G45	**If often, how do you feel about this?**				
	1. Very intolerant or disturbed	0	1	0	0
	2. Moderately intolerant or disturbed	0	0	3	1
448:G46	**Fainting?**				
	1. Occasionally (n)	0	1	1	1
	2. Never	147	147	149	149
	3. Occasionally (p)	1	2	0	0
	† 4. Seldom	48		2	
449:G47	**If often, how do you feel about this?** (This question was never asked in view of responses to preceding question.)				
450:G48	**Temper tantrums?**				
	1. Very often (n)	0	0	0	3
	2. Quite often (n)	11	7	7	11
	3. Occasionally (n)	69	58	65	58
	4. Never	51	62	58	61
	5. ?	0	0	1	0
	6. Very often (p)	0	2	0	0
	7. Quite often (p)	0	1	0	0
	8. Occasionally (p)	19	20	19	17

Item No.: IBM Card and Column No.	Item; or Question and Response Codings; or Computed Values	Study II Control Group (N = 50) F	M	Study II Experimental Group (N = 50) F	M	Study III Control Group (N = 150) F	M	Study III Experimental Group (N = 150) F	M
451:G49	† 9. Often		2		5				
	† 10. Seldom		13		21				
	If often, how do you feel about this?								
	1. Very intolerant or disturbed					1	2	1	5
	2. Moderately intolerant or disturbed					6	4	5	7
	3. Indifferent; no attitude apparent					0	1	0	0
	4. Moderately tolerant; not disturbed much					2	2	0	1
	5. Very tolerant; not disturbed at all					2	1	0	1
452:G50	Running **away?**								
	1. Very often (n)					1	0	0	1
	2. Quite often (n)					1	1	1	1
	3. Occasionally (n)					3	5	5	6
	4. Never	44		38		143	139	143	139
	5. ?					0	1	0	0
	6. Quite often (p)					0	1	0	0
	7. Occasionally (p)					2	3	1	3
	† 8. Often	1		1					
	† 9. Seldom	5		11					
453:G51	If often, how do you feel about this?								
	1. Very intolerant or disturbed								
	2. Moderately intolerant or disturbed					0	1	0	2
	3. Indifferent; no attitude apparent					0	0	1	0
454:G52	Whining?								
	1. Very often (n)					2	0	0	0
	2. Quite often (n)					1	4	3	4
	3. Occasionally (n)					17	22	25	22
	4. Never	25		21		95	77	85	80
						24	30	37	40

5. Very often (p)			0	2	0	0
6. Quite often (p)			0	2	0	1
7. Occasionally (p)			13	13	0	3
†8. Often	8	10				
†9. Seldom	17	19				
455:G53 If often, how do you feel about this?						
1. Very intolerant or disturbed			3	14	14	13
2. Moderately intolerant or disturbed			10	9	10	13
3. Indifferent; no attitude apparent			2	3	1	0
4. Moderately tolerant; not disturbed much			2	4	2	1
5. Very tolerant; not disturbed at all			1	0	1	0
456:G54 Stealing?						
1. Quite often (n)			1	0	0	1
2. Occasionally (n)	46		9	7	12	9
3. Never		45	139	134	138	138
4. Occasionally (p)			1	9	0	2
†5. Seldom	4	5				
457:G55 If often, how do you feel about this?						
1. Indifferent; no attitude apparent			1	0	0	0
2. Very tolerant; not disturbed at all			0	0	0	1
458:G56 Teasing?						
1. Very often (n)			11	14	3	9
2. Quite often (n)			34	48	35	39
3. Occasionally (n)	10	24	81	64	89	82
4. Never			19	22	22	20
5. ?			1	0	1	0
6. Occasionally			4	2	0	0
†7. Often	13	5				
†8. Seldom	27	21				
459:G57 If often, how do you feel about this?						
1. Very intolerant or disturbed			2	9	3	12
2. Moderately intolerant or disturbed			13	25	15	19

Item No.: IBM Card and Column No.	Item; or Question and Response Codings; or Computed Values	Study II Control Group (N = 50) F	M	Study II Experimental Group (N = 50) F	M	Study III Control Group (N = 150) F	M	Study III Experimental Group (N = 150) F	M
	3. Indifferent; no attitude apparent					8	5	1	5
	4. Moderately tolerant; not disturbed much					5	9	12	7
	5. Very tolerant; not disturbed at all					13	12	5	5
	6. Thinks behavior is "funny, cute"					3	2	1	0
460:G58	Bullying?								
	1. Very often (n)					0	2	1	1
	2. Quite often (n)					5	8	5	8
	3. Occasionally (n)					43	45	57	45
	4. Never		32		32	94	88	83	95
	5. ?					1	0	2	0
	6. Very often (p)					1	0	0	0
	7. Quite often (p)					0	0	0	1
	8. Occasionally (p)					6	7	1	0
	†9. Often		3		5				
	†10. Seldom		15		13				
461:G59	If often, how do you feel about this?								
	1. Very intolerant or disturbed					2	2	1	3
	2. Moderately intolerant or disturbed					0	6	3	5
	3. Indifferent; no attitude apparent					0	0	0	0
	4. Moderately tolerant; not disturbed much					2	1	2	2
	5. Very tolerant; not disturbed at all					1	1	0	0
462:G60	Disobedience?								
	1. Very often (n)					2	4	6	4
	2. Quite often (n)					18	19	15	28
	3. Occasionally (n)					109	107	116	105
	4. Never		4		2	13	15	13	13
	5. ?					1	0	0	0

463:G51	6. Occasionally (p)				
	†7. Often	14	13		
	†8. Seldom	32	35		
	If often, how do you feel about this?				
	1. Very intolerant or disturbed	0	0		
	2. Moderately intolerant or disturbed	3	2	9	11
	3. Indifferent; no attitude apparent	11	13	10	15
	4. Moderately tolerant; not disturbed much	1	3	2	0
	5. Very tolerant; not disturbed at all	4	6	0	3
464:G62	*Do you wish he were more or less obedient?*				
	1. Less	0	2	1	0
	2. More	72	71	69	70
	3. Stay as he is	78	77	80	80
465:G63	*Do you wish he were less well or better behaved?*				
	1. Less well behaved	2	2	0	1
	2. Better behaved	52	58	56	61
	3. Stay as he is	92	87	94	86
	4. ?	2	0	0	1
466:G64	*Does your wife (husband) wish he were less well or better behaved?*				
	1. Less well behaved	3	1	0	0
	2. Better behaved	70	69	65	66
	3. Stay as he is	74	78	78	78
	4. ?	2	2	7	6
467:G65	*Does child meet your ideal standards?*				
	1. Very well	73	56	71	50
	2. Quite well	63	71	59	72
	3. As often acceptable as not	6	15	11	15
	4. Falls quite short	2	1	3	9
	5. Falls very short	0	1	0	1
	6. Parent does not have ideal standards	5	5	6	3

Item No.: IBM Card and Column No.	Item; or Question and Response Codings; or Computed Values	Study II Control Group (N = 50) F	M	Study II Experimental Group (N = 50) F	M	Study III Control Group (N = 150) F	M	Study III Experimental Group (N = 150) F	M
	† 7. Yes	22	31	30	22				
	† 8. No	10	10	16	25				
	† 9. Have no ideal standards because of acceptance of child as he is	15	9	4	3				
	†10. Have no ideal standards because of generally low standards for social behavior	1	1	0	0				
	†11. ?								
468*	Wherein is child deficient?[101]								
	1. Nothing					48	34	31	19
	2. Speech					5	4	46	39
	3. Relations with parents or with others					29	38	26	49
	4. Physical appearance and/or intelligence					15	11	12	7
	5. Childish					17	18	8	8
	6. Character traits; personality					31	42	24	41
	7. Care of self and possessions					10	16	9	15
	8. ?					6	11	6	4
469:c66	Do you think the child meets your wife's (husband's) ideal standards?								
	1. Very well					69	56	66	56
	2. Quite well					65	69	66	58
	3. As often acceptable as not					6	8	11	14
	4. Falls quite short					4	4	2	12
	5. Falls very short					1	1	0	0
	6. ?	1	1	0	0	4	12	5	10
	† 7. Yes	28	35	35	23				
	† 8. No	8	4	11	22				

[101]More specific responses were reported than those listed; many different individual wordings of response have been grouped as here indicated for practical purposes of presentation. Some respondents gave more than one response.

† 9. Have no ideal standards because of acceptance of child as he is	9	7	3	2
† 10. Have no ideal standards because of generally low standards for social behavior	1	0	1	3

470* Wherein is he deficient in your wife's (husband's) opinion?[102]

1. Nothing	42	44	28	22
2. Speech	3	5	39	32
3. Relations with parents or with others	33	37	33	41
4. Physical appearance and/or intelligence	8	5	6	4
5. Childish	22	20	8	13
6. Character traits; personality	21	28	18	23
7. Care of self and possessions	18	15	13	10
8. ?	15	18	19	22

471:G67 Compared with other children, how much does he explain away his faults and mistakes? (Study II: Does he usually rationalize his faults and mistakes?)

1. Much more than average	2	4	2	0
2. Somewhat more than average	13	16	16	20
3. About average	93	102	113	107
4. Somewhat less than average	27	18	12	14
5. Much less than average	8	6	3	3
6. ?	7	4	3	5

472:G68 Compared with other children, how readily does your child give up on hard tasks as a rule? (In Study II the phrase "Compared with other children" was not included in this

† 7. Yes	23	29	29	37
† 8. No	26	20	16	10
† 9. ?	0	0	1	0

102 See footnote 98.

		Study II				Study III			
Item No.: IBM Card and Column No.	Item; or Question and Response Codings; or Computed Values	Control Group (N = 50)		Experimental Group (N = 50)		Control Group (N = 150)		Experimental Group (N = 150)	
		F	M	F	M	F	M	F	M
	question or in subsequent corresponding questions in this series.)								
	1. Much more than average					2	0	0	3
	2. Somewhat more than average					18	22	23	26
	3. About average					91	90	80	79
	4. Somewhat less than average					31	32	40	26
	5. Much less than average					5	6	5	3
	6. ?					3	0	2	3
	†7. Gives up much too readily	5	2	11	9				
	†8. Rather readily gives up	20	16	9	15				
	†9. Reluctant to give up	23	28	24	21				
	†10. Never gives up	1	3	6	5				
473:G69	As compared with other children, how attractive do you feel your child is?								
	1. Much more than average	10	3	2	6	13	13	12	13
	2. Somewhat more than average	25	29	21	19	71	49	61	50
	3. About average	15	18	27	25	65	84	75	85
	4. Somewhat less than average	0	0	0	0	0	4	2	2
	5. ?	0	0	0	0	1	0	0	0
474:G70	How attractive does your wife (husband) feel the child is?								
	1. Much more than average	17	7	5	6	21	22	16	15
	2. Somewhat more than average	26	29	25	20	72	49	62	58
	3. About average	7	12	16	21	53	68	69	71
	4. Somewhat less than average	0	1	0	0	0	1	1	1
	5. ?	0	1	4	3	4	10	2	5
475:G71	Do you wish he were better looking or less good looking?								
	1. Less					1	1	0	0
	2. Better					10	7	4	6
	3. Stay as he is					139	142	144	142
	4. ?					0	0	2	0

476:G72 Compared with other children of his age, how good an athlete do you think your child is?[103]

1. Much better than average	1	2	2	9	6	4	5
2. Somewhat better than average	8	5	8	27	23	29	16
3. About average	25	22	17	66	62	61	65
4. Somewhat below average	9	9	10	4	11	10	17
5. Much below average	1	0	1	1	2	1	1
6. ?	0	0	0	0	2	1	3

477:G73 How good an athlete does your wife (husband) think he is?

1. Much better than average	1	2	2	7	7	4	5
2. Somewhat better than average	8	6	11	25	20	28	15
3. About average	29	19	12	64	57	60	61
4. Somewhat below average	5	10	9	6	13	8	20
5. Much below average	1	0	1	0	1	1	0
6. ?	0	1	3	5	8	5	6

478:G74 Do you wish he were a better or less good athlete?

1. Less good				0	0	0	1
2. Better				27	13	26	20
3. Stay as he is				78	92	79	83
4. ?				2	1	1	3

479:G75 Compared with other children, how much does your child read?

1. Much more than average	10	2	3	18	19	12	14
2. Somewhat more than average	19	15	12	57	59	48	42
3. About average	14	19	23	64	58	71	66
4. Somewhat less than average	1	8	7	8	9	7	14
5. Much less than average	1	1	1	0	1	0	2
6. ?	0	5	4	1	1	1	2

480-484

480:G76 Compared with other children, how afraid is your child:

Of dogs?

1. Much more than average				6	6	12	10

[103] Items 476-478 were asked with reference to boys only.

Item No.: IBM Card and Column No.	Item; or Question and Response Codings; or Computed Values	Study II				Study III			
		Control Group (N = 50)		Experimental Group (N = 50)		Control Group (N = 150)		Experimental Group (N = 150)	
		F	M	F	M	F	M	F	M
	2. Somewhat more than average					22	14	27	14
	3. About average					61	55	54	63
	4. Somewhat less than average					26	33	37	40
	5. Much less than average					34	42	18	22
	6. ?					1	0	2	1
	† 7. Very much	3	0	2	3				
	† 8. Rather	1	4	3	4				
	† 9. Not very	6	4	3	2				
	†10. Not at all	35	42	39	40				
481:G77	Of doctors?								
	1. Much more than average					2	7	0	1
	2. Somewhat more than average					7	8	10	11
	3. About average					64	54	86	79
	4. Somewhat less than average					39	40	35	39
	5. Much less than average					32	39	17	19
	6. ?					6	2	2	1
	† 7. Very much	0	0	3	6				
	† 8. Rather	9	3	3	4				
	† 9. Not very	4	11	0	1				
	†10. Not at all	34	36	40	38				
482:G78	Of strangers?								
	1. Much more than average					0	1	0	1
	2. Somewhat more than average					10	6	14	15
	3. About average					71	67	88	77
	4. Somewhat less than average					39	43	34	42
	5. Much less than average					30	32	14	14
	6. ?	0	0	0	1	0	1	0	1
	† 7. Very much	1	0	0	0				
	† 8. Rather	4	2	0	0				
	† 9. Not very	5	5	0	1				
	†10. Not at all	38	43	47	47				

483:C79 Of the dark?

Response								
1. Much more than average					0	1	1	2
2. Somewhat more than average					12	12	14	20
3. About average					75	73	87	80
4. Somewhat less than average					37	33	37	33
5. Much less than average					24	29	9	12
6. ?		0	0	1	2	2	2	3
† 7. Very much	3	2	1	3				
† 8. Rather	12	8	5	3				
† 9. Not very	7	14	1	6				
10. Not at all	23	26	40	36				

484:G80 Of other children?

1. Much more than average				0	1	0	0
2. Somewhat more than average				6	1	5	6
3. About average				68	71	101	103
4. Somewhat less than average				39	35	31	26
5. Much less than average				35	41	12	11
6. ?				2	0	1	2
† 7. Rather	4	2	3				
† 8. Not very	4	1	0				
† 9. Not at all	42	44	46				

485:H6-7 What (other) strong fears does the child have?[104]

Response						
1. None	16	30	108	99	118	94
2. Thunder	5	4	0	1	3	6
3. Loud noises	1	0	1	1	4	4
4. Unusual sounds	7	0	0	0	1	1
5. Large animals	6	0	1	0	1	1
6. Insects			3	3	0	0
7. Lightning	1	2	0	2	1	1
8. Fires			0	1	1	1
9. Thunder; lightning			6	4	4	3
10. Shots from the doctor	4	1	0	3	0	1

[104] For both Studies II and III there were 99 additional fears reported, each by fewer than three of the informants represented in any one column of the table; 57 of these 99 were reported by the control and 58 by the experimental group respondents. Some respondents in Study II gave more than one response.

Item No.: IBM Card and Column No.	Item; or Question and Response Codings; or Computed Values	Study II Control Group (N = 50) F	M	Study II Experimental Group (N = 50) F	M	Study III Control Group (N = 150) F	M	Study III Experimental Group (N = 150) F	M
486:H8	11. Parents leaving him					0	0	0	3
	12. High places; height					4	1	1	1
	Do you wish the child were less or more afraid of things?								
	1. Less					21	19	28	38
	2. More					18	17	11	13
	3. Stay as he is					111	113	110	99
	4. ?					0	1	1	0
487:H9	Compared with other children, how easily does the child cry?								
	1. Much more than average		0		2	1	2	4	7
	2. Somewhat more than average		6		10	23	24	27	29
	3. About average		25		22	100	89	96	95
	4. Somewhat less than average		15		13	20	32	20	18
	5. Much less than average		4		2	5	3	3	1
	6. ?		0		1	1	0	0	0
488:H10	Do you wish the child would cry less or more easily?								
	1. Less					46	49	49	52
	2. More					1	0	2	0
	3. Stay as he is					103	101	98	98
	4. ?					0	0	1	0
489:H11	Compared with other children, how happy is your child?								
	1. Much more than average	6	1	4	2	10	12	10	7
	2. Somewhat more than average	23	24	21	13	60	47	49	35
	3. About average	18	24	23	31	77	88	84	95
	4. Somewhat less than average	2	1	2	4	3	2	7	12
	5. Much less than average	0	0	0	0	0	1	0	0
	6. ?	0	0	0	0	0	0	0	1

490:HI2-13

How do siblings treat the child?[105]

1. Tease him, bully him, make him the goat, reject him from games	11	11	1	4	2	0	0	0
2. Tease, bully, fight him but accept him					10	5	29	21
3. Accept him into activities without question	11	15	12	8	2	0	5	8
4. Follow his leadership; respect him	3	4	13	13	8	5	11	12
5. Tease but favor him more than they do themselves					2	4	0	0
6. Share, fight, make up--play together fairly well					22	23	4	5
7. Older sibs tease, fight, bully him but accept him into activities; younger sib follows him					4	6	1	4
8. Accept him; play together; sometimes follow him					3	5	5	3
9. Has no siblings					15	15	24	24
10. Tease him but follow him					0	2	5	4
11. Follow him; imitate him					6	6	8	8
12. Act affectionate toward him					1	0	5	10
13. Sibling an infant; too young					9	9	8	8
14. Have protective attitude toward him; play together					11	9	0	2
15. Very well					3	3	1	0
16. Tease case but play with her often					8	8	5	2
17. Tease each other					2	4	4	3
18. Idolize him					2	2	0	3
19. Tease, fight him but play together and seem to accept him					19	21	0	2
20. Much fighting and teasing					0	0	3	2

[105]For both Studies II and III there were 59 additional behaviors reported, each by fewer than three of the informants represented in any one column of the table; 37 of these 59 were reported by the control and 40 by the experimental group respondents. Some respondents in Study II gave more than one response.

Item No.: IBM Card and Column No.	Item; or Question and Response Codings; or Computed Values	Study II				Study III			
		Control Group (N = 50)		Experimental Group (N = 50)		Control Group (N = 150)		Experimental Group (N = 150)	
		F	M	F	M	F	M	F	M
	21. Tease her; play together fairly well								
	22. Boss, dominate him								
	†23. Tease him but accept him	10	10	8	11	1	2	3	1
	†24. Doesn't want him in her room; prefers not to be with him	0	0	1	3	0	1	3	2
	†25. Mothers him	0	3	1	3				
491:H14	Toward which sibling does the child show the greatest rivalry?								
	1. None	3	6	16	12	51	57	63	61
	2. ?					0	1	0	2
	3. Oldest	8	9	1	0	26	25	21	21
	4. Next older	6	8	1	0	19	15	5	8
	5. Youngest	1	2	1	1	24	18	21	21
	6. Twin	1	0	1	0	0	0	1	1
	7. Next younger	2	5	3	5	10	12	7	6
	8. All siblings the same	1	0	0	2	3	4	2	2
	9. No siblings--only child	5	5	11	11	15	15	24	24
	10. Two next older sibs	0	0	0	0	1	0	0	0
	11. Third child	0	0	0	0	1	1	7	2
	†12. Boy	7	8	2	3				
	†13. Girl	6	5	3	2				
	†14. One sibling--some rivalry	3	1	3	7				
	†15. One sibling--much rivalry	2	1	2	3				
	†16. Second younger	1	0	1	0				
492:H15	Do you wish that the brothers and sisters would get along better or less well?								
	1. Better					52	56	38	51
	2. Stay as they are					81	76	84	71
	3. ?					1	2	0	0

493:H16 Compared with other youngsters, how much is the child laughed at by other children? Made fun of?

1. Much more than average	0	0	1	1
2. Somewhat more than average	1	1	5	7
3. About average	75	80	99	99
4. Somewhat less than average	44	36	29	28
5. Much less than average	21	23	5	5
6. ?	9	9	10	10
(Study II: Do other children usually laugh at him?)				
†1. Yes	1	0	1	1
†2. No	44	45	48	48
†3. ?	0	0	1	1

494:H17-18 If more than average, why?

1. Speech	0	0	6	6
2. Large size	1	1	0	0
3. Know how easily they can make her cry	0	0	0	0
4. Because the child doesn't fight back	0	0	0	1
(Study II: If yes, why?)				
†1. Speech	0	1	0	0
†2. Consider stuck up	0	0	0	1

495:H19 Compared with other youngsters, how much is he teased by other children?

1. Much more than average	0	0	0	1
2. Somewhat more than average	10	13	11	15
3. About average	93	98	101	103
4. Somewhat less than average	30	25	30	20
5. Much less than average	11	9	5	6
6. ?	6	5	3	5
(Study II: Do other children usually tease him?)				
†1. Yes	10	3	3	6
†2. No	32	42	46	44
†3. ?	0	0	1	0

Item No.: IBM Card and Column No.	Item; or Question and Response Codings; or Computed Values	Study II Control Group (N=50) F	M	Study II Experimental Group (N=50) F	M	Study III Control Group (N=150) F	M	Study III Experimental Group (N=150) F	M
496:H20	What do they tease the child about?[106]								
	1. His speech	0	0	4	7	0	2	8	13
	2. Nothing specific					131	127	98	103
	3. ?					7	5	33	22
	4. Playing with dolls	2	1	2	1	0	1	3	2
497:H21-22	What does the child usually do when teased?[107]								
	1. Cries	5	4	7	8	14	18	15	27
	2. Answers back	3	1	2	0	6	4	6	2
	3. Fights, aggressive behavior	7	8	14	21	23	20	25	17
	4. Teases back	0	0	3	3	27	15	18	13
	5. Whines	3	2	4	9	1	1	1	0
	6. Laughs	3	3	5	5	6	7	4	4
	7. Quits playing, withdraws	1	2			11	19	13	17
	8. Doesn't answer			1		1	1	2	2
	9. Not aware, nothing	2	0	2	0	1	4	7	5
	10. Acts as if it doesn't bother him					7	6	3	8
	11. Hits back after teasing persists					2	7	0	0
	12. ?	2	3	8	3	15	6	30	14
	13. Teases back; cries if teasing persists								
	14. Cries; gets angry					0	1	1	3
	15. Gets angry	10	8	14	20	16	22	0	3
	16. Tells parents					5	3	15	13

[106] For both Studies II and III there were 30 additional characteristics reported, each by fewer than three of the informants represented in any one column of the table; 22 of these 30 were reported by the control and 15 by the experimental group respondents.

[107] For both Studies II and III there were 29 additional actions reported, each by fewer than three of the informants represented in any one column of the table; 19 of these 29 were reported by the control and 22 by the experimental group respondents. Some respondents in Study II gave more than one response. Note that in Study II apparently few of the parents who answered 495 by saying that their children were "not usually" teased meant, according to their answers to 497, that they were "never" teased.

		C1	C2	C3	C4	C5	C6	C7	C8
	17. Child is not teased (Study II: never teased)					0	1	1	2
	† 18. Fights					4	3	10	14
498:H23	Do you think the child feels generally picked on?								
	1. Very much					3	1	1	1
	2. Moderately					8	4	9	4
	3. Slightly					25	12	13	9
	4. Not at all					114	132	125	136
	5. ?					0	1	2	0
499:H24	In comparison with other children, how much do you believe your child is picked on?								
	1. Much more than average	0	0	1	0	2	0	1	0
	2. Somewhat more than average	1	1	2	5	13	9	10	4
	3. About average	17	18	33	34	111	110	96	95
	4. Somewhat less than average	24	22	7	6	22	26	27	33
	5. Much less than average	5	9	6	4	2	4	15	16
	6. ?	0	0	0	0	0	1	1	2
500:H25	Does the child go to Sunday school?								
	1. Yes					110	106	73	79
	2. No					38	39	54	49
	3. No Sunday school in church					2	5	23	22
501:H26-27	Does the child belong to other organizations? (Study II: What organizations does the child belong to, or what meetings does the child attend?)108								
	1. No (Study II: none)	6	2			131	132	126	130
	2. Scouts (Study II: Boy Scouts)	9	4			0	0	0	0
	3. Dancing class or club	0	3			7	8	0	2
	4. Preschool or nursery school					6	6	15	13
	† 5. Sunday school	32	36						

108For both Studies II and III there were 16 additional organizations reported, each by fewer than three of the informants represented in any one column of the table; 12 of these 16 were reported by the control and 8 by the experimental group respondents. Some respondents in Study II gave more than one response.

Item No.: IBM Card and Column No.	Item; or Question and Response Codings; or Computed Values	Study II				Study III			
		Control Group (N = 50)		Experimental Group (N = 50)		Control Group (N = 150)		Experimental Group (N = 150)	
		F	M	F	M	F	M	F	M
	† 6. Cub Scouts		3		5				
	† 7. YMCA swimming club or other swim club		3		5				
	† 8. Boys' club		7		0				
	† 9. 4-H Club		6		1				
	†10. FFA		3		0				
	†11. Church Youth Fellowship		2		6				
	†12. Church choir		3		3				
	†13. Band or orchestra		1		4				
	†14. Church		3		1				
502:H28	How much freedom has the child in determining how he shall use his own play time?								
	1. Thorough control by parent					3	1	1	2
	2. Moderate control					12	12	15	15
	3. Relative freedom		11		6	12	15	27	27
	4. Practically complete freedom, but parent interested					122	121	105	106
	5. Parent negligent and indifferent		0		0	1	0	2	0
	† 6. Rigid control by parent		1		1				
	† 7. Complete freedom, but parent interested		30		40				
	† 8. A good deal of control		6		2				
503:H29	Does the child have any live pets? (Dogs, cats, rabbits, sheep, etc., but not goldfish or guppies. That is, they must be pets he can handle, hold,								

or fondle.) (Study II: What pets does the child have?)[109]

	C1	C2	C3	C4	C5	C6
1. More than one	15	17	25	24	13	13
2. One	19	17	41	43	29	28
3. None	1	3	84	83	108	109
† 4. One dog	12	7				
† 5. More than one dog	2	3				
† 6. One cat	3	0				
† 7. More than one cat	4	1				
† 8. Canary or other birds	4	0				
† 9. Guinea pig						
† 10. Turtle						

504:H30-31 If none, why not? (Most important reason)[110]

	C1	C2	C3	C4	C5	C6
1. Not permitted by owner of home	3	3	11	11	12	18
2. Not desired by mother	1	2	8	16	23	28
3. Not desired by father (or not permitted)	2	0	8	0	9	5
4. Child has shown no desire for any	0	1	3	2	3	3
5. Unable to find suitable pet	0	1	1	0	3	7
6. No room	2	1	7	9	20	12
7. Parents want child to wait until he is older	1	2	4	7	4	4
8. Have had hard luck with dogs (accidents, etc.)		1	2	1	4	
9. Too much trouble; town no place for them (Study II: inconvenient in town)	1		2	0	2	5
10. City is no place for pets			9	10	3	2

[109]In Study II there were 10 additional pets reported, each by fewer than three of the informants represented in any one column of the table; 6 of these 10 were reported by the control and 6 by the experimental group respondents. Some respondents in Study II gave more than one response.

[110]For both Studies II and III there were 33 additional reasons reported, each by fewer than three of the informants represented in any one column of the table; 21 of these 33 were reported by the control and 19 by the experimental group respondents. Some respondents in Study II gave more than one response.

Item No.: IBM Card and Column No.	Item; or Question and Response Codings; or Computed Values	Study II Control Group (N=50) F	M	Study II Experimental Group (N=50) F	M	Study III Control Group (N=150) F	M	Study III Experimental Group (N=150) F	M
	11. Not desired by parents					11	1	15	7
	12. Dog died, never replaced him					4	6	0	2
	13. Enough in the neighborhood		4		5	1	4	0	0
	14. Neighbor doesn't like pets					2	3	0	2
	15. Poor location for a pet					2	3	0	0
505:H32	Do you wish the child played better or less well with other children?								
	1. Better					29	26	35	47
	2. Stay as he is					119	123	114	103
	3. ?					2	0	1	0
506:H33	Do you wish the child would play more or less quietly?								
	1. Less quietly					5	1	3	2
	2. More quietly					44	28	31	31
	3. Stay as he is					101	121	115	117
	4. ?					0	0	1	0
507:H34	Do you encourage or discourage or say nothing about the child's reading?								
	1. Very much encourage					25	21	21	24
	2. Moderately encourage					51	53	57	58
	3. Moderately discourage					0	0	3	1
	4. Very much discourage					0	0	0	1
	5. Say nothing either way					58	61	64	61
	† 6. Encourage		40		38				
	† 7. Discourage		1		0				
	† 8. Indifferent		7		6				
508:H35	Do you encourage or discourage or say nothing about the child's playing alone?								
	1. Very much encourage					4	4	2	8
	2. Moderately encourage					14	36	14	35

	C1	C2	C3	C4	C5	C6	C7	C8
3. Moderately discourage								
4. Very much discourage								
5. Say nothing either way								
†6. Encourage	15	10	5	11	5	3	10	5
†7. Discourage	2	4	1	1	8	6	2	11
†8. Indifferent	90	119	104	120	36	41	38	33

509:H36-37 What do you want him to be when he grows up?[111]

	C1	C2	C3	C4	C5	C6	C7	C8
1. ?; what he wants to be	123	126	121	120				
2. Engineer	1	3	0	1				
3. Doctor	7	4	5	1				
4. Professional man or woman	4	7	10	16				
5. Schoolteacher	3	0	0	1				

510* What are his very favorite activities? What would he rather do than anything else?[112]

	C1	C2	C3	C4	C5	C6	C7	C8
1. Active or outdoor activities	97	87	124	87	38	27	23	36
2. Quiet or indoor activities	68	58	104	71	9	5	10	15
3. Mechanical activities	35	30	37	36	6	3	2	2
4. Movies, TV, radio	13	9	10	12	1	3	4	6
5. Music, singing	6	3	11	10	4	2	0	3
6. Playing with friends or sibs	4	8	8	10	1	5	3	6
7. School	3	2	7	7	0	2	0	0
8. Doing things with parent	1	2	6	6	1	1	1	0
9. Pretend games	5	6	12	9	3	1	2	0
10. No preference	1	2	3	9	0	1	0	0
11. ?	2	4	1	4	1	1	1	1

511:H38 How much does the child masturbate?

	C1	C2	C3	C4	C5	C6	C7	C8
1. More than once a week	15	12	7	3	1	1	1	1

111For both Studies II and III there were 28 additional occupations reported, each by fewer than three of the informants represented in any one column of the table; 18 of these 28 were reported by the control and 16 by the experimental group.

112More specific responses were reported than those listed; variations of individual wording of responses have been grouped as here indicated for practical purposes of presentation. Some respondents in both studies gave more than one response.

Item No.: IBM Card and Column No.	Item; or Question and Response Codings; or Computed Values	Study II Control Group (N = 50) F	M	Study II Experimental Group (N = 50) F	M	Study III Control Group (N = 150) F	M	Study III Experimental Group (N = 150) F	M
	2. About once a week					5	8	3	5
	3. Less than once a week					9	12	17	22
	4. Never					120	119	111	107
	5. ?					13	4	6	1
512:H39	How often has the child been caught stealing things?								
	1. Chronically					1	0	0	0
	2. Occasionally					8	7	4	7
	3. Isolated case					11	19	10	11
	4. Never					130	124	136	132
513:H40	How does the child adjust to new situations and new friends?								
	1. Shuns all new contacts and experiences	0	0	1	0	0	0	0	0
	2. Very shy; avoids meeting new situations if possible	7	4	2	4	2	1	2	5
	3. Finds it difficult to meet new situations; appears embarrassed	7	5	2	5	13	21	16	22
	4. Usually makes satisfactory adjustment to new situations and people	17	27	25	15	126	116	104	100
	5. Unusual poise and ability to adjust; definitely positive reaction	17	13	20	25	9	12	28	23
514:H41	How much does your child irritate and annoy you?								
	1. A great deal	2	2	4	9	1	9	8	13
	2. Moderately					30	60	27	53
	3. Slightly	13	13	10	5	91	69	85	71
	4. None; not at all	0	0	0	0	28	12	30	12
	5. ?					0	0	0	1
	†6. Some	8	15	14	20				
	†7. Hardly any	26	20	22	16				

515:H42 How much does your child irritate and annoy your wife (husband)?

1. A great deal	2	0	5	5	3	2	6	15
2. Moderately					49	47	50	39
3. Slightly					77	81	68	70
4. None; not at all	11	16	7	10	17	18	22	24
5. ?	1	0	0	1	4	2	4	2
†6. Some	11	14	18	16				
†7. Hardly any	25	20	20	18				

516* What does your child do that irritates or annoys you?[113]

1. Noisy	12	9	8	3
2. Teases brother (sib)	4	3	2	3
3. Bothers parent when working or reading (wants attention)	11	12	8	5
4. Wants constant attention	2	3	1	1
5. Noisy; fighting	0	1	2	3
6. Running in house; sliding on rugs	6	3	0	1
7. Wants to play when father is tired	10	0	1	0
8. Won't mind; disobedient	3	10	7	14
9. Fights with sibs	0	5	1	1
10. Talk too much--too loudly	2	2	0	3
11. Constant chattering	5	5	0	1
12. Whines	9	9	3	4
13. Interrupting conversation of parents or others	1	1	0	5
14. Nothing specific	4	4	5	2
15. Nothing	16	5	22	8
16. ?	2	2	3	4

517* What does your child do that irritates your wife (husband)?[114]

1. Gets in way in kitchen	3	0	2	0

[113]For both Studies II and III there were 55 additional actions reported, each by fewer than three of the informants represented in any one column of the table; 20 of these 55 were reported by the control and 45 by the experimental group respondents.

[114]There were 47 additional actions reported, each by fewer than three of the informants represented in any one column of the table; 18 of these 47 were reported by the control and 35 by the experimental group respondents.

Item No.: IBM Card and Column No.	Item; or Question and Response Codings; or Computed Values	Study II Control Group (N = 50)		Study II Experimental Group (N = 50)		Study III Control Group (N = 150)		Study III Experimental Group (N = 150)	
		F	M	F	M	F	M	F	M
	2. Noisy					10	7	6	8
	3. Teases brother (sib)					4	2	1	2
	4. Bothers parent when latter is working or reading (wants attention)								
	5. Cries					5	15	5	5
	6. Wants constant attention					1	1	2	3
	7. Won't mind; disobedient					2	3	1	3
	8. Slow in eating					11	14	12	18
	9. Fights with sibs					2	3	0	0
	10. Whines					3	1	3	0
	11. Interrupting conversation of parents or others					6	8	4	3
	12. Nothing specific					1	1	0	5
	13. Nothing					1	2	4	2
	14. ?					13	11	15	20
	X. No response; does not annoy sufficiently					7	6	15	5
						70	64	57	53
518:H47	How often do you take time out and definitely play with your child? (Study II: How often do you play with your child?)								
	1. Two or three times per day or more	5	12	4	14	21	33	17	44
	2. Once a day	16	20	20	13	67	69	62	61
	3. Several times a week	14	10	14	8	44	32	50	25
	4. Once a week	6	2	6	5	12	10	13	8
	5. Occasionally, but not as often as once a week					4	4	2	8
	6. Practically never					2	2	4	3
	7. Never	3	0	0	1	0	0	2	1
	†8. Hardly ever	6	6	6	9				

519* What do you usually do when you spend time together?[115]

Activity				
1. Read	61	26	57	30
2. Color pictures	4	2	0	3
3. Color; read; play indoor games	2	0	5	1
4. Read; play with trucks; put puzzles together	3	2	2	0
5. Play indoor-outdoor games	3	3	3	1
6. Rough-tumble play, wrestle	1	29	4	32
7. Physical affection (hugging); read; "rough house"	1	3	1	0
8. Read and color	2	2	4	1
9. Read; play ball; swing	3	1	1	1
10. Read; play games	9	5	12	8
11. Read; do housekeeping tasks together	2	0	16	1
12. Read; talk	5	2	4	4
13. Child reads to parent	3	1	0	0
14. Whatever child wants to do	3	4	2	6
15. Play ball	0	3	2	9
16. Swing	1	0	3	0
17. Talk	5		1	4

520:H50 How often does your wife (husband) play with the child?

Activity								
1. Two or three times per day or more	15	46	17	53	14	4	15	7
2. Once a day	59	61	63	62	18	20	14	16
3. Several times a week	44	22	43	20	9	19	8	13
4. Once a week	18	4	17	5	1	1	3	4
5. Occasionally, but not as often as once a week	7	1	9	3				
6. Practically never	4	3	1	2	2	0	2	0
7. ?								
8. Never	0	13	0	5	0	0	2	2
†9. Hardly ever	3	0	0	0	6	6	6	8

115There were 35 additional activities reported, each by fewer than three of the informants represented in any one column of the table; 23 of these 35 were reported by the control and 25 by the experimental group respondents.

Item No.: IBM Card and Column No.	Item; or Question and Response Codings; or Computed Values	Study II Control Group (N = 50)		Study II Experimental Group (N = 50)		Study III Control Group (N = 150)		Study III Experimental Group (N = 150)	
		F	M	F	M	F	M	F	M
521*	What does your wife (husband) usually do when she (he) and the child spend time together?116								
	1. Read					56	28	65	18
	2. Color pictures					3	1	5	1
	3. Talk					3	7	6	2
	4. Do carpentry work together; work in father's workshop					0	5	0	4
	5. Read; walk; play with toys					3	0	4	0
	6. Read; indoor games; "rough house"					3	9	2	7
	7. Read; "rough house"					2	12	1	14
	8. Go for rides; walks; play with blocks; trucks					0	1	3	4
	9. Go for auto rides					0	4	0	4
	10. Read; color; cut out					11	1	5	0
	11. Read; play games					11	2	4	2
	12. Play ball					3	8	1	3
	13. "Rough house"					1	33	0	21
	14. Play games					5	0	1	2
	15. Watch TV					0	5	0	3
	16. Child helps parent do things around the house, chores					8	0	2	1
	17. Play cards					0	0	0	3
	18. ?					9	0	13	2
522:H53	How often do you make an effort to get your child to converse with you? (Study II: Do you make an effort to get your child to converse with you?)								
	1. Two or three times per day or more					23	17	30	17

116There were 38 additional activities reported, each by fewer than three of the informants represented in any one column of the table; 23 of these 38 were reported by the control and 27 by the experimental group respondents.

2. Once a week
3. Several times a week
4. Once a week
5. Occasionally, but not as often as once a week
6. Practically never
7. Don't have to (Study II: not necessary)
† 8. Yes
† 9. No

Response	1	2	3	4	5	6	7	8
2. Once a week	25	23	11	8	21	18	13	23
3. Several times a week	13	17	28	36	13	7	6	6
4. Once a week	12	10	11	6	0	1	0	3
5. Occasionally					2	1	4	1
6. Practically never					2	4	5	6
7. Don't have to								
† 8. Yes					89	102	92	94
† 9. No								

523:H54 How often does your wife (husband) make an effort to get your child to converse with her (him)? (Study II: Does your wife (husband) make an effort to get your child to converse with her (him)?)

1. Two or three times per day or more
2. Once a day
3. Several times a week
4. Once a week
5. Occasionally, but not as often as once a week
6. Practically never
7. ?
8. Don't have to (Study II: not necessary)
† 9. Yes
†10. No

Response	1	2	3	4	5	6	7	8
1. Two or three times per day or more	25	24	10	5	27	13	18	30
2. Once a day	16	17	34	34	22	21	24	11
3. Several times a week	8	9	4	10	7	8	10	1
4. Once a week					0	4	1	3
5. Occasionally					0	1	4	
6. Practically never					1	4	4	
7. ?					5	1	1	
8. Don't have to								
† 9. Yes					88	98	88	93
†10. No								

524:H55 How does your child respond to your corrections and suggestions?

1. Extremely sensitive; easily hurt; sulks or becomes tearful
2. Belligerent, or may "go off halfcocked"; shows a temper (Study II coding does not include "shows a temper")
3. Inclined to be stubborn

Response	1	2	3	4
1. Extremely sensitive	4	4	5	6
2. Belligerent	2	0	2	2
3. Inclined to be stubborn (part a)	3	2	7	12
3. Inclined to be stubborn (part b)	10	14	49 / 38 / 29	23

		Study II				Study III			
Item No.: IBM Card and Column No.	Item; or Question and Response Codings; or Computed Values	Control Group (N = 50) F	M	Experimental Group (N = 50) F	M	Control Group (N = 150) F	M	Experimental Group (N = 150) F	M
	4. Usually tractable; occasionally only seems to assume attitude of tractability	16	20	11	9	102	93	72	66
	5. Intelligent and reasonable attitude and response	17	13	27	22	11	11	27	18
	6. Ignores parent					1	3	0	1
	7. Half the time stubborn; half the time responds well					0	1	2	0
525:H56	How does your child respond to the corrections and suggestions of your wife (husband)?								
	1. Extremely sensitive; easily hurt; sulks, or becomes tearful	5	0	1	2	5	9	4	5
	2. Belligerent, or may "go off halfcocked"; shows a temper (Study II coding does not include "shows a temper")	2	13	2	6	7	4	8	8
	3. Inclined to be stubborn	13	13	15	8	38	24	54	31
	4. Usually tractable; occasionally only seems to assume attitude of tractability	16	14	13	5	87	98	63	81
	5. Intelligent and reasonable attitude and response	14	21	19	29	9	12	18	25
	6. Ignores parent					3	2	0	0
	7. Half the time stubborn; half the time responds well					0	1	2	1
526:H57	8. How does the child usually evaluate his abilities and accomplishments?								
	1. Very modest; tends to be depreciative					1	3	1	6
	2. Moderately modest					8	4	2	4

3. Noncommittal	3	6	11	9
4. Moderately proud	121	118	104	109
5. Very proud; tends to exaggerate his accomplishments	17	19	28	25
6. ?	0	0	0	1
† 7. Very depreciative	0	0	1	2
† 8. Rather depreciative	4	6	6	6
† 9. Rather proud; normal reaction	29	37	33	35

527-530 In comparison with other children, does the child seem to be a perfectionist. (Study II: coding does not include "In comparison with other children"):

527:H58 About home tasks?

1. Much more than average	8	8	8	8
2. Somewhat **more** than average	19	16	23	16
3. About average	98	108	111	112
4. Somewhat less than average	21	12	7	11
5. Much less than average	0	3	1	0
6. ?	4	3	0	3
† 7. Yes	10	9	15	13
† 8. No	37	39	31	35

528:H59 About his neatness?

1. Much more than average	5	4	10	10
2. Somewhat more than average	29	26	39	38
3. About average	98	104	95	92
4. Somewhat less than average	14	11	6	10
5. Much less than average	3	4	0	0
6. ?	1	1	0	0
† 7. Yes	10	9	21	24
† 8. No	39	40	27	24

529:H60 About his schoolwork?

1. Much more than average	2	3	3	4
2. Somewhat more than average	16	11	13	13
3. About average	42	43	51	42
4. Somewhat less than average	2	4	1	3
5. Much less than average	0	0	0	0

175

Item No.: IBM Card and Column No.	Item; or Question and Response Codings; or Computed Values	Study II				Study III			
		Control Group (N = 50)		Experimental Group (N = 50)		Control Group (N = 150)		Experimental Group (N = 150)	
		F	M	F	M	F	M	F	M
	6. ?	0	0	0	1	3	2	2	4
	†7. Yes	14	16	15	19				
	†8. No	33	30	26	21				
530:H61	About his speech?								
	1. Much more than average					5	6	3	6
	2. Somewhat more than average					18	12	11	15
	3. About average					119	122	122	121
	4. Somewhat less than average					5	3	7	5
	5. Much less than average					0	1	0	0
	6. ?	0	0	2	2	3	6	7	3
	†7. Yes	11	9	11	20				
	†8. No	37	41	35	26				
531*	How does the child make bids for attention?117								
	1. Crying	6	6	0	0	1	3	0	1
	2. Temper tantrums	1	2	0	0	2	3	1	1
	3. Asks questions					2	1	8	2
	4. Interrupts conversations of parents and others	8	7	4	4	12	10	18	14
	5. Talking a lot	25	31	16	12	12	13	25	19
	6. Gets affectionate (climbs onto parent's lap)					5	2	2	4
	7. Pesters					1	1	3	0
	8. Whines	4	2	0	1	6	1	0	2
	9. Talks loudly					18	27	6	8
	10. Yells	0	1	0	1	9	8	3	4
	11. Climbs onto parent's lap and pulls parent's face toward him					4	2	0	1

117For both Studies II and III there were 60 additional behaviors reported, each by fewer than three of the informants represented in any one column of the table; 22 of these 60 were reported by the control and 55 by the experimental group respondents. Some respondents in Study II gave more than one response.

	1	2	3	4	5	6	7
12. Makes noise	2	0	1	4	2	2	0
13. Acts silly, "clowns"	0	0	1	6	8	3	4
14. Says "Nobody's paying any attention to me"							
15. Does forbidden things				1	3	0	0
16. Pulls parent's clothing				1	7	3	2
17. Jumps or climbs onto parent's lap				0	4	0	4
18. Does something he knows is annoying	0	2	3	5	2	3	1
19. Does not make bids for attention	4	1	3	0	1	0	0
20. Have not noticed	2	11	13	6	5	0	7
†21. Telling about actual achievement	5	2	3	1	0	5	5
†22. Doing things well	4	0	4				
†23. Asks to be played with	0	4	5				
†24. Shows off	11	9	3				
X. No response; child does not sufficiently make bids for attention				18	16	27	31
532:H64 How often does child do this?							
1. Several times a day	13	7	18	42	36	63	61
2. Daily	4	11	5	46	36	44	30
3. Several times a week	31	32	26	38	48	33	40
4. Weekly	2	0	1	11	15	4	4
5. Two or three times a month	4	1	3	4	3	1	3
6. Monthly	1	0	0	1	1	0	0
7. Less than once a month	0	2	0	0	2	0	0
8. ?	1	4	3	1	4	3	5
9. Never	9	7	2	4	2	2	7
533:H65 Which parent does the child prefer?							
1. Mother	13	7	18	46	36	63	54
2. Father	4	11	5	25	32	26	30
3. Neutral	31	32	26	70	75	49	57
4. ?	2	0	1	9	7	12	9

Item No.: IBM Card and Column No.	Item; or Question and Response Codings; or Computed Values	Study II Control Group (N = 50) F	M	Study II Experimental Group (N = 50) F	M	Study III Control Group (N = 150) F	M	Study III Experimental Group (N = 150) F	M
534:H66-67	Why is this probably true?[118]								
	1. With that parent more	6	6	11	7	27	21	41	34
	2. That parent does not punish (discipline) child	0	2	5	5	9	6	7	11
	3. That parent is not with child as much	1	2	2	7	10	7	4	7
	4. Because same sex as child; better companion					0	3	1	0
	5. That parent more lenient; plays with child more	1	3	1		1	1	3	3
	6. That parent plays with child a great deal (more)				2	5	5	5	4
	7. That parent takes care of him when sick, nursed him			3					
	†8. Natural (normal) to favor mother	0	0	0	1	0	3	0	0
	†9. That parent "babies" child more	1	0	0	4				
	X. No response; not sufficient preference expressed	37	35	30	27	79	82	61	66
535:H68	In comparison with other children, how well behaved do you think your child is?								
	1. Much more than average	6	9	3	3	7	4	3	5
	2. Somewhat more than average	14	18	11	10	42	29	44	28
	3. About average	27	22	33	31	99	110	95	96
	4. Somewhat less than average	0	1	3	5	2	6	7	20
	5. Much less than average	0	0	0	1	0	1	0	1

[118] For both Studies II and III there were 54 additional reasons reported, each by fewer than three of the informants represented in any one column of the table; 16 of these 54 were reported by the control and 38 by the experimental group respondents. Some respondents in Study II gave more than one response.

536:H69 How frequently is the child punished? (Punishment to be defined as correction that goes beyond words.)

1. 5 to 25 times a day	3	2	1	0	0	0	1	3
2. 5 to 25 times a week	25	31	21	19	4	9	12	6
3. 5 to 20 times a month	62	69	56	66	16	16	10	15
4. Some but less often than 3 above	44	38	57	47	21	22	22	23
5. Practically never	15	8	14	13	2	0	0	0
6. ?	0	0	0	0				
7. Never	1	2	1	5	6	3	4	3

537:H70 How frequently do you think your child is punished in comparison with other children?

1. Much more than average	0	1	1	2	0	0	0	0
2. Somewhat more than average	12	18	15	25	1	3	2	2
3. About average	73	76	88	69	26	20	18	18
4. Somewhat less than average	49	41	31	39	14	17	25	24
5. Much less than average	11	11	8	8	4	6	4	3
6. ?	5	3	7	7	5	3	1	1

538:H71 From ages 1 to 4 approximately how frequently was the child punished?

1. 5 to 25 times a day	1	2	1	0	1	1	5	0
2. 5 to 25 times a week	26	30	22	15	8	11	16	20
3. 5 to 20 times a month	62	66	60	62	9	20	7	14
4. Some but less often than 3 above	44	38	46	47	25	15	12	9
5. Practically never	16	11	21	21	1	0	1	2
6. ?	0	2	0	2				
7. Never	1	1	0	3	3	3	7	1

539:H72-73 What methods of punishment have you used? (Method most often used)[119]

1. Spanking or paddling	32	38	33	44	71	61	65	58

[119] For both Studies II and III there were 38 additional methods reported, each by fewer than three of the informants represented in any one column of the table; 29 of these 38 were reported by the control and 16 by the experimental group respondents. Some respondents in Study II gave more than one response.

Item No.: IBM Card and Column No.	Item; or Question and Response Codings; or Computed Values	Study II Control Group (N = 50)		Study II Experimental Group (N = 50)		Study III Control Group (N = 150)		Study III Experimental Group (N = 150)	
		F	M	F	M	F	M	F	M
	2. Having privilege taken away	14	25	16	31	9	7	14	18
	3. Having to stay in	4	8	1	1	0	0	0	4
	4. Being sent to bed	13	7	11	14	1	3	6	5
	5. Being sent to room; loss of privilege					2	4	0	3
	6. Having to sit in chair	9	9	7	18	7	7	12	11
	7. Slap hands	1	0	0	0	3	0	1	0
	8. Sit on chair; sent to room					1	1	4	1
	9. Sent to room	26	11	8	24	10	6	15	16
	10. Spanking; sent to bed					2	2	1	3
	11. Spanking; loss of privilege					12	11	8	2
	12. Spanking; privilege taken away; sent to room.								
	13. Spanking; sit on chair					0	6	2	4
	14. Spanking; sent to room					3	5	3	8
	15. Spanking; being in from out-doors; sent to room					6	9	2	8
	16. Spanking; sit on chair; sent to room					0	4	0	0
	17. Privilege taken away; sit on chair					1	3	0	0
	18. None	0	1	1	2	1	3	0	1
	†19. Having allowance taken away	1	1	0	3	4	2	5	2
	†20. Being separated from friends or siblings	5	11	1	5				
	†21. Playthings taken away	2	6	0	1				
	†22. Slapped	1	1	1	4				
	†23. Strap	0	2	2	3				
540:H74-75	What method have you found to be most effective? (Study II:								

Which one or two of these methods have you used most?)[120]

#	Method								
1.	Spanking or paddling	19	23	18	24	65	58	53	52
2.	Having privilege taken away	10	17	13	15	14	19	25	23
3.	Having to stay in	2	1	0	1	0	0	0	4
4.	Being sent to bed	8	2	1	3	2	4	7	10
5.	Being sent to room; loss of privilege	1	0	0	0	1	4	0	1
6.	Having to stay in room alone	2	6	6	8	4	3	4	2
7.	Having to sit in chair	1	0	0	0	9	7	12	11
8.	Slap hands					4	0	0	0
9.	Being sent to room	15	5	6	14	12	8	12	19
10.	Spanking; loss of privilege					1	3	4	1
11.	Spanking; sent to room					2	6	3	0
12.	None					15	15	14	12
13.	?					5	4	8	5
14.	Being separated from friends or siblings	1	3	0	1				

542-558 **Is the child punished regularly or has he been punished a number of times for the following behavior (Study II: Is the child ever punished for the following behavior?):**

541:H76 For messing up his room?

1. Yes	4	3			17	13	14	7
2. No	46	47			133	137	136	142
3. ?	0	0			0	0	0	1

542:H77 For spilling what he was eating or drinking (Study II: food or drink)?

1. Yes	6	17			32	25	24	28
2. No	44	32			118	125	126	121
3. ?	0	1			0	0	0	1

[120] For both Studies II and III there were 28 additional methods reported, each by fewer than three of the informants represented in any one column of the table; 22 of these 28 were reported by the control and 14 by the experimental group respondents. Some respondents in Study II gave more than one response.

Item No.: IBM Card and Column No.	Item; or Question and Response Codings; or Computed Values	Study II				Study III			
		Control Group (N = 50)		Experimental Group (N = 50)		Control Group (N = 150)		Experimental Group (N = 150)	
		F	M	F	M	F	M	F	M
543:H78	Talking back								
	1. Yes		29		27	70	70	51	74
	2. No		21		23	79	80	99	75
	3. ?		0		0	1	0	0	1
544:H79	Disobedience?								
	1. Yes		47		37	109	111	99	103
	2. No		3		13	41	38	51	46
	3. ?		0		0	0	1	0	1
545:H80	Talking too much?								
	1. Yes		2		2	8	3	6	5
	2. No		48		48	142	147	144	144
	3. ?		0		0	0	0	0	1
546:I6	Interrupting the conversation of others?								
	1. Yes		5		4	16	15	14	21
	2. No		45		46	134	135	136	129
547:I7	Wetting the bed?								
	1. Yes		0		5	5	5	7	3
	2. No		50		45	145	145	143	147
548:I8	Stuttering?								
	1. Yes		0		1	0	0	0	1
	2. No		50		49	93	96	150	149
	3. ?		0		0	0	0	0	0
549:I9	Lying?								
	1. Yes		14		9	24	16	24	17
	2. No		36		41	126	133	125	133
	3. ?		0		0	0	0	1	0
550:I10	Swearing?								
	1. Yes		6		11	16	13	8	11
	2. No		44		39	134	137	142	139

551:I11	Yelling around the house; being noisy?						
	1. Yes	12	17	55	39	37	39
	2. No	38	33	95	111	113	111
552:I12	Playing with sex organs?						
	1. Yes	1	0	5	2	5	1
	2. No	49	50	145	148	145	149
553:I13	Fighting with other children?						
	1. Yes	16	23	46	59	43	49
	2. No	34	27	103	91	107	101
	3. ?	0	0	1	0	0	0
554:I14	Quarreling with other children?						
	1. Yes	26	29	41	52	25	26
	2. No	24	21	109	98	124	124
	3. ?	0	0	0	0	1	0
555:I15	Not doing his chores around the house (Study II: not helping with housework)?						
	1. Yes	7	11	35	16	17	15
	2. No	43	39	115	134	132	135
556:I16	Being rude?						
	1. Yes	16	11	46	40	40	28
	2. No	34	39	104	110	110	121
	3. ?	0	0	0	0	0	1
557:I17	Destroying things?						
	1. Yes	15	25	66	65	57	53
	2. No	35	25	83	85	92	97
	3. ?	0	0	1	0	1	0
558:I18	Getting dirty (Study II: appearance; getting dirty)?						
	1. Yes	5	9	16	12	17	10
	2. No	45	41	134	138	133	140
	3. ?	0	0	0	0	0	0
559:I19-20	Total number of above answered "yes":						
	1. One			18	17	22	18
	2. Two			14	28	28	19

Item No.: IBM Card and Column No.	Item; or Question and Response Codings; or Computed Values	Study II Control Group (N = 50)		Study II Experimental Group (N = 50)		Study III Control Group (N = 150)		Study III Experimental Group (N = 150)	
		F	M	F	M	F	M	F	M
	3. Three					21	20	16	27
	4. Four					20	16	16	17
	5. Five					22	21	12	12
	6. Six					11	14	8	12
	7. Seven					8	7	4	11
	8. Eight					12	5	4	3
	9. Nine					3	4	3	1
	10. Ten					4	3	3	2
	11. Eleven					2	1	2	1
	12. Twelve					0	0	3	1
	13. Thirteen					0	0	1	0
	14. Fourteen					0	1	0	0
	15. None					15	13	28	26
	16. Total "yes" responses					606	566	486	490
	17. Average					4.0	3.8	3.2	3.3
	18. Average, exclusive of "none"					4.5	4.1	4.0	4.0
560:I21	How do you reprimand the child?[121]								
	1. Yell, shout at him	7	6	14	21	10	6	17	27
	2. Sharply tell him not to	24	17	25	32	48	39	68	51
	3. Quietly tell him not to	15	22	6	11	5	6	12	15
	4. Threaten him in a sharp way					5	3	9	13
	5. Explain why he shouldn't-- quietly					21	18	11	7
	6. Explain why he shouldn't-- sharply					18	21	10	10
	7. Tell him what he should do instead of what he has done					8	3	1	2

[121] For both Studies II and III there were 14 additonal methods reported, each by fewer than three of the informants represented in any one column of the table; 12 of these methods were reported by the control and 8 by the experimental group respondents. Some respondents in Study II gave more than one response.

8. Try to reason with him	15	13	9	11		2		0
9. Sometimes quietly, sometimes sharply tell him not to	7	5	31	17		21		15
10. First reason with him; then yell at him	1	0	10	2		6		0
†11. Get him to promise to do better					8		2	
†12. Explain why he shouldn't					32		27	
†13. Threaten him					11		6	
561:I22 When you compare yourself with other parents, how strict do you feel you are?								
1. Much more than average	8	4	4	11	3	2	1	1
2. Somewhat more than average	29	38	42	37	9	11	9	9
3. About average	72	66	66	64	23	21	25	32
4. Somewhat less than average	36	34	34	37	13	11	13	6
5. Much less than average	5	8	2	0	2	5	2	1
6. ?	0	0	2	1				
562:I23 When you compare your wife (husband) with other parents, how strict do you feel she (he) is?								
1. Much more than average	7	1	5	3	2	3	0	2
2. Somewhat more than average	39	29	37	47	9	8	8	6
3. About average	69	75	74	59	24	23	27	27
4. Somewhat less than average	28	40	28	39	13	13	12	13
5. Much less than average	7	5	4	2	2	3	3	0
6. ?	0	0	2	0				
563:I24 Do you feel you are								
1. Too strict	26	26	25	22	10	7	4	2
2. Too lax	46	33	32	29	12	13	13	7
3. About right	75	87	81	87	26	30	33	38
4. ?	3	4	12	12	2	0	0	0
564:I25 Do you feel your wife (husband) is								
1. Too strict	34	15	24	15	7	5	4	3
2. Too lax	39	45	22	31	6	11	10	17
3. About right	76	89	90	99	35	34	35	28

Item No.: IBM Card and Column No.	Item; or Question and Response Codings; or Computed Values	Study II Control Group (N = 50) F	M	Study II Experimental Group (N = 50) F	M	Study III Control Group (N = 150) F	M	Study III Experimental Group (N = 150) F	M
	4. ?	0	0	0	2	5	14	1	1
	†5. Too strict--about neatness	0	1	0	0				
565:I26	Do you think the child is spoiled?								
	1. Very					3	6	1	7
	2. Quite					18	11	15	23
	3. Not very					51	62	59	57
	4. No					77	71	75	62
	5. ?					1	0	0	1
566:I27	How much have you worried about spoiling your child?								
	1. A great deal	1	4	4	3	3	7	7	9
	2. Some	6	6	7	9	23	13	13	25
	3. Not much	7	14	3	2	31	36	43	41
	4. None	35	26	36	36	93	93	87	75
	5. ?					0	1	0	0
567:I28	How much has the other parent worried about spoiling the child?								
	1. A great deal	0	2	1	1	3	2	9	5
	2. Some	2	5	5	4	20	15	15	16
	3. Not much	9	11	5	4	33	33	38	28
	4. None	38	30	37	36	92	94	85	95
	5. ?	0	1	2	5	2	6	3	6
568:I29	How much does it bother you when your child makes a mess around the house?								
	1. Severely disapproving; bothers a great deal	2	2	1	9	8	10	17	26
	2. Rather disapproving; bothers some	27	23	13	20	71	81	54	78
	3. Noncommittal; indifferent; appears not to bother	18	20	34	16	70	54	73	43

4. Expressed approval of his right	2	4	2	5
5. Inconsistent—sometimes bothers a great deal, sometimes indifferent	1	4	5	2
569:I30-31 Age the child entered first grade (in years)				
a. Minimum	6.0	6.5	5.8	4.8
b. Maximum	7.0	6.9	6.6	6.8
c. Mean	6.2	6.2	6.2	6.1
d. Median	6.0	6.1	6.1	6.0
e. 90th percentile	6.6	6.7	6.5	6.6
f. N	41	40	29	33
570:I32-33 Why was child's starting to school delayed?				
1. Sick	0	1	0	0
2. No school available before	2	1	0	0
3. Speech difficulty thought to be too great a handicap	0	3	0	0
4. Repeated kindergarten	0	2	0	14
5. Way his birthday fell	9	15	19	0
6. Small for age	0	0	0	0
X. No response; no delay	39	28	131	136
571:I34 Why was child started to school early?				
1. Advanced for age; very bright	0	0	0	0
2. Way his birthday fell	0	2	7	13
3. Child large for his age	1	0	0	1
X. No response; not started early	49	48	143	136
572:I35-36 Grade attending now				
1. 1B	4	5	7	4
2. 1A	1	1	14	22
3. 2B	3	2	3	2
4. 2A	2	4	5	5
5. 3B	4	3	0	0
6. 3A	2	1	0	0
7. 4B	3	3	0	0

Item No.: IBM Card and Column No.	Item; or Question and Response Codings; or Computed Values	Study II Control Group (N = 50) F	M	Study II Experimental Group (N = 50) F	M	Study III Control Group (N = 150) F	M	Study III Experimental Group (N = 150) F	M
	8. 4A		3		1		0		0
	9. 5B		1		3		0		0
	10. 5A		3		2		0		0
	11. 6B		0		3		0		0
	12. 6A		3		2		0		0
	13. 7B		3		3		0		0
	14. Kindergarten		1		3		39		29
	†15. 7A		1		4				
	†16. 8B		4		0				
	†17. 8A		1		1				
573-583; 587-595; I37-50; I55-66[122]									
584:I51-52	Age (in years) at which child learned to read:								
	a. Minimum					5.0	5.0	5.0	5.5
	b. Maximum					8.4	7.0	6.8	6.8
	c. Mean					6.2	6.1	6.1	6.1
	d. Median					6.6	6.5	6.0	6.0
	e. 90th percentile					6.6		6.6	6.6
	f. N					27	29	32	32
585:I53	Conditions under which reading was learned; where child learned to read:								
	1. Preschool age--at home					0	0	2	0
	2. Kindergarten					2	3	3	1
	3. First grade					23	26	26	29
	4. Kindergarten age, at home					1	0	1	2
586:I54	Was first writing learned mainly:								
	1. Cursive					0	0	1	0
	2. Printing					52	53	52	54

[122] These items have to do with school attendance, greade retardation and acceleration, adjustment to school, grades or marks, and related matters; the relatively small number of subjects for whom the items were appropriate precludes meaningful analysis of data.

596:I67 How well satisfied are you with your child's intelligence?

Response	1	2	3	4	5	6	7	8
1. Completely satisfied	41	32	40	39	104	123	111	114
2. Fairly well satisfied	1	11	7	6	45	27	34	32
3. Undecided; noncommittal (Study II: coding does not include "noncommittal")	2	0	1	3				
4. Not very well satisfied	0	0	2	2	0	0	3	1
5. Not at all satisfied	1	1	0	0	0	0	1	3
†6. ?	0	1	0	0	0	0	0	0

597:I68 How do you think your child compares in intelligence with the neighborhood children?

Response	1	2	3	4	5	6	7	8
1. Much more intelligent than average	5	6	5	2	10	12	13	11
2. Somewhat more than average	25	17	12	15	61	50	62	42
3. About average	17	24	30	29	76	84	70	90
4. Somewhat less than average	0	1	3	3	1	1	3	5
5. Much less than average	1	1	0	0	0	0	0	0
6. ?	0	0	0	1	1	3	1	2

598:I69 Which child do you enjoy most? (Study II: Who is your favorite child?)

Response	1	2	3	4	5	6	7	8
1. Present case	10	3	4	4	39	32	29	32
2. Other than present case	4	2	6	3	27	25	22	19
3. No preference	31	40	29	32	65	74	70	68
4. ?					4	4	4	6
5. Only child	5	5	11	11	15	15	25	25

599:I70 Age of the child you enjoy most (Study II: Age of favorite child)

Response	1	2	3	4	5	6	7	8
1. Oldest	4	1	0	4	17	7	20	16
2. Youngest					37	38	23	32
3. Second	2	1	4	1	5	8	4	1
4. Third	1	2	3	2	4	4	1	0
5. Fourth	0	0	1	0	1	0	2	0
6. Fifth	0	0	2	0	1	0	0	1
7. One of younger twins					0	0	1	0

Item No.: IBM Card and Column No.	Item; or Question and Response Codings; or Computed Values	Study II Control Group (N = 50)		Study II Experimental Group (N = 50)		Study III Control Group (N = 150)		Study III Experimental Group (N = 150)	
		F	M	F	M	F	M	F	M
	8. Youngest child but a younger sib deceased					1	0	0	0
	9. Only child	5	5	11	11	15	15	25	25
	10. No preference	37	41	29	32	69	78	74	75
	†11. Twin	1	0	0	0				
600:I71	Sex of child you enjoy most (Study II: Sex of favorite child)								
	1. Male	6	3	8	2	46	35	28	29
	2. Female	4	1	1	5	20	22	23	21
	X. Only child; no preference	40	46	41	43	84	93	99	100
601:I72-73	Why is that child the one you enjoy most? (Study II: Why?)123								
	1. Most like me	1	0	0	0	0	0	5	0
	2. Cuter ways					4	3	3	1
	3. Easier to manage					2	3	1	4
	4. Can do more things with him (recreation)	2	2	2	1	10	2	5	7
	5. The youngest; a baby					3	5	3	10
	6. The youngest					8	3	2	4
	7. Happier; easier to get along with					0	4	0	0
	8. Plays with parent more; with parent more					3	0	4	2
	9. More pleasant; better temperament					0	3	1	0
	10. Because a boy					3	1	1	1
	11. The oldest; older	1	0	0	0	2	0	4	3

123For both Studies II and III there were 95 additional reasons reported, each by fewer than three of the informants represented in any one column of the table; 59 of these reasons were reported by the control and 51 by the experimental group respondents. Some respondents in Study II gave more than one response.

602:I74 Which child does your wife (husband) enjoy most? (Study II: Who is your wife's (husband's) favorite child?)								
1. Present case	7	4	7	6	30	38	19	34
2. Other than present case	7	2	4	5	35	29	25	27
3. No preference	30	36	27	25	60	58	63	50
4. ?	1	3	1	3	10	10	18	14
5. Only child	5	5	11	11	15	15	25	25
603:I75 Age of child the other parent enjoys most (Study II: Age of the other parent's favorite child)								
1. Oldest	1	1	3	3	10	18	19	23
2. Youngest	4	2	5	5	44	36	23	31
3. Second	3	1	1	1	9	10	1	4
4. Third	0	0	1	1	0	2	1	1
5. Fourth	0	0	1	1	1	0	0	1
6. Fifth			1	1	1	1	0	1
7. One of younger twins								
8. Youngest child, but a younger sib deceased					1	0	0	0
9. Only child	5	5	11	11	15	15	25	25
X. No preference; uncertain	37	41	28	28	79	68	69	86
604:I76 Sex of child the other parent enjoys most (Study II: Sex of the other parent's favorite child)								
1. Male	5	2	7	8	40	47	19	32
2. Female	6	2	4	3	25	20	25	29
X. Only child; no preference	39	46	39	39	85	83	106	89
605:I77-78 Why is this child the one enjoyed most by the other parent? (Study II: Why?)[124]								
1. A boy					2	6	0	6

[124] For both Studies II and III there were 98 additional reasons reported, each by fewer than three of the informants represented in any one column of the table; 67 of these reasons were reported by the control and 45 by the experimental group respondents. Some respondents in Study II gave more than one response.

191

Item No.: IBM Card and Column No.	Item; or Question and Response Codings; or Computed Values	Study II Control Group (N = 50)		Study II Experimental Group (N = 50)		Study III Control Group (N = 150)		Study III Experimental Group (N = 150)	
		F	M	F	M	F	M	F	M
	2. Easier to take care of					1	0	4	0
	3. A girl					3	1	5	4
	4. The baby; easier to manage					3	0	1	2
	5. Older; prefers older children; easier to play with; doesn't get hurt easily								
	6. Parent not at home when other child was an infant; has watched case grow up					0	3	0	3
	7. Older; can talk and reason better with child					0	1	0	1
	8. Can do more things together; better companion					5	10	2	4
	9. Because the youngest and a boy			0	3	3	0	0	6
	10. The youngest	2	1			6	2	3	0
	11. Cuter; smallest					2	2	3	4
	12. The oldest	2	0	0	1	2	1	1	2
	13. With that child more	0	0	1	0	4	1	0	3
	14. ?					3	0	5	3
606:I79	Which of the children do you consider the brightest?								
	1. Present case	8	6	4	7	20	19	31	29
	2. Other than present case	11	10	19	18	53	44	34	33
	3. No difference	22	26	11	11	45	54	48	42
	4. ?	4	3	5	3	17	18	12	21
	X. No response; only child	5	5	11	11	15	15	25	25
607:I80	Which of your children do you consider slowest (dullest)?								
	1. Present case	6	6	16	12	29	22	24	26
	2. Other than present case	8	7	9	11	35	37	35	34
	3. No difference	22	25	10	11	48	52	48	42

608.J6									
4. ?	9	7	4	5	23	24	23	18	23
X. No response; only child	5	5	11	11	15	15	15	25	25
Of which child do you demand most?									
1. Present case					35	45		49	54
2. Other than present case					68	72		56	57
3. No difference					26	14		18	12
4. ?					5	4		2	2
5. Present case and one other than present case, equally					1	0		0	0
X. No response; only child					15	15		25	25
609.J7-8									
(Answered by interviewer)									
Informant refused to talk about what subjects?									
1. How child's condition and behavior compared with ideals					2	0		1	1
2. None					146	149		147	148
3. Child's speech					0	1		1	0
4. How child's condition and behavior compared with spouse's ideals					0	0		1	0
5. Husband's attitudes					0	0		0	1
6. Wife's feelings					1	0		0	0
610									
(Answered by interviewer)									
Characteristics of informant:[125]									
1. Much blaming of other parent	0	0	2	3	0	0		1	0
2. Some blaming of other parent	5	0	0	2	0	0		0	1
3. Seemed objective about self, family; cooperative					11	16		11	13
4. Cooperative; willing to answer questions	15	15	46	47	10	15		40	39
5. Rationalized own behavior; found excuses to justify his behavior	0	0	2	2	0	0		3	4
6. Restrained; reserved	2	1	0	1	1	0		5	3
7. Reserved but thoughtful					2	1		3	1

125 For both Studies II and III there were 27 additional characteristics reported, each by fewer than three of the informants represented in any one column of the table; 16 of these characteristics were reported for the control and 22 for the experimental group respondents. Some informants in Study II were assigned more than one characteristic.

Item No.: IBM Card and Column No.	Item; or Question and Response Codings; or Computed Values	Study II Control Group (N = 50)		Study II Experimental Group (N = 50)		Study III Control Group (N = 150)		Study III Experimental Group (N = 150)	
		F	M	F	M	F	M	F	M
8.	Sincere but not productive					1	1	6	2
9.	Deliberate; thoughtful					11	1	1	4
10.	Talkative; gave indirect answers and had to be asked for clarification								
11.	Friendly; interested	2	6	3	4	3	10	6	3
12.	Straightforward and simple					6	20	1	3
13.	Frank; friendly					13	17	4	1
14.	Interested					6	13	6	11
15.	Frank; direct					10	2	4	4
16.	Cooperative, interested; memory is vague					10	4	11	11
17.	Polite but not motivated					4	6	2	1
18.	Defensive	1	0	1	1	0	0	2	1
19.	Very talkative	2	10	5	6	2	1	1	3
X.	No comment					39	38	35	35
†20.	Some blaming of others (other than parent)	1	0	0	4				
†21.	Animated, dynamic	0	2	6	21				
†22.	Gave cryptic, brief answers; taciturn	4	1	8	1				
†23.	Attempted to dominate interview	3	1	0	0				
†24.	Gave well-reasoned answers with qualifications	6	3	10	4				
†25.	Noncommittal	0	0	3	2				
†26.	Needed much explanation; had difficulty understanding questions	4	1	4	3				
†27.	Slow in answering	6	0	4	1				
†28.	Gave answers very quickly	3	7	6	6				
†29.	Mild manner	4	0	5	0				

	1	2	3	4	5	6	7	8
† 30. Very vague answers; much "I don't know"	2	0	2	3	3	2	5	5
† 31. A good deal of talking of blame	3	0	3	3	3	0	1	0
611:J11 (Answered by interviewer) Conduct of interview:								
1. All at one sitting	122	143	144	148	33	47	50	50
2. Two sessions	28	7	6	2	15	3	0	0
3. Three sessions	0	0	0	0	2	0	0	0
612:J12 (Answered by interviewer) Amount of interruption:								
1. No interruptions	88	113	59	117	18	32	0	1
2. One or a few minor interruptions	55	31	57	27	20	15	9	5
3. Moderate amount of interruption	6	6	32	5	5	3	12	12
4. Many interruptions severely interfered with effectiveness of interview	0	0	2	1	0	0	3	3
613:J13-14 Score on Iowa Scale of Attitude toward Stuttering								
a. Minimum	1.0	1.0	1.0	1.0	1.0	1.1	1.3	1.2
b. Maximum	3.3	3.5	3.5	3.6	2.8	3.9	3.0	2.8
c. Mean	1.9	1.9	1.9	1.9	2.0	2.0	2.1	2.0
d. Median	1.9	1.8	1.8	1.8				
e. 90th percentile	2.5	2.5	2.4	2.4				
f. N	146	138	149	149				
614:J15 Interviewer's rating of severity of child's stuttering[126]								
1. 1, none	47	7	148	50	48	49	43	43

126 See Chapter I for a description of the criteria for selecting the experimental group children. All children in the experimental group met these criteria. With two exceptions in which ratings were made by two persons, the interviewer and a second clinical worker who made a tape recording of the child's speech, each child in Study III was rated by the interviewer. In Study II ratings were made by one or more other clinical workers, in addition to the interviewer, and the ratings made of each child's speech were averaged. In this table all fractional values have been rounded to the nearest whole number, with any value lying midway between two whole numbers being converted to the higher one of the two. For example, an average rating of 1.5 was entered in the table as 2.

Item No.: IBM Card and Column No.	Item; or Question and Response Codings; or Computed Values	Study II Control Group (N = 50) F	M	Study II Experimental Group (N = 50) F	M	Study III Control Group (N = 150) F	M	Study III Experimental Group (N = 150) F	M
	2. 2, very mild		0		11		0		39
	3. 3, mild		0		14		0		30
	4. 4, average		0		10		0		11
	5. 5, moderately severe		0		6		0		14
	6. 6, severe		0		2		0		1
	7. 7, very severe		0		0		0		1
	X. Unrated		0		0		2		7
615	Score on Minnesota Multiphasic Personality Inventory[127]								
616	Child's speech sample[128]								
617-621:J16-J20[129]									
622:J21-22	Total score on Warner Index of Status Characteristics								
	a. Minimum					20		21	
	b. Maximum					69		76	
	c. Mean					45.3		45.5	
	d. Median					45		46	
	e. 90th percentile					58		58	
	f. N					150		150	
623:J23	Social-class rating of family:								
	1. Upper	2		2		3		4	
	2. Upper-middle	19		19		33		33	
	3. Lower-middle	19		19		70		68	
	4. Upper-lower	9		9		42		42	
	5. Lower-lower	1		1		2		3	

[127]See Chapter 7 for presentation of the data obtained from administration of the MMPI.
[128]See Chapter 8 for presentation of the data obtained from analysis of the tape-recorded samples of the children's speech.
[129]Responses to these items, concerned with father's occupation, source of income, house type, and parents' education, were used in deriving the scores and ratings summarized in 622 and 623.

624:J24 How stable has your employment been?

Response		
1. Rarely work	2	1
2. Work when can find job, but irregularly	0	0
3. Usually employed but change jobs frequently	17	9
4. Steadily employed; infrequently change jobs	131	140

625:J25 How well-to-do do you consider yourself to be now?

1. Totally dependent	0	1	0	0	0	0	0
2. Partially dependent	0	1	0	5	5	2	6
3. Meagerly independent	22	14	25	26	36	49	42
4. Adequately independent	27	32	22	114	103	92	98
5. Well-to-do	1	0	3	3	4	7	3
6. ?	0	0	0	2	2	0	1

626:J26 How regular is your income?

Response						
1. Steady	43	40	45	42	139	139	139
2. Irregular	6	7	5	8	11	10	9
3. None	0	0	0	0	0	1	1
X. No response; uncertain	1	3	0	0	0	0	1

627:J27 Husband: How secure do you consider your job to be? Wife: How secure do you consider your husband's job to be?

1. Very secure	26	20	29	30	101	108	92
2. Quite secure	13	19	14	9	40	31	47
3. Rather insecure	2	3	2	4	5	6	9
4. Very insecure	7	7	5	6	0	2	1
5. ?	2	1	0	1	3	1	0
6. Slightly insecure					0	0	0
7. Husband unemployed					1	1	1

628:J28 Husband only: How secure does your wife consider your job to be?

Response			
1. Very secure	27	30	101	106
2. Quite secure	10	12	37	28
3. Rather insecure	3	0	5	6

Item No.: IBM Card and Column No.	Item; or Question and Response Codings; or Computed Values	Study II Control Group (N = 50) F	M	Study II Experimental Group (N = 50) F	M	Study III Control Group (N = 150) F	M	Study III Experimental Group (N = 150) F	M
	4. Very insecure	6		5		0		2	
	5. ?	4		3		6		7	
	6. Husband unemployed	0		0		1		1	
629:J29	Husband: How well do you like your present employment? Wife: How well do you like your husband's present employment?								
	1. Very much	30	25	41	29	99	82	100	66
	2. Moderately well	17	18	4	9	37	41	38	49
	3. Indifferent	1	2	1	3	3	6	7	16
	4. Moderately dislike	2	3	4	4	6	11	2	14
	5. Strongly dislike	0	2	0		1	4	3	3
	6. ?	0	0	0	3	3	5	0	2
	7. Unemployed					1	1	0	0
630:J30	Husband: How well do you think your present employment uses and demonstrates your abilities? Wife: How well do you think your husband's present employment uses and demonstrates his abilities?								
	1. Beyond my (his) capacities					2	0	2	3
	2. Challenging, demands all my (his) powers					63	33	27	8
	3. Average, well suited to abilities					53	74	104	106
	4. Rather easy, not very challenging					23	26	12	24
	5. Far below capacities					4	7	4	6
	6. ?					4	7	0	1
	7. Demonstrates abilities but not suited to interests					0	2	1	2
	8. Unemployed					1	1	0	0

631:J31 How well does your wife think your present employment uses and demonstrates your abilities?

1. Beyond my capacities	0	1	4
2. Challenging, demands all my powers	49	19	5
3. Average, well suited to abilities	52	104	38
4. Rather easy, not very challenging	21	11	19
5. Far below capabilities	5	5	5
6. ?	21	10	48
7. Unemployed	2	0	2

632:J32 How often have you changed your residence from one community to another on the average since marriage?

1. Twice a year or more often	4	4	6
2. Once every year	13	12	4
3. Every two years	31	32	35
4. Every three years	29	31	18
5. Every four years	10	12	6
6. Every five years	28	22	50
7. Every seven or eight years	4	4	2
8. In same locale for ten years or more	9	10	6
9. Never changed	20	23	23

633:J33 For what reasons have you changed your community of residence since marriage?[130]

1. Chance to better business opportunities	4	5	10	8	6	8
2. To take new job	6	9	40	36	25	23
3. House too small; moved to larger quarters			13	11	28	23
4. In Navy or Army; to change jobs			6	7	2	5
5. Husband in service, transferred; husband transferred (not in service)			2	4	11	12

[130]For both Studies II and III there were 34 additional reasons reported, each by fewer than three of the informants represented in any one column of the table; 28 of these reasons were reported by the control and 13 by the experimental group respondents. Some respondents in Study II gave more than one response.

Item No.: IBM Card and Column No.	Item; or Question and Response Codings; or Computed Values	Study II Control Group (N=50) F	M	Study II Experimental Group (N=50) F	M	Study III Control Group (N=150) F	M	Study III Experimental Group (N=150) F	M
	6. Bought a house					12	14	17	16
	7. Health reasons; to take new job					21	25	25	23
	8. To improve living conditions					20	22	29	30
	9. To take new job; attend school					1	3	0	0
	10. Informant (husband) changed schools; educational reasons								
	11. To take new job; bought a house					4	5	0	0
†12.	Transferred by employer		6		6	4	2	0	0
†13.	To take advantage of particular educational advantage		3		0				
†14.	Military service		4		4				
†15.	Opportunity to buy, rent, find permanent quarters		15		1				
634:J34	How proud are you of your abilities and accomplishments?								
	1. Very depreciative	0	0	1	3	0	0	0	2
	2. Rather depreciative	4	6	6	15	14	9	11	24
	3. Noncommittal	5	4	2	1	9	10	8	13
	4. "Normal" reaction; rather proud	40	37	41	31	123	127	118	107
	5. Very proud; exaggerates accomplishments	1	2	0	0	3	3	13	3
	6. ?	0	0	0	0	1	1	0	1
635:J35	How proud is your wife (husband) of your abilities and accomplishments?								
	1. Very depreciative					1	0	0	1
	2. Rather depreciative					7	5	3	7
	3. Noncommittal					7	8	21	15
	4. "Normal" reaction; rather proud					112	116	101	107
	5. Very proud; exaggerates accomplishments					7	7	18	14
	6. ?					16	14	7	6

636-640:J36-J40[131]					
641:J41-42	Informant's father's total score on Warner Index of Status Characteristics (at present time)				
	a. Minimum	20	15	18	18
	b. Maximum	76	69	73	65
	c. Mean	48.3	46.0	50.1	46.7
	d. Median	48	47	51	48
	e. 90th percentile	66	60	65	59
	f. N	102	87	111	122
642:J43	Social-class rating of informant's father (at present time)				
	1. Upper	3	3	2	2
	2. Upper-middle	17	16	12	15
	3. Lower-middle	42	39	46	57
	4. Upper-lower	31	26	42	48
	5. Lower-lower	9	3	9	0
643:J44	Is home owned or rented?				
	1. Owned	19	24	68	57
	2. Rented	13	15	40	47
	3. In process of buying	12	8	36	43
	4. Live in home owned by relative (no rent)	1	3	4	2
	5. Live in home owned by relative (pay rent)			1	1
	6. Live in home owned by friend (no rent)	1	3	1	0
644:J45-46	Number of rooms[132]				
	a. Minimum	2	3	3	2
	b. Maximum	14	17	15	10
	c. Mean	6.6	6.7	5.7	5.4
	d. Median			6	5
	e. 90th percentile			7	7
	f. N	50	50	150	150

[131]Responses to these items, concerned with the informant's father's occupation, source of income, house type, and education, were used in deriving the scores and ratings summarized in 641 and 642.

[132]Bathrooms were excluded from room count.

Item No.: IBM Card and Column No.	Item; or Question and Response Codings; or Computed Values	Study II Control Group (N = 50) F	M	Study II Experimental Group (N = 50) F	M	Study III Control Group (N = 150) F	M	Study III Experimental Group (N = 150) F	M
645:J47-48	Number living in home								
	a. Minimum		3		3		3		2
	b. Maximum		9		8		9		8
	c. Mean		4.8		4.5		4.8		4.3
	d. Median						5		4
	e. 90th percentile						6		6
	f. N		50		50		150		150
646:J49-50	Ratio of overcrowdedness (number of rooms divided by number of persons living in home)								
	a. Minimum		.6		.5		.5		.7
	b. Maximum		3.5		3.25		2.5		2.7
	c. Mean		1.5		1.6		1.2		1.3
	d. Median						1.2		1.2
	e. 90th percentile						1.7		1.8
	f. N		50		50		150		150
647*	What magazines do you and the other members of your family read?[133]								
648:J51	Number of magazines taken or read								
	1. One to three		12		2	45	34	51	40
	2. Four to six		11		9	66	74	70	77
	3. Seven to nine		11		13	28	33	21	18
	4. Ten to fifteen		13		22	7	4	3	9
	5. Over fifteen		0		4	0	1	0	0
	6. None					4	4	5	6
649:J52	Does the child have adequate play space inside the house?								
	1. Yes					128	123	126	121

133 see 648 for summary of data.

	1	2	3	4	5	6	7	8
2. No	29	22	26	22				
3. ?	0	2	1	0				

650:J53 Does the child have adequate play space outside the house?

	1	2	3	4	5	6	7	8
1. Yes	137	136	143	140				
2. No	13	13	7	9				
3. ?	0	1	0	1				

651* To what community organizations do you belong?[134]

652:J54 Total number of organizations to which you belong:

	1	2	3	4	5	6	7	8
a. Minimum	0	0	0	0	0	0	0	0
b. Maximum	9	7	7	7	13	8	7	9
c. Mean	1.6	1.4	2.1	1.8	2.8	2.0	3.0	2.9
d. Median	1	1	2	1				
e. 90th percentile	3	4	4	4				
f. N	150	150	150	150	49	50	50	50

653:J55 Total number of organizations in which you have held office:

	1	2	3	4	5	6	7	8
a. Minimum	0	0	0	0	0	0	0	0
b. Maximum	9	4	4	4	4	5	4	6
c. Mean	0.3	0.2	0.7	0.5	0.6	0.7	0.7	1.2
d. Median	0	0	0	0				
e. 90th percentile	1	1	2	2				
f. N	150	150	150	150	49	50	50	50

654-661 How frequently do you take part in the following sparetime activities?

654:J56 Movies

	1	2	3	4	5	6	7	8
1. Daily	1	0	0	0	0	0	0	0
2. Several times a week	3	3	1	0	1	0	3	4
3. Once a week	4	5	6	7	8	13	11	7
4. Two or three times a month	22	24	16	21	4	5	6	5
5. Once a month	20	24	16	26	11	9	6	8
6. Every two or three months	25	25	36	31	12	6	7	8
7. Once in six months	31	28	32	24	8	1	10	10

[134] See 652 for summary of data.

Item No.: IBM Card and Column No.	Item; or Question and Response Codings; or Computed Values	Study II Control Group (N = 50)		Study II Experimental Group (N = 50)		Study III Control Group (N = 150)		Study III Experimental Group (N = 150)	
		F	M	F	M	F	M	F	M
	8. Once a year or less	2	3	4	6	21	17	25	24
	9. Never	3	3	3	2	20	26	16	20
655:J57	Dancing								
	1. Once a week	0	0	2	1	1	3	0	2
	2. Two or three times a month	3	3	1	4	6	4	5	4
	3. Once a month	4	3	7	4	19	12	13	11
	4. Every two or three months	6	6	4	4	24	28	17	19
	5. Once in six months	7	11	3	5	19	22	35	30
	6. Once a year or less	16	12	9	9	37	25	29	33
	7. Never	14	14	23	23	44	56	51	51
656:J58	Playing cards								
	1. Daily	0	0	2	2	0	0	2	0
	2. Several times a week	3	4	9	8	4	2	5	4
	3. Once a week	16	9	13	7	18	20	16	29
	4. Two or three times a month	7	14	6	7	31	34	27	23
	5. Once a month	5	3	5	12	29	23	28	22
	6. Every two or three months	3	5	5	2	25	19	23	21
	7. Once in six months	2	3	3	5	10	15	15	12
	8. Once a year or less	1	3	2	3	13	10	11	11
	9. Never	12	7	4	6	20	27	23	28
657:J59	Musical activities								
	1. Daily	1	2	1	4	2	8	1	0
	2. Several times a week	4	7	0	1	4	12	2	2
	3. Once a week	2	2	1	4	8	7	2	4
	4. Two or three times a month	0	3	2	1	3	2	2	3
	5. Once a month	1	2	0	1	3	5	4	3
	6. Every two or three months	2	3	0	0	3	2	0	0
	7. Once in six months	0	2	0	0	1	0	0	0
	8. Once a year or less	0	0	0	0	1	0	2	0
	9. Never	2	3	0	0	5	5	3	3
658*	Sports participation[135]	37	26	45	39	121	109	133	134

[135] Data on file in University of Iowa Speech Clinic.

659*								
660:J62 Sports enjoyment[136]								
Travel (vacation trips; family pleasure trips, including short ones)								
1. Daily	0	0	1	0	0	0	0	0
2. Once a week	0	0	0	0	0	0	1	2
3. Two or three times a month	0	3	2	1	0	0	1	1
4. Once a month	2	1	3	2	1	1	1	1
5. Every two or three months	8	11	10	7	0	1	5	10
6. Once in six months	17	21	18	19	6	9	15	10
7. Once a year or less	86	86	92	94	34	30	25	25
8. Never	37	28	24	27	9	9	2	1
661:J63 Parties								
1. Several times a week	0	0	4	1	3	0	1	0
2. Once a week	15	8	17	10	5	5	4	5
3. Two or three times a month	23	20	25	27	10	7	13	10
4. Once a month	33	38	45	49	4	11	9	6
5. Every two or three months	30	39	28	39	11	9	15	18
6. Once in six months	30	28	18	17	12	11	5	6
7. Once a year or less	11	5	7	4	3	1	3	2
8. Never	8	12	6	3	2	5	0	3
662:J64 Interviewer's evaluation of informant's social interests:								
1. Very few or none; rarely or never attends functions outside home	38	42	19	17	3	4	10	9
2. Chiefly superficial; commercial recreation but few other interests	72	77	85	82	20	20	26	18
3. Limited to one or two types	19	11	9	14	3	2	3	2
4. Varied; includes at least three	21	20	37	37	24	23	11	21
In comparison with others, how many friends do you have?								
663:J65								
1. Many more than average	5	4	2	9	1	2	1	1
2. Somewhat more than average	24	29	33	23	5	4	14	7
3. About average	103	93	100	102	36	38	28	32

[136]Data on file in University of Iowa Speech Clinic.

Item No.: IBM Card and Column No.	Item; or Question and Response Codings; or Computed Values	Study II Control Group (N = 50) F	M	Study II Experimental Group (N = 50) F	M	Study III Control Group (N = 150) F	M	Study III Experimental Group (N = 150) F	M
	4. Somewhat fewer than average	9	6	5	6	15	12	20	17
	5. Many fewer than average	1	1	1	2	1	3	4	1
664:J66	How important are your friendships to you?								
	1. Very important; essential; could not do without	24	31	37	34	71	101	74	77
	2. Rather important	16	13	6	8	63	45	48	52
	3. Not very important	8	5	5	4	15	4	24	20
	4. Not at all important	2	1	2	4	1	0	3	0
	5. ?	0	0	0	0	0	0	0	1
	6. Indifferent	0	0	0	0	0	0	1	0
665:J67	How important are friendships to your wife (husband)?								
	1. Very important; essential; could not do without	29	25	40	29	79	77	84	55
	2. Rather important	14	16	4	13	57	44	50	57
	3. Not very important	5	6	4	2	10	20	14	29
	4. Not at all important	1	2	2	5	4	2	1	1
	5. ?	1	1	0	1	0	6	1	6
	6. Indifferent	0	0	0	0	0	1	0	2
666:J68	In comparison with others, how careful are you of your general appearance in social situations?								
	1. Much more than average	5	2	3	0	4	6	3	4
	2. Somewhat more than average	17	14	15	15	39	30	34	27
	3. About average	24	32	27	31	88	107	106	113
	4. Somewhat less than average	4	2	5	4	15	6	7	6
	5. Much less than average	0	0	0	0	4	1	0	0
667:J69	In comparison with others, how careful is your wife (husband) of her (his) general appearance in social situations?								
	1. Much more than average	8	1	6	4	15	9	8	7

2. Somewhat more than average	17	15	22	16	50	38	53	36
3. About average	20	32	21	23	82	94	86	99
4. Somewhat less than average	4	2	1	6	2	0	3	8
5. Much less than average	0	0	0	1	0	0	0	0
6. ?	0	0	0	0	1	1	0	0
668:J70 How much do you care about the impression you make on others?								
1. Very sensitive	16	5	14	12	12	19	15	30
2. Quite sensitive	12	14	13	15	65	71	55	69
3. Not very sensitive	8	11	11	14	50	47	49	38
4. Not at all sensitive	8	17	8	9	15	9	15	5
5. Indifferent; noncommittal	3	2	2	0	4	1	11	1
6. Sensitive, if care for person	2	0	2	0	4	3	4	5
7. ?	0	0	0	0	0	0	1	2
669:J71 How easily do you adjust to new situations and new friends?								
1. Shuns all new contacts and experiences	0	0	0	0	1	0	0	1
2. Very shy; avoids meeting new situations if possible	3	0	5	2	2	2	4	0
3. Finds it difficult to meet new situations	13	8	8	8	17	21	19	26
4. Usually makes satisfactory adjustment to new situations and people	22	28	17	22	118	121	98	102
5. Unusual ability to adjust; unusual poise; positive reaction	11	10	20	18	12	6	29	21
6. ?	0	1	0	0	0	0	0	0
670:J72 How easily does your wife (husband) adjust to new situations and new friends?								
1. Shuns all new contacts and experiences	0	0	0	0	1	1	0	0
2. Very shy; avoids meeting new situations if possible	0	0	3	2	0	4	5	5
3. Finds it difficult to meet new situations	6	6	5	4	18	15	20	12

Item No.: IBM Card and Column No.	Item; or Question and Response Codings; or Computed Values	Study II				Study III			
		Control Group (N = 50)		Experimental Group (N = 50)		Control Group (N = 150)		Experimental Group (N = 150)	
		F	M	F	M	F	M	F	M
	4. Usually makes satisfactory adjustment to new situations and people	29	29	23	17	114	112	92	93
	5. Unusual ability to adjust; unusual poise; positive reaction	14	14	18	27	17	17	33	36
	6. ?	0	1	1	0	0	1	0	4
671:J73	Were you previously married?								
	1. Yes	2	3	4	1	4	4	5	4
	2. No	48	47	46	49	146	144	144	146
	3. Yes, then remarried to same person					0	2	0	0
672:J74	How was previous marriage terminated?								
	1. Death	0	0	1	0	0	3	0	1
	2. Divorce	1	2	3	1	4	3	5	3
	†3. Annulled	1	1	0	0				
673:J75	Number of children of previous marriage								
	1. One	0	0	2	0	1	1	2	0
	2. Two	0	0	1	1	0	1	0	0
	3. Four	0	0	0	0	1	0	0	0
	4. None	2	3	1	0	2	2	3	4
674:J76	Have children of previous marriages lived in present home?[137]								
675*	Date of present marriage								
676:J77-79	Age (in years) at present marriage								
	a. Minimum					16.8	17.4	18.3	18.1
	b. Maximum					42.4	33.6	45.3	35.0
	c. Mean					24.2	22.0	26.0	23.4

[137]There were too few children to warrant a detailed report.

		1	2	3	4	5	6	7	8
	d. Median	22.6	25.0	21.5	23.5				
	e. 90th percentile	27.5	31.8	25.4	29.1				
	f. N	149	149	150	150				
677:J80	**How well do you and your wife (husband) like being alone together?**								
	1. Greatly enjoy being together	91	78	107	95	38	40	44	38
	2. Moderately enjoy being together	53	61	39	50	8	8	4	9
	3. Indifferent	5	7	2	5	4	2	2	2
	4. Moderately dislike being together	1	2	0	0				
	5. Strongly dislike being together	0	1	0	0	0	0	0	0
	6. No opinion	0	0	1	0	0	0	0	1
678:K6	**How often have you been separated (estranged)?**								
	1. No history of separation	146	143	144	144	44	47	47	48
	2. Once	3	5	3	5	5	2	1	1
	3. Twice	1	2	1	1	1	1	0	0
	4. Now separated	0	0	0	0	0	0	1	1
	5. One separation and one divorce	0	0	2	0				
679:K7	**How much do you quarrel, as compared with your married friends?**								
	1. Much more than average	2	2	0	0	0	1	1	0
	2. Somewhat more than average	11	15	6	5	2	0	4	2
	3. About average	53	68	60	63	16	17	18	24
	4. Somewhat less than average	57	44	47	44	11	13	17	21
	5. Much less than average	24	20	34	32	21	18	10	3
	6. ?	1	1	3	6	0	1	0	0
680-693	**Here are some things about which some husbands and wives have differences. How strong are your differences about the following?**								
680:K8	**Religion**								
	1. Very serious	2	1	2	2	1	0	1	2
	2. Moderately serious	12	8	8	6	1	1	4	3
	3. Slight	17	27	30	30	9	8	10	9
	4. None	119	114	110	112	39	41	35	36

Item No.: IBM Card and Column No.	Item; or Question and Response Codings; or Computed Values	Study II				Study III			
		Control Group (N = 50)		Experimental Group (N = 50)		Control Group (N = 150)		Experimental Group (N = 150)	
		F	M	F	M	F	M	F	M
681:K9	Use of money								
	1. Very serious	1	2	1	1	2	3	4	2
	2. Moderately serious	8	5	5	4	17	10	15	15
	3. Slight	21	25	14	18	67	54	66	69
	4. None	18	18	30	27	64	83	65	64
682:K10	Discipline of children								
	1. Very serious	1	0	1	2	1	1	2	4
	2. Moderately serious	7	4	2	5	15	18	9	22
	3. Slight	24	33	22	29	91	85	88	79
	4. None	18	13	25	14	43	45	51	45
	5. ?					0	1	0	0
683:K12	Amount of social life								
	1. Very serious	0	0	1	0	3	0	0	1
	2. Moderately serious	8	2	2	1	17	10	16	13
	3. Slight	24	18	15	18	68	53	75	54
	4. None	18	30	32	31	62	87	59	82
684:K13	Kind of entertainment								
	1. Moderately serious	4	2	2	2	7	6	11	8
	2. Slight	19	12	10	9	65	36	49	41
	3. None	27	36	38	39	78	108	90	101
685:K14	Types of friends								
	1. Very serious	1	0	0	0	0	0	0	0
	2. Moderately serious	5	3	1	2	9	5	4	3
	3. Slight	14	10	6	7	46	41	46	35
	4. None	30	37	43	41	95	104	100	112
686:K15	Ambition								
	1. Very serious	0	0	0	0	1	0	3	1
	2. Moderately serious	1	1	0	3	9	5	7	5
	3. Slight	18	7	11	12	56	31	37	32
	4. None	31	41	39	35	84	114	103	112
687:K16	Employment of husband								
	1. Very serious	1	0	0	0	0	2	2	1

2. Moderately serious	2	0	0	0	8	2	3	4
3. Slight	12	6	4	6	23	15	27	19
4. None	35	44	46	44	119	131	118	126

688:K17 Employment of wife

1. Very serious	0	1	0	0	1	0	0	2
2. Moderately serious	1	0	1	1	1	1	5	4
3. Slight	2	1	1	4	12	12	18	15
4. None	47	48	48	46	137	137	127	129

689:K18 In-laws

1. Very serious	0	1	0	2	3	4	2	2
2. Moderately serious	2	4	3	1	8	4	7	10
3. Slight	15	11	4	9	40	51	44	32
4. None	33	34	43	38	98	91	97	106

690:K19 How to spend vacations

1. Very serious	2	0	0	0	0	0	0	0
2. Moderately serious	1	0	1	0	7	3	2	1
3. Slight	19	7	4	5	36	25	22	22
4. None	28	43	43	42	107	122	126	127

691:K20 Recreation (as distinct from entertainment)

1. Very serious	0	0	0	0	0	0	1	0
2. Moderately serious	2	2	0	2	7	2	8	6
3. Slight	20	10	10	6	49	38	45	32
4. None	28	38	40	42	94	110	96	112

692:K21 Politics

1. Very serious	0	0	0	0	2	1	1	0
2. Moderately serious	1	2	0	0	4	2	6	3
3. Slight	9	6	7	11	28	22	13	17
4. None	39	42	43	39	116	125	130	130

693:K22 Radio and TV listening

1. Very serious	0	1	0	0	2	0	1	0
2. Moderately serious	2	3	3	2	8	3	5	4
3. Slight	26	14	16	20	47	39	43	49
4. None	22	32	31	28	95	108	102	97

694:K23 Husband: How well satisfied are you with the way your wife is rearing the child? Wife: How well

Item No.: IBM Card and Column No.	Item; or Question and Response Codings; or Computed Values	Study II Control Group (N = 50)		Study II Experimental Group (N = 50)		Study III Control Group (N = 150)		Study III Experimental Group (N = 150)	
		F	M	F	M	F	M	F	M
	satisfied are you with the way your husband participates in home training and discipline of the child?								
	1. Highly satisfied	27	30	37	29	104	80	95	65
	2. Moderately well satisfied	19	15	8	12	43	57	48	62
	3. Undecided or indifferent	3	0	0	0	2	0	1	1
	4. Moderately dissatisfied	3	5	4	6	1	12	5	18
	5. Highly dissatisfied	1	0	1	3	0	1	1	4
695:K24-25	If dissatisfied, why?138								
696:K26	How well satisfied are you with your present marital relationship?								
	1. Completely satisfied	45	45	44	43	111	118	98	96
	2. Fairly well satisfied	4	3	5	3	37	28	44	47
	3. Undecided or indifferent	0	0	0	1	1	0	1	1
	4. Moderately dissatisfied	0	1	1	3	0	4	6	4
	5. Highly dissatisfied	1	1	0	0	1	0	1	2
697:K27	How readily do you confide in your wife (husband)?								
	1. Very readily; all the time	30	41	39	41	71	96	63	96
	2. Quite readily; often	4	6	4	4	50	42	54	39
	3. Not very readily; occasionally	12	2	2	4	27	9	20	11
	4. Not at all readily; seldom or never	3	1	5	1	2	3	13	4
	5. ?	1	0	0	0	0	0	0	0
698:K28	How readily do you confide in others?								
	1. Very readily; all the time	2	6	4	4	4	8	10	7
	2. Quite readily; often	4	15	7	5	18	26	14	22
	3. Not very readily; occasionally	21	19	11	8	79	74	58	72
	4. Not at all readily; seldom or never	21	10	28	33	48	42	68	49
	5. ?	1	0	0	0	1	0	0	0

138There were too few responses to warrant a detailed report.

699:K29 As a general rule, how tense are you?

1. Very	1	7	5	10	6	13	11	21
2. Quite	15	21	14	15	33	51	43	66
3. Not very	16	20	22	21	96	81	85	58
4. Not at all	18	2	9	4	15	4	11	5
5. ?					0	1	0	0

700:K30 How irritable are you?

1. Very	2	2	0	4	5	7	9	6
2. Quite	11	15	8	14	23	41	32	51
3. Not very	24	33	36	30	117	100	101	86
4. Not at all	13	0	6	2	5	1	8	5
5. ?					0	1	0	2

701:K31 How easygoing?

1. Very	8	3	11	8	31	16	38	20
2. Quite	26	29	29	23	100	101	80	84
3. Not very	14	17	10	18	19	27	31	40
4. Not at all	2	0	0	1	0	3	1	6
5. ?					0	3	0	0

702:K32 How high are your standards of conduct (which you use in judging conduct of your family or others)?

1. Very	20	14	12	15	47	43	35	31
2. Quite	26	27	36	34	85	93	98	106
3. Not very	4	9	2	1	17	10	17	13
5. ?	0	0	0	0	1	4	0	0

703:K33 How high are your standards of neatness?

1. Very	15	11	7	12	24	36	33	34
2. Quite	25	17	34	33	95	87	97	98
3. Not very	10	20	9	5	31	26	20	18
4. Not at all	0	2	0	0	0	1	0	0

704:K34 How tense is your wife (husband)?

1. Very	2	3	4	3	8	8	21	15
2. Quite	14	8	22	12	49	35	43	38
3. Not very	26	30	20	28	78	88	81	72

Item No.: IBM Card and Column No.	Item; or Question and Response Codings; or Computed Values	Study II Control Group (N = 50) F	M	Study II Experimental Group (N = 50) F	M	Study III Control Group (N = 150) F	M	Study III Experimental Group (N = 150) F	M
	4. Not at all	8	9	4	7	12	18	3	25
	5. ?	0	0	0	0	3	1	2	0
705:K35	How irritable?								
	1. Very	0	1	2	1	4	2	8	7
	2. Quite	5	8	11	8	30	20	41	26
	3. Not very	34	30	31	29	103	100	93	94
	4. Not at all	11	11	6	12	12	28	8	23
	5. ?	0	0	0	0	1	0	0	0
706:K36	How easygoing?								
	1. Very	5	17	11	19	29	47	29	46
	2. Quite	20	20	28	19	90	78	79	76
	3. Not very	19	12	10	9	30	21	41	26
	4. Not at all	5	1	1	3	1	3	1	2
	5. ?					0	1	0	0
707:K37	How high are her (his) standards of conduct?								
	1. Very	28	12	25	17	60	55	60	39
	2. Quite	20	26	25	31	86	79	85	94
	3. Not very	1	11	0	2	2	12	5	14
	4. Not at all	1	0	0	0	0	1	0	1
	5. ?					2	3	0	2
708:K38	How high are her (his) standards of neatness?								
	1. Very	21	12	27	25	60	52	68	47
	2. Quite	19	23	20	20	78	79	68	80
	3. Not very	6	13	3	5	12	17	14	22
	4. Not at all	3	1	0	0	0	1	0	1
	5. ?						1	0	0
709:K39	Do you consider the other parent to have spoiled the child?								
	1. Yes	11	8	10	8	15	17	26	34
	2. No	37	41	40	42	134	132	122	115
	3. ?	0	0	0	0	1	1	1	1

710:K40 To be too easy going concerning the child?								
1. Yes	14	7	13	9	22	31	38	34
2. No	36	42	37	41	125	117	110	114
3. ?	0	0	0	0	3	2	1	2
711:K41 To be too demanding of the child?								
1. Yes	12	8	4	13	19	24	18	41
2. No	37	40	46	36	130	124	129	109
3. ?	0	0	0	1	1	2	2	0
4. Yes, occasionally	1	0	0	0	0	0	0	0
712:K42 To worry too much?								
1. Yes	26	11	25	13	34	21	50	27
2. No	23	38	24	37	116	129	98	123
3. ?	0	0	1	0	0	0	1	0
713:K43 To be away from home too much?								
1. Yes	3	13	2	10	9	37	4	31
2. No	47	35	48	40	140	112	145	119
3. ?	0	0	0	0	1	1	0	0
714:K44 To be with the child too much?								
1. Yes	10	0	9	0	14	4	24	5
2. No	40	48	39	50	136	145	125	145
3. ?	0	0	2	0	0	1	0	0
715:K45 To be inconsistent in treatment of the child?								
1. Yes	14	9	4	12	26	25	26	38
2. No	36	39	46	38	122	120	121	110
3. ?	0	0	0	0	2	5	2	1
716:K46 How often do you side with the child against the other parent in the presence of the child?								
1. Constantly	0	0	0	0	0	0	0	0
2. Quite often	1	3	2	1	4	1	2	6
3. Now and then	4	9	4	2	18	30	14	31
4. Hardly ever	13	17	11	8	39	40	45	42
5. Never	30	20	33	27	89	79	89	71

Item No.: IBM Card and Column No.	Item; or Question and Response Codings; or Computed Values	Study II				Study III			
		Control Group (N = 50)		Experimental Group (N = 50)		Control Group (N = 150)		Experimental Group (N = 150)	
		F	M	F	M	F	M	F	M
717:K47	How often does the other parent side with the child against you in the presence of the child?								
	1. Constantly	2	0	1	1	0	0	0	0
	2. Quite often	6	2	1	0	5	3	6	7
	3. Now and then	9	9	7	4	15	12	16	18
	4. Hardly ever	11	20	13	9	45	42	45	38
	5. Never	22	18	28	36	85	93	83	87
718:K48	How often do you wish you were single?								
	1. Constantly	0	0	0	0	0	0	3	0
	2. Quite often	0	0	0	1	1	4	2	5
	3. Now and then	2	9	1	1	18	10	17	16
	4. Hardly ever	11	12	8	4	41	24	32	33
	5. Never	34	28	41	44	90	112	96	95
	6. ?					0	0	0	1
719:K49	How do you think your married life compares in happiness with that of your married friends?								
	1. Much more than average					21	26	17	14
	2. Somewhat more than average					55	61	41	44
	3. About average					69	58	82	84
	4. Somewhat less than average					4	4	7	6
	5. Much less than average					0	1	2	1
	6. ?					1	0	0	1
720*	If you could make two improvements in your wife (husband), what would they be?139								
	1. None					48	37	38	19

139More specific responses were reported than those listed; many different, individual wordings of response have been grouped as here indicated for practical purposes of presentation. Some respondents gave more than one response.

2. Attitude toward money	2	10	38	19
3. Physical appearance	10	14	5	11
4. House upkeep	29	7	15	9
5. Work habits	3	8	3	13
6. Health	5	0	7	4
7. Behavior details	12	16	9	17
8. Relationship with child	14	17	5	18
9. Relationship with spouse	13	9	13	20
10. Spend more time at home	0	9	0	10
11. Personality traits; decreased incompatability	63	73	70	90
12. Other	0	12	0	5

721* If you could make two improvements in your home life, what two things would you change?[140]

1. Nothing	32	29	41	30
2. Arrangements with regard to money	16	4	12	9
3. Physical setup	47	43	44	43
4. Personal problems or sources of discomfort	5	16	4	7
5. Relationships with in-laws or relatives	1	5	6	3
6. Routine and organization (more or less)	10	16	5	9
7. Outside interests	7	5	2	4
8. Have husband (wife) home more	15	9	13	9
9. Family relations	23	25	14	20
10. Social life	10	5	1	11
11. Arrangements with regard to work	3	17	11	9
12. Spend more time with spouse	5	1	0	7
13. Spend more time as family	22	23	14	15

722* What in you (what personal trait or characteristic about yourself) makes

[140] See footnote 139.

217

Item No.: IBM Card and Column No.	Item; or Question and Response Codings; or Computed Values	Study II				Study III			
		Control Group (N = 50)		Experimental Group (N = 50)		Control Group (N = 150)		Experimental Group (N = 150)	
		F	M	F	M	F	M	F	M
	you most unhappy or discontented or dissatisfied with yourself?[141]								
	1. Nothing					24	6	24	11
	2. Physical appearance					3	13	4	13
	3. Financial problems					5	3	6	0
	4. Health problems					2	2	4	2
	5. Work problems					25	28	34	26
	6. Personality (personal problems)					28	34	28	34
	7. Behavior at home					12	6	10	2
	8. Lack of abilities					4	4	4	9
	9. Speech problems					0	0	5	2
	10. Relations with children					4	20	3	9
	11. Relations to the outside world (social, religious, political)					18	11	5	17
	12. Temperament; disposition					34	44	27	55
723*	What in you makes your wife (husband) most unhappy or discontented or dis- satisfied with you?[142]								
	1. Nothing					12	12	11	17
	2. Work problems					8	0	5	0
	3. Disposition; temperament					22	24	26	33
	4. Social problems					13	5	11	5
	5. Personal characteristics					39	37	38	36
	6. Relations with spouse					13	13	15	5
	7. ?; has never said					18	15	28	24
	8. Too much time away from home; too many activities					8	3	3	3
	9. House upkeep or organization					8	20	8	13
	10. Relations with children					7	12	1	7

141See footnote 139.
142See footnote 139.

11. Physical appearance
12. Financial problems

724:K50-51
What is the usual mood of your wife (husband)?143

1. Unusually happy (Study II: "and expressive")	15	23	14	14	8	6	4	9
2. Very excitable; lacks control	4	0	2	1	0	0	1	0
3. Even-keeled; even-tempered (Study II: even disposition; neutral; even-keeled)	8	14	12	11	7	10	11	7
4. Usually happy person	0	8	0	2	43	30	57	42
5. Quiet					5	4	1	8
6. Variable: cross and contented	6	8	0	2	1	4	2	1
7. Good-natured			1		7	9	2	8
8. Fairly happy				1	4	5	8	14
9. Congenial	6	0	1	1	4	7	5	2
10. Happy; contented					5	7	5	5
11. Noncommittal (doesn't say what's on mind; doesn't react)					8	7	8	3
12. Serious; sober	3	2	0	1	3	0	0	0
13. Cheerful					0	5	4	6
14. Happy; tranquil				1	16	12	14	9
15. Tense					1	3	2	0
16. Variable: moody, pouty, and good-natured				1	1	3	4	2
17. Pleasant					0	3	1	1
18. Easygoing					12	11	5	3
19. Moody					4	4	3	10
20. Agreeable	1	1	0	0	1	2	3	0
21. Jolly					2	3	0	1
22. Happy but quiet					2	0	0	1
23. Good mood					3	2	0	3

143For both Studies II and III there were 64 additional moods reported, each by fewer than three of the informants represented in any one column of the table; 40 of these moods were reported by the control and 36 by the experimental group respondents. Some respondents in Study II gave more than one response.

Item No.: IBM Card and Column No.	Item; or Question and Response Codings; or Computed Values	Study II Control Group (N=50) F	M	Study II Experimental Group (N=50) F	M	Study III Control Group (N=150) F	M	Study III Experimental Group (N=150) F	M
725:K52	Total number of children of present marriage:								
	1. One		5		11		15		25
	2. Two		17		25		57		77
	3. Three		19		8		46		32
	4. Four		5		4		22		9
	5. Five		2		2		5		5
	6. Six		0		0		2		2
	7. Seven		1		0		0		0
	†8. Eight		1		0		0		
	†9. Total		141		111		412		348
726:K53	Birth order of child being studied:								
	1. Oldest						41		56
	2. Youngest						53		45
	3. Second						27		16
	4. Third						11		6
	5. Fourth						1		2
	6. Fifth						1		0
	7. Sixth						1		0
	8. Only child						15		24
	9. Only child; sib died at birth						0		1
727:K54	Do you expect to have any more children?								
	1. Yes	19	20	9	10	49	54	37	53
	2. No	27	28	33	38	76	74	81	72
	3. ?	3	1	2	1	25	22	32	25
728:K55-56	If no, why not?144								
	1. Not physically able (post-menopause, sterile, etc.)	9	13	2	8	7	9	15	17

144For both Studies II and III there were 37 additional reasons reported, each by fewer than three of the informants represented in any one column of the table; 19 of these reasons were reported by the control and 25 by the experimental group respondents. Some respondents in Study II gave more than one response.

2. Can't afford more children	6	6	8	3	6	6	1	2	1
3. Too old for children emotionally	7	9	5	9					
4. Too much trouble or work	2	0	2	3					
5. Present number is satisfactory (Study II: "ideal number")									
6. Large enough family for financial reasons	17	16	15	21	6	10	2	2	
7. Wife (husband) doesn't want more children	9	10	14	15		3	3	1	0
8. Doctor advises against it	3	6	1	2	1	0	0	0	
† 9. Too old for children chronologically; age discrepancy too great	2	2	7	3	4	1	1	6	6
†10. Just prefer not to have more; reason not sharply verbalized	3	1	2	3	6	6	6		
†11. Have all can handle and raise	2	8	3	2	1	10	3		
†12. Apparently unable (trying 10 years, for example)	3	0	2	1					
729:K57 Husband's present employment									
1. Full time	146	143							
2. Part time	2	4							
3. Not at all	2	3							
730:K58 Wife's employment outside home									
1. Full time	21	18	23	21					
2. Part time	129	131	126	129					
3. Not at all	0	1	0	0					
731:K59 Did both parents work during infancy or early childhood of child?									
1. Yes	9	8							
2. No	8	9							
3. ?	133	133							
732:K60 How frequently are both parents home in the evening while the child is still up?									
1. Six to seven nights per week	97	89	77	75	32	23	29	25	
2. Four to five nights per week	30	40	43	48	8	10	12	10	

Item No.: IBM Card and Column No.	Item; or Question and Response Codings; or Computed Values	Study II Control Group (N = 50)		Study II Experimental Group (N = 50)		Study III Control Group (N = 150)		Study III Experimental Group (N = 150)	
		F	M	F	M	F	M	F	M
733*	3. Three nights per week	9	5	2	5	15	11	10	12
	4. One to two nights per week	6	3	5	5	11	16	10	10
	What other persons have lived in the home at some time during the lifetime of the child (other than immediate family, not including those living in room or apartment rented out and frequently seen)?[145]								
	1. Paternal grandfather		5		4		7		6
	2. Paternal grandmother		10		5		7		12
	3. Maternal grandfather		9		3		8		10
	4. Maternal grandmother		16		12		20		19
	5. Paternal aunt		1		3		1		2
	6. Paternal uncle		0		4		3		9
	7. Maternal aunt		1		4		10		14
	8. Maternal uncle		2		1		4		7
	9. Cousin of child		3		3		7		4
	10. Other relative		1		6		9		2
	11. Friends; neighbor		0		2		6		6
	12. Hired help; nurse		1		12		4		4
	13. Others		10		8		3		0
734:K61	Total number living in the home during the lifetime of the child, other than members of immediate family unit								
	1. One					34		32	
	2. Two					10		17	
	3. Three					3		4	

[145]More specific responses were reported than those listed; many different individual wordings of response have been grouped as here indicated for practical purposes of presentation. Some respondents in both studies gave more than one response.

	4. Four	3	3
	5. Five	1	2
	6. Eight	1	0
	7. None	92	98

735:K62 — What is the maximum number of persons, other than members of the immediate family unit, who have lived in the home at one time during the lifetime of the child?

1. One	12	9	36	36
2. Two	15	7	10	18
3. Three	3	3	3	2
4. Four	1	6	3	2
5. Five	0	6		
6. Six	0	3		
7. Seven	0	2		
8. Eight	0	1		
9. Nine	0	1		
10. None	15	11	98	92

736:K63 — How long did this number of persons live in the home?

1. Less than one month	1	3
2. One month	3	1
3. 1 to 3 months	11	19
4. 4 to 6 months	13	7
5. 6 to 12 months	9	7
6. 13 to 18 months	1	4
7. 19 to 24 months	5	3
8. 25 to 36 months	2	5
9. 3 to 5 years	4	9
10. Over 5 years	3	1

737:K64 — How often does the child meet visitors in the home?

1. Daily	5	2	21	18	27	19
2. Several times a week	20	15	78	64	69	60
3. Once a week	16	16	33	41	31	47

223

Item No.: IBM Card and Column No.	Item; or Question and Response Codings; or Computed Values	Study II Control Group (N = 50)		Study II Experimental Group (N = 50)		Study III Control Group (N = 150)		Study III Experimental Group (N = 150)	
		F	M	F	M	F	M	F	M
	4. Two or three times a month		4		9	16	17	21	16
	5. Once a month or less		4		8	2	6	6	8
738:K65	Do you feel that, as a general rule, a child should be seen and not heard?								
	1. Yes	3	0	1	1	10	4	5	7
	2. Usually yes	8	1	1	1	7	6	6	4
	3. Usually no	8	12	3	7	15	25	15	29
	4. No	29	36	45	41	118	114	123	108
	5. ?					0	1	1	2
739:K66	Does your wife (husband) feel that, as a general rule, a child should be seen and not heard?								
	1. Yes	3	0	1	3	13	3	8	14
	2. Usually yes	3	1	1	1	7	10	3	3
	3. Usually no	10	13	0	7	13	24	15	29
	4. No	32	35	46	38	114	105	123	100
	5. ?			2	1	3	8	1	4
740:K67	How well do you like your neighbors?								
	1. Like most or all, with possibly one or two exceptions	46	46	45	41	124	131	122	126
	2. Indifferent; noncommittal	1	1	2	4	5	4	6	3
	3. Dislike most or all	0	1	1	1	3	1	5	4
	4. Don't know neighbors well; no close neighbors	0	0	1	3	14	11	7	6
	5. Half like; half dislike	2	1	1	1	0	0	0	1
	†6. Like but little contact because of remoteness	2	0	0	0				
	7. Uncertain; no response	0	1	0	0	4	3	0	0
741:K68	In comparison with what you know of most people's neighbors, how friendly are your neighbors?								
	1. Much more than average	3	5	1	1	8	15	5	7

	1	2	3	4	5	6	7	8
2. Somewhat more than average	17	19	16	8	48	38	24	25
3. About average	24	23	23	28	79	75	102	94
4. Somewhat less than average	5	2	7	8	10	15	11	18
5. Much less than average	1	0	0	4	2	2	0	2
6. ?	0	0	2	0	1	4	7	3

742:K69 How do your neighbors usually treat your child?

	1	2	3	4	5	6	7	8
1. Like one of the family	17	15	41	36	16	12	28	28
2. Friendly attitude	31	33	6	12	127	131	113	113
3. Indifferent; ignore him	1	0	0	0	3	2	3	5
4. Slightly antagonistic	1	0	0	1	0	0	1	0
5. Strongly antagonistic	0	0	0	0	0	0	1	0
6. ?	0	0	0	0	2	2	1	0
7. No contact	0	0	2	1	1	2	3	4

743-747 How often do you and your family all together:

743:K70 Go on picnics?

	1	2	3	4	5	6	7	8
1. Daily			0	0	1	1	1	0
2. Several times per week			3	3	7	7	9	13
3. Once a week			7	9	30	37	26	40
4. Two or three times per month			9	12	38	45	30	20
5. Once a month			11	9	35	31	39	32
6. Every two or three months			3	14	23	17	14	7
7. Once in six months			1	9	7	2	8	8
8. Once a year or less			3	5	5	5	13	18
9. Never			0	0	4	5	10	12

744:K71 Make auto trips, go for auto drives?

	1	2	3	4	5	6	7	8
1. Daily		0	2	2	0	1	7	
2. Several times per week		5	10	24	30	30	26	
3. Once a week		19	18	66	60	48	52	
4. Two or three times per month		8	4	31	29	35	22	
5. Once a month		6	7	19	12	21	16	
6. Every two or three months		2	3	4	7	7	13	
7. Once in six months		1	1	1	4	0	2	
8. Once a year or less		6	1	0	1	1	3	
9. Never		2	4	3	6	7	9	

Item No.: IBM Card and Column No.	Item; or Question and Response Codings; or Computed Values	Study II				Study III			
		Control Group (N = 50)		Experimental Group (N = 50)		Control Group (N = 150)		Experimental Group (N = 150)	
		F	M	F	M	F	M	F	M
745:K72	Go to the movies?								
	1. Several times per week		1		1	1	1	1	2
	2. Once a week		10		4	2	2	4	2
	3. Two or three times per month		7		3	8	4	2	7
	4. Once a month		8		3	16	13	8	7
	5. Every two or three months		11		9	15	20	15	9
	6. Once in six months		1		7	15	17	14	12
	7. Once a year or less		4		4	16	14	17	11
	8. Never		7		18	77	79	89	100
746:K73	Go to ball games or other sports events?								
	1. Daily		0		0	0	0	2	0
	2. Several times per week		0		3	0	2	1	0
	3. Once a week		1		6	0	0	1	3
	4. Two to three times per month		6		5	4	9	1	3
	5. Once a month		7		3	5	5	7	3
	6. Every two or three months		6		4	10	10	8	3
	7. Once in six months		1		1	16	4	6	4
	8. Once a year or less		12		4	15	8	4	8
	9. Never		15		24	100	111	119	124
747:K74	Play parlor or card games? (The words "parlor or" were not used in Study II.)								
	1. Daily		0		2	5	4	2	2
	2. Several times per week		9		13	15	10	9	8
	3. Once a week		3		9	27	19	8	16
	4. Two or three times per month		6		2	15	20	11	15
	5. Once a month		4		5	25	20	18	9
	6. Every two or three months		5		1	12	9	8	8
	7. Once in six months		1		2	8	3	8	3
	8. Once a year or less		10		1	1	5	4	5
	9. Never		11		15	42	60	82	84

748:K75 — In comparison with others, how much do you laugh wholeheartedly?

1. Much more than average	5	1	2	6	11	5	3
2. Somewhat more than average	12	7	12	39	28	32	30
3. About average	26	27	30	89	94	88	97
4. Somewhat less than average	7	15	6	15	14	21	19
5. Much less than average	0	0	0	1	2	3	1
6. ?				0	1	0	0

749:K76 — In comparison with others, how much does your wife (husband) laugh wholeheartedly?

1. Much more than average	2	0	1	8	7	6	2
2. Somewhat more than average	14	19	9	35	34	28	27
3. About average	29	26	33	90	96	101	102
4. Somewhat less than average	5	5	7	16	9	12	18
5. Much less than average	0	0	0	0	4	2	1
6. ?				1	0	0	0

750:K77 — Did the child's father serve in the armed forces or has he been absent from home for any extended period of time (six months or more) for other reasons since marriage?

1. No		31	36	87	87	104	103
2. Army		10	7	5	24	27	27
3. Navy		5	2	27	26	11	11
4. Air Corps				7	8	4	4
5. Coast Guard, Marines, Merchant Marine		2	1	2	2	2	3
6. Other reasons (work, travel, education)		2	4	2	3	2	2

751:K78 — What was the nature of service or reason for absence?

1. Combat overseas		14		20	23	14	16
2. Noncombat overseas		11		12	9	11	10
3. Stateside duty		14		18	19	14	14
4. Stateside and overseas (combat and noncombat)		4		8	7	4	3

Item No.: IBM Card and Column No.	Item; or Question and Response Codings; or Computed Values	Study II Control Group (N = 50) F	M	Study II Experimental Group (N = 50) F	M	Study III Control Group (N = 150) F	M	Study III Experimental Group (N = 150) F	M
752:K79	5. Stateside and overseas (noncombat)					1	2	1	1
	6. Other (work, travel, education)					4	3	3	4
	(Instruction to interviewer: Ask this question and number 753 if child was alive at the time) Did wife worry about his (husband's) safety?								
	1. Yes		10		7	3	2	3	4
	2. No		7		3	5	6	5	5
	3. ?					0	0	1	0
753:K80	Did child worry about his (father's) safety?								
	1. Yes		5		2	1	0	0	0
	2. No		9		7	7	8	7	8
	3. ?		1		0	0	0	1	0
754:L6-7	For what total time during his whole lifetime has the child been separated from his father (in months)?[146]								
	a. Minimum						0		0
	b. Maximum						42		36
	c. Mean						4.2		3.9
	d. Median						1		1
	e. 90th percentile						10		12
	f. N						150		150
755:L8-9	From his mother (in months)?								
	a. Minimum						0		0
	b. Maximum						5		4
	c. Mean						1.2		1.1
	d. Median						1		1

[146] Two experimental group mothers in Study III gave the following response: "Very long period--first seven years home only weekends" and "Very long period--half the time." These responses were not included in computing the mean, median, and 90th percentiles.

| | e. 90th percentile | | | | | | | |
| | f. N | | | | 2 150 | | 2 150 | |

756:I110 — How is your present health?

1. Good	41	38	35	36	139	131	137	129
2. Fair	9	10	9	12	10	18	13	21
3. Poor	0	1	1	2	0	1	0	0
4. Unable to rate health					1	0	0	0

757:I111 — How was it at onset of stuttering? (For controls: At time corresponding to the onset age for other member of pair?)

1. Good	42	37	37	36	137	136	135	119
2. Fair	2	2	6	11	10	12	14	22
3. Poor	0	4	2	2	2	2	1	9
4. Unable to rate health					1	0	0	0

758:I112 — How is your wife's (husband's) present health?

1. Good	33	36	36	43	139	131	137	134
2. Fair	15	11	6	6	10	18	13	12
3. Poor	1	2	3	1	0	1	0	4
4. Unable to rate health	0	0	0	0	1	0	0	0

758A:I113 — How was it at onset of stuttering? (For controls: At time corresponding to the onset age for other member of pair?)

1. Good	37	37	34	41	132	138	132	132
2. Fair	4	4	9	7	16	10	15	15
3. Poor	2	2	1	0	2	2	3	3
4. Unable to rate health	0	0	1	1	0	0	0	0
†5. Overseas	0	0	0	1				

759:I114 — How many times during the lifetime of the child have you, your wife (husband), the other children in the family, or others living in the home had any severe illness

Item No.: IBM Card and Column No.	Item; or Question and Response Codings; or Computed Values	Study II Control Group (N = 50)		Study II Experimental Group (N = 50)		Study III Control Group (N = 150)		Study III Experimental Group (N = 150)	
		F	M	F	M	F	M	F	M
	or injury requiring severe restriction of activities and care by others?								
	1. Once						42		44
	2. Twice						39		32
	3. Three times						20		25
	4. Four times						8		7
	5. Five to ten times or more						8		3
	6. Never						31		31
760:I115	What is the total illness time covered by the answer to 759?								
	1. Less than one month						76		74
	2. One month						9		8
	3. One to three months						22		24
	4. More than three months						10		6
761:I116	Where were these persons during their illnesses?								
	1. At home						13		22
	2. In hospital						59		42
	3. In relative's or neighbor's home						1		2
	4. Home and hospital						44		43
	5. In hospital; in hotel resort						0		1
	6. Hospital and parents' home						0		1
762:I117	If they were at home, who usually looked after these who were ill? (Person who most often looked after them.)								
	1. No one						5		2
	2. Husband or wife						36		35
	3. Relative						6		5
	4. Grandparent						6		15
	5. Nurse, neighbor, other						4		9

Question / Response								
763:L18 During these illnesses, what was usually (most frequently) done with the child?[147]								
1. Looked after by self								
2. Looked after by mother or father					6	27	1	32
3. Looked after by a parent or relative					44	14	40	19
4. Sent to grandparents' home								
5. Sent to home of neighbor or relative					8		6	
6. Looked after by hired help					37		47	
7. Looked after by nurse					3		1	
764:L19 How much do you worry about getting sick?								
1. A great deal; very much worried	4	1	0	2	1	4	0	5
2. Some; occasionally; quite worried	4	3	5	6	16	21	12	20
3. Hardly ever; not very worried	6	7	7	5	35	37	31	46
4. Never; not at all	36	38	38	37	98	88	107	79
765:I20 How much does your wife (husband) worry about getting sick?								
1. A great deal; very much worried	1	2	3	1	2	10	4	7
2. Some occasionally; quite worried	6	3	4	8	25	16	22	12
3. Hardly ever; not very worried	14	8	4	1	38	30	35	35
4. Never; not at all	27	36	39	40	75	87	84	92
5. ?	1	0	0	0	10	7	5	4
766:L21 How is your appetite now?								
1. Good	47	46	40	49	145	144	136	138
2. Fair	3	3	9	1	5	5	14	9
3. Poor	0	0	1	0	0	1	0	3
767:L22 How well do you sleep?								
1. Very well	38	37	38	43	138	127	128	120
2. Fairly well	10	10	8	2	11	14	15	20
3. Not too well	1	2	4	4	1	8	7	9
4. Very poorly	1	0	0	1	0	1	0	1

147For both Studies II and III there were 12 additional responses reported, each by fewer than three of the informants represented in any one column of the table; 9 of these responses were reported by the control and 6 by the experimental group respondents.

231

Item No.: IBM Card and Column No.	Item; or Question and Response Codings; or Computed Values	Study II Control Group (N = 50) F	M	Study II Experimental Group (N = 50) F	M	Study III Control Group (N = 150) F	M	Study III Experimental Group (N = 150) F	M
768:I23	How is your wife's (husband's) appetite?								
	1. Good	44	46	43	42	132	142	131	139
	2. Fair	3	2	5	8	15	8	15	7
	3. Poor	0	0	1	0	3	0	4	4
769:I24	How well does he (she) sleep?								
	1. Very well	30	41	37	39	120	121	108	125
	2. Fairly well	13	5	9	7	24	24	31	19
	3. Not too well	3	2	2	3	6	3	10	5
	4. Very poorly	0	0	1	1	0	1	1	0
	5. ?	0	0	0	0	0	1	0	1
770:I25	Do you have many food dislikes?								
	1. Yes	8	1	8	3	15	8	22	5
	2. No	40	46	42	47	135	142	128	145
771:I26	Does your wife (husband) have many food dislikes?								
	1. Yes	6	4	1	15	11	19	12	24
	2. No	42	43	49	35	139	131	137	125
	3. ?	0	0	0	0	0	0	1	1
772:I26A	Number among immediate family and ancestors reported to have had epilepsy								
	1. One					2	3	2	3
	2. Two					0	0	0	1
	3. None					139	137	127	130
773:I26B	Number among immediate family and ancestors reported to have had diabetes								
	1. One					12	12	19	19
	2. Two					0	0	2	1
	3. Three					0	0	0	1
	4. None					130	129	108	112

774:I26C Number among immediate family and ancestors reported to have had an allergy (hay fever, rashes, asthma, etc.)

1. One	32	37	30	32
2. Two	12	15	10	17
3. Three to seven	4	9	4	6
4. None	94	81	85	79

775:I27-29 Informant's handedness: score on Brief Handedness Questionnaire

a. Minimum	0	0	0	0
b. Maximum	100	100	100	100
c. Mean	93	93	91	95
d. Median	100	100	100	100
e. 90th percentile	100	100	100	100
f. N	149	150	143	146

776:L30 Have you ever changed your handedness?

1. Yes, completely or nearly so	4	4	8	5
2. Yes, partially	10	2	8	9
3. No	134	142	129	135
4. ?	2	2	4	1

(additional figures appearing in this block: 2 1 2 4 ; 48 48 48 46)

777:L31 Number of informant's siblings who are right-handed

1. One	43	27	31	31
2. Two	28	25	29	27
3. Three	25	24	26	26
4. Four	13	11	15	18
5. Five	7	13	6	10
6. Six	8	5	8	6
7. Seven	5	4	2	2
8. Eight	1	6	5	1
9. Nine	4	2	3	0
10. Ten	0	0	8	9
11. Eleven	0	4	2	4
12. Twelve	0	1	0	0
13. Thirteen	0	1	0	0

Item No.: IBM Card and Column No.	Item; or Question and Response Codings; or Computed Values	Study II				Study III			
		Control Group (N = 50)		Experimental Group (N = 50)		Control Group (N = 150)		Experimental Group (N = 150)	
		F	M	F	M	F	M	F	M
	14. None					15	26	12	14
	15. Total right-handed					388	451	488	471
778:I32	Number of informant's siblings who are left-handed								
	1. One					16	19	13	20
	2. Two					2	2	4	3
	3. None					131	128	130	125
	4. Total left-handed					20	23	21	26
779:I33	Number of informant's siblings significantly mixed in handedness								
	1. One					2	5	4	2
	2. Two					0	0	0	1
	3. None					147	144	143	145
780:I34	What is the handedness of your mother?								
	1. Right					144	138	140	145
	2. Left					5	8	3	1
	3. Mixed					0	1	4	3
	4. ?					1	3	3	0
781:I35	What is the handedness of your father?								
	1. Right					138	139	145	139
	2. Left					5	6	0	8
	3. Mixed					5	1	4	1
	4. ?					2	4	1	1
782*	Scores on Unimanual Handedness Questionnaire148								
783:I36-37	Informant's handedness: score on Iowa Unimanual Hand Usage Questionnaire								
	a. Minimum					-1.7	-2	-1.5	-1.1

148 Data summarized in 783 are punched on IBM cards in the University of Iowa Statistical Service Office. The score can vary from -2.0, complete left-handedness, through 0.0, complete ambidexterity or lack of preference, to 2.0, complete right-handedness.

	Col 1	Col 2	Col 3	Col 4
b. Maximum	2	2	2	2
c. Mean	1.3	1.5	1.3	1.5
d. Median	1.5	1.6	1.5	1.7
e. 90th percentile	2	2	2	2
f. N	150	150	143	146

784:L38-39 Number right-handed in child's immediate family

a. Minimum	2	5
b. Maximum	24	22
c. Mean	11	11
d. Median	11	11
e. 90th percentile	18	16
f. N	150	138

785:L40-41 Number left-handed in child's immediate family

a. Minimum	0	0
b. Maximum	4	4
c. Mean	0.7	0.6
d. Median	0	0
e. 90th percentile	2	2
f. N	150	138

786:L42 Number significantly mixed in child's immediate family

a. Minimum	0	0
b. Maximum	5	4
c. Mean	1.2	1.1
d. Median	1	1
e. 90th percentile	3	2
f. N	150	138

787:L43 Number with undetermined handedness (too young) in child's immediate family

a. Minimum	0	0
b. Maximum	2	2
c. Mean	0.4	0.4
d. Median	0	0
e. 90th percentile	1	1
f. N	150	138

Item No.: IBM Card and Column No.	Item; or Question and Response Codings; or Computed Values	Study II				Study III			
		Control Group (N = 50)		Experimental Group (N = 50)		Control Group (N = 150)		Experimental Group (N = 150)	
		F	M	F	M	F	M	F	M
788:L44-45	Child's handedness: score on Iowa Unimanual Hand Usage Questionnaire								
	a. Minimum						-2		-2
	b. Maximum						2		2
	c. Mean						1.3		1.4
	d. Median						1.6		1.6
	e. 90th percentile						2		2
	f. N						150	144	144
789:L46	Are you a twin?								
	1. Yes, like-sexed, probably identical					0	1	0	0
	2. Yes, like-sexed, probably non-identical					2	1	2	1
	3. Yes, unlike-sexed					0	1	0	1
	4. No	49	49	50	50	148	147	148	149
	5. Yes	1	1	0	0				
790:L47-48	Are there any cases of twins in your immediate family (among your blood relations)?[149]								
	1. None	33	30	32	25	129	122	131	129
	2. Paternal grandmother	2	1	0	0	11	3	5	4
	3. Paternal grandfather	0	1	1	1	0	0	1	0
	4. Maternal grandmother	1	1	1	1	3	9	2	7
	5. Maternal grandfather	0	0	1	1	1	0	0	1
	6. Paternal uncle	1	1	1	1	1	0	2	1
	7. Paternal aunt	1	1	2	1	2	3	0	3
	8. Maternal uncle	1	1	4	4	1	3	1	1
	9. Maternal aunt	1	1	3	4	1	9	1	1

[149] Some respondents reported more than one relative. Note that in Study II, in responses 19-23, there were more kinds of relatives, and more distant ones, included than in Study III.

10. Brother of child	0	0	0	0	0	0	0	0
11. Sister of child	1	1	0	0	0	0	1	0
12. Maternal cousin	2	1	1	1	1	0	1	1
13. Paternal cousin	0	0	1	1	0	0	1	1
14. Paternal aunt and uncle	0	0	0	0	0	0	2	0
15. Maternal aunt and uncle	0	0	0	0	0	0	0	1
16. Paternal grandfather; paternal uncle								
17. Paternal grandfather; paternal aunt	0	0	0	0	0	1	0	0
18. ?; unable to identify	0	0	0	0	0	0	1	1
†19. Mother's grandfather	0	0	1	1	0	0	2	0
†20. Uncle/aunt of parent of case	5	3	3	10	0			
†21. Cousin of parent of case	4	4	5	5	0			
†22. More remote relative	2	0	0	3	0			
†23. Other relative	1	10		4	1			
24. N responding	10	50	50	50	50	150	150	150	150

791*

Are there any cases of speech defects in your immediate families (among your blood relatives)?[150]

1. None	45	42	33	26	141	128	107	104
2. Paternal grandmother	0	0	0	0	0	0	0	0
3. Paternal grandfather	2	0	0	0	0	1	2	3
4. Maternal grandmother	0	0	1	2	0	1	0	1
5. Maternal grandfather	0	0	8	1	1	2	3	4
6. Paternal uncle	0	0	0	4	1	1	6	7
7. Paternal aunt	0	0	2	1	2	1	1	1
8. Maternal uncle	0	2	0	3	1	4	5	7
9. Maternal aunt	0	3	1	1	0	2	1	1
10. Brother of child	0	0	0	2	0	0	8	7
11. Sister of child	0	0	1	0	0	1	0	1
12. Maternal cousin	1	1	1	4	1	10	4	5

[150]Some respondents in both studies reported more than one relative; all of each type of relative reported by one or more respondents are listed and enumerated in the table. These data are to be taken as constituting only a rough approximation; the question proved to be extraordinarily difficult for most respondents. See item 325 for data on stutterers in the families of the control and experimental group informants.

Item No.: IBM Card and Column No.	Item; or Question and Response Codings; or Computed Values	Study II				Study III			
		Control Group (N = 50)		Experimental Group (N = 50)		Control Group (N = 150)		Experimental Group (N = 150)	
		F	M	F	M	F	M	F	M
	13. Paternal cousin	0	0	3	4	3	0	2	3
	†14. Cousin of parent	0	0	4	4				
792:L51-52	What were these speech defects (exclusive of mild articulatory imperfections)?L51								
793:L53	Comparing yourself with others, how much physical energy do you believe you have?								
	1. Much more than average	7	1	0	2	9	7	14	4
	2. Somewhat more than average	16	13	20	9	26	29	45	34
	3. About average	24	26	25	32	111	89	78	84
	4. Somewhat less than average	3	8	4	7	4	23	13	27
	5. Much less than average	0	1	0	0	0	0	0	1
794:L54	Comparing your wife (husband) with others, how much physical energy do you believe she (he) has?								
	1. Much more than average	1	5	1	3	5	10	6	8
	2. Somewhat more than average	18	24	12	17	29	45	33	52
	3. About average	24	20	34	28	97	87	92	79
	4. Somewhat less than average	7	0	2	2	18	6	19	11
	5. Much less than average	0	0	0	0	1	1	0	0
	6. Can't say	0	0	0	0	0	1	0	0
795:L55	How often do you use alcohol (drink intoxicating beverages)?								
	1. No use	10	22	14	20	33	51	17	34
	2. Occasional use outside home	15	11	9	5	11	15	10	6
	3. Occasional use in home	4	3	2	3	12	9	11	17
	4. Occasional use inside and outside home	20	12	19	19	85	70	101	87

151 Exclusive of stuttering there were too few identifications to warrant detailed presentation of data; see item 325 for complete presentation of responses to "Are there any other stutterers in your family?"

	1	2	3	4	5	6	7	8
5. Frequent use	1	0	4	2	9	5	11	6
6. Chronic use	0	0	2	1	0	0	0	0
796:I56 How often does your wife (husband) use alcohol?								
1. No use	23	10	17	17	51	37	36	22
2. Occasional use outside home	10	22	9	7	8	14	5	6
3. Occasional use in home	2	3	3	2	10	10	11	14
4. Occasional use inside and outside home	14	11	17	18	77	79	91	95
5. Frequent use	0	1	3	4	4	10	7	13
6. Chronic use	0	1	1	2	0	0	0	0
797:I57 Evaluation of quality of speech of parent (answered by interviewer)								
1. No defect noticed	33	35	38	40	146	141	124	137
2. Minor articulation errors	0	3	5	4	2	3	12	8
3. Numerous articulation errors	2	1	0	0	0	0	0	0
4. Foreign dialect	1	1	1	0	0	1	4	1
5. Regional dialect	10	5	5	1	0	1	0	0
6. Voice defect	0	3	5	4	0	3	0	0
7. Stuttering	0	0	1	0	0	0	9	2
8. Rapid rate	1	1	1	2	0	0	0	1
9. Jerkiness	0	0	1	0	0	1	0	0
10. Jerkiness; very mild stuttering	0	0	1	1	2	0	1	1
11. Voice and articulation defect	0	0			0	0	0	
†12. Stumbling	0	0	2	0				
†13. Very halting speech; unable to find words	2	0	1	0				
†14. Plaintive voice	0	0	0	1				
798:I58 Estimate by interviewer of amount of speech of parent in this situation								
1. Very high verbal output	6	1	2	1	6	6	2	14
2. More than average verbal output	15	5	4	7	12	26	13	35
3. Average verbal output	21	30	34	41	112	110	105	92
4. Less than average verbal output	6	11	9	1	19	7	21	6
5. Very low verbal output	0	2	1	0	1	1	9	3

799-803:I59-I63[152]

[152]Responses to these items, concerned with the occupation, source of income, house type, and education of the inform-ant's father during the informant's preschool years, were used in deriving the scores and ratings summarized in 804 and 805.

Item No.: IBM Card and Column No.	Item; or Question and Response Codings; or Computed Values	Study II Control Group (N = 50)		Study II Experimental Group (N = 50)		Study III Control Group (N = 150)		Study III Experimental Group (N = 150)	
		F	M	F	M	F	M	F	M
804:I64-65	Informant's father's total score on Warner Index of Status Characteristics before informant's entrance into school (preschool age)								
	a. Minimum					21	15	18	18
	b. Maximum					74	73	73	73
	c. Mean					42.2	47.1	49.3	48.5
	d. Median					50	46	49	50
	e. 90th percentile					67	63	64	62
	f. N					141	146	128	121
805:I66	Social-class rating of informant's father before informant's entrance into school (preschool age)								
	1. Upper					2	4	3	4
	2. Upper-middle					26	26	12	14
	3. Lower-middle					56	64	61	49
	4. Upper-lower					48	43	44	48
	5. Lower-lower					14	8	8	5
	6. ?					3	4	0	3
806-810:I67-I71 153									
811:I72-73	Informant's father's total score on Warner Index of Status Characteristics during informant's youth (12-18 years)								
	a. Minimum					20	15	18	18
	b. Maximum					77	78	73	73
	c. Mean					47.8	47.9	48.9	47.8
	d. Median					49	47	48.5	51
	e. 90th percentile					64	66	65	62
	f. N					141	141	126	122

153 Responses to these items, concerned with the occupation, source of income, house type, and education of the informant's father during the informant's youth, 12-18 years, were used in deriving the scores and ratings summarized in 811 and 812.

812:L74 Social-class rating of informant's father during informant's youth (12-18 years)

1. Upper	5	5	2	4	
2. Upper-middle	21	23	15	17	
3. Lower-middle	58	54	56	47	
4. Upper-lower	46	46	45	45	
5. Lower-lower	11	12	8	9	
6. ?	3	7	0	1	

813:L75-76 Number of months (to nearest month) between onset of stuttering (196; for controls, date corresponding to onset of stuttering) and date of interview

a. Minimum	0	0	3	0	0	1
b. Maximum	120	133	58	54	50	39
c. Mean	50.1	56.6	22.4	18.8	18.2	17.5
d. Median	46.0	44.3	19.5	16	17	17.5
e. 90th percentile			42	38	35	34
f. N	49	49	56	51	141	150

814:L77-78 Discrepancy (to nearest month) between mother's and father's report of age at onset (196A; for control group, age of child when attention was first given to nonfluency aspects of speech

a. Minimum	0	0	0
b. Maximum	108	38	37
c. Mean	15.3	10.7	5.5
d. Median	10.5	9	3
e. 90th percentile		21.4	12.9
f. N	48	39	141

815:L79-80 Difference (in months) between 196 and 237 (? responses excluded)

a. Minimum	0	0
b. Maximum	48	36
c. Mean	4.8	5.2
d. Median	2	2
e. 90th percentile	12	15.9
f. N	115	131

Statistically Significant Values of Chi-Square, Tables 2 through 37, and Associated Degrees of Freedom (E, C, M, and F Refer, Respectively, to Experimental Group, Control Group, Mother, and Father)

Item No. in Summary Table	Groups Compared	Value of Chi-Square	df	Item No. in Summary Table	Groups Compared	Value of Chi-Square	df
12	CM - EM	10.64	3	229	CM - EM	34.67	1
12	CF - EF	11.02	4	229	CF - EF	4.53	1
13	EF - EM	18.60	4	231	CF - CM	6.86	1
13	CF - CM	30.04	4	234	CM - EM	37.06	1
17	CF - CM	10.27	3	234	CF - EF	37.26	1
19	CM - EM	83.30	1	241	CM - EM	11.64	1
20	CM - EM	6.95	1	241	CF - EF	6.43	1
22	CF - CM	5.44	1	250	CM - EM	13.24	1
25	CM - EM	6.43	2	250	CF - EF	10.21	1
26	CM - EM	5.48	1	253	EF - EM	11.92	2
29	CM - EM	5.14	1	256	EF - EM	10.85	1
50	CM - EM	4.33	1	262	CM - EM	147.06	3
50	CF - CM	7.95	1	262	CF - EF	113.78	3
56	CM - EM	12.87	6	262	EF - EM	11.95	3
61	CF - CM	13.58	3	263	CM - EM	118.00	3
82	CM - EM	11.68	2	263	CF - EF	147.95	3
82	CF - CM	6.12	2	264	CM - EM	69.34	3
85	CF - EF	7.31	1	264	CF - EF	63.32	3
87	CF - EF	5.30	1	265	CM - EM	22.58	3
87	CF - CM	4.96	1	265	CF - EF	29.48	3
96	CF - EF	5.51	1	268	CM - EM	34.24	3
110	CM - EM	25.12	2	268	CF - EF	36.63	3
110	CF - EF	22.42	2	269	CM - EM	32.09	3
111	CM - EM	21.10	2	269	CF - EF	42.00	3
111	CF - EF	16.17	2	270	CM - EM	39.94	3
120	EF - EM	78.00	2	270	CF - EF	24.56	3
120	CF - CM	39.54	2	273	CM - EM	8.44	1
122	CM - EM	10.33	2	273	CF - EF	5.49	1
122	CF - EF	6.68	2	274	CM - EM	119.57	1
122	EF - EM	49.46	3	274	CF - EF	96.77	1
122	CF - CM	18.98	3	275	CM - EM	25.85	1
123	EF - EM	156.78	2	275	CF - EF	9.12	1
123	CF - CM	21.22	2	276	CM - EM	56.48	1
124	EF - EM	9.14	2	276	CF - EF	26.60	1
153	CM - EM	10.39	1	276	EF - EM	6.31	1
153	CF - EF	5.77	1	277	CM - EM	13.54	1
163	CM - EM	13.52	2	277	CF - EF	6.92	1
163	CF - EF	19.78	2	277	EF - EM	4.26	1
164	CM - EM	8.05	2	279	CM - EM	10.92	1
164	CF - EF	11.83	1	283	CM - EM	21.45	1
170	CM - EM	23.10	2	283	CF - EF	11.74	1
170	CF - EF	17.18	2	283	EF - EM	5.19	1
182	CM - EM	13.74	4	284	CM - EM	8.05	1
188	CF - EF	8.09	2	297	EF - EM	5.87	1
190	CM - EM	246.71	1	321	CM - EM	150.71	3
190	CF - EF	216.94	1	321	CF - EF	136.10	3
191	CM - EM	233.25	1	322	CM - EM	151.06	3
191	CF - EF	246.16	1	322	CF - EF	171.94	3
192	CM - EM	115.75	1	323	CM - EM	11.46	1
192	CF - EF	72.66	1	324	CM - EM	5.40	1
215	EF - EM	7.85	1	324	CF - EF	4.49	1
218	CM - EM	5.91	1	328	EF - EM	15.90	3
221	CM - EM	67.40	1	328	CF - CM	22.57	3
221	CF - EF	72.07	1	352	CM - EM	9.44	3
224	CM - EM	10.16	1	352	CF - EF	10.01	3
224	CF - EF	10.16	1	357	EF - EM	10.86	2
227	CF - EF	7.10	1	360	EF - EM	35.75	1
228	CM - EM	7.89	1	361	EF - EM	18.36	2
228	CF - EF	8.28	1	364	CM - EM	28.07	2

Item No. in Summary Table	Groups Compared	Value of Chi-Square	df	Item No. in Summary Table	Groups Compared	Value of Chi-Square	df
364	CF - EF	32.11	2	532	CF - EF	10.86	3
365	CM - EM	8.50	3	533	CM - EM	6.11	2
367	CF - EF	11.20	4	533	CF - EF	6.34	2
371	CM - EM	7.96	2	535	CM - EM	7.96	2
372	CM - EM	15.32	2	535	EF - EM	9.45	2
372	EF - EM	6.00	2	536	CM - EM	8.36	3
375	CM - EM	8.81	3	543	CF - EF	4.70	1
376	CM - EM	9.04	2	543	EF - EM	6.91	1
378	CM - EM	4.14	1	554	CM - EM	10.83	1
387	CF - EF	8.06	3	554	CF - EF	4.25	1
387	CF - CM	9.24	3	555	CF - CM	7.65	1
388	CM - EM	10.73	2	564	CM - EM	7.07	2
389	CM - EM	7.37	2	564	EF - EM	8.80	2
391	CF - EF	8.69	2	568	CM - EM	8.54	2
391	CF - CM	7.43	2	596	CF - CM	5.44	1
399	CM - EM	6.46	2	597	EF - EM	6.88	2
399	CF - EF	8.46	2	599	CM - EM	5.01	1
400	CF - CM	6.98	2	611	EF - EM	12.94	1
402	CM - EM	6.90	2	612	EF - EM	8.26	1
402	CF - EF	11.78	2	612	CF - CM	49.44	2
406	CM - EM	49.29	3	625	CM - EM	4.27	1
406	CF - EF	41.00	2	629	EF - EM	18.41	3
418	CM - EM	13.57	2	630	CM - EM	16.56	2
418	CF - EF	12.10	1	630	CF - EF	33.62	2
420	CM - EM	11.34	2	630	EF - EM	12.39	2
420	CF - EF	9.24	2	630	CF - CM	15.12	2
421	CF - CM	5.42	1	633	CF - EF	11.13	2
422	CM - EM	8.29	2	634	EF - EM	9.10	2
422	CF - EF	4.50	1	652	CM - EM	15.50	4
425	EF - EM	12.03	2	652	EF - EM	5.66	1
428	CF - EF	6.28	2	652	CF - CM	8.57	1
430	CF - EF	8.82	2	653	CM - EM	15.78	2
430	EF - EM	9.10	2	653	CF - EF	13.94	1
436	CF - EF	5.13	1	657	CM - EM	19.17	2
438	CM - EM	9.72	3	657	CF - CM	8.36	3
472	CM - EM	6.63	2	662	CM - EM	15.42	3
472	EF - EM	7.59	2	662	CF - EF	21.50	3
473	CF - CM	7.49	2	664	CM - EM	14.40	2
478	CF - CM	5.22	1	664	CF - CM	15.44	2
480	CF - EF	9.07	3	665	CM - EM	6.82	2
481	CF - EF	7.88	2	666	CF - CM	8.02	2
482	CM - EM	11.26	3	668	EF - EM	12.94	2
483	CM - EM	9.67	3	669	CM - EM	10.28	2
484	CM - EM	25.74	2	669	CF - EF	9.10	2
485	EF - FM	8.05	1	670	CM - EM	8.79	2
493	CM - EM	16.18	2	670	CF - EF	8.28	2
493	CF - EF	17.58	2	679	CF - EF	9.41	3
498	EF - EM	7.28	1	683	EF - EM	7.32	2
500	CM - EM	15.78	2	683	CF - CM	9.40	2
502	CF - EF	6.92	2	684	CF - CM	11.90	1
503	CM - EM	9.96	2	686	CF - CM	12.49	1
506	CF - CM	4.11	1	694	EF - EM	15.94	2
508	EF - EM	16.68	2	694	CF - CM	7.44	1
508	CF - CM	9.43	1	696	CM - EM	7.19	1
513	CF - EF	12.14	2	697	EF - EM	16.02	2
514	EF - EM	18.60	3	697	CF - CM	11.48	2
514	CF - CM	23.86	2	698	CF - EF	6.76	2
518	EF - EM	22.30	4	699	CM - EM	7.08	2
520	EF - EM	36.99	3	699	EF - EM	14.82	2
524	CM - EM	10.24	2	699	CF - CM	8.78	1
524	EF - EM	7.08	2	700	CF - CM	6.54	1
525	CM - EM	6.47	2	701	CF - EF	6.26	2
525	CF - EF	8.24	2	701	EF - EM	8.20	2
527	CF - EF	6.86	2	701	CF - CM	7.23	2
528	CF - EF	8.01	2	704	CF - EF	6.42	2
532	CM - EM	9.91	3	704	EF - EM	19.13	3

Item No. in Summary Table	Groups Compared	Value of Chi-Square	df	Item No. in Summary Table	Groups Compared	Value of Chi-Square	df
705	EF - EM	10.38	2	794	CF - CM	11.04	2
705	CF - CM	9.00	2	795	EF - EM	7.52	2
706	CF - CM	6.01	2	795	CF - CM	6.02	2
707	EF - EM	9.90	2	797	EF - EM	4.24	1
709	CM - EM	6.06	1	798	EF - EM	30.22	2
710	CF - EF	4.58	1	798	CF - CM	9.08	2
711	CM - EM	4.77	1	108 x 109	EM vs. EM by EF*	7.58	2
711	EF - EM	9.69	1	369 x 370	CM vs. CM by CF	6.51	2
712	CF - EF	4.02	1	369 x 370	CF vs. CF by CM	11.40	3
712	EF - EM	8.88	1	467 x 469	EF vs. EF by EM	6.59	2
713	EF - EM	21.67	1	473 x 474	CM vs. CM by CF	14.90	2
713	CF - CM	18.74	1	514 x 515	CF vs. CF by CM	6.80	2
714	EF - EM	12.50	1	518 x 520	CM vs. CM by CF	8.38	3
714	CF - CM	4.72	1	634 x 635	EM vs. EM by EF	10.12	2
716	EF - EM	10.44	2	634 x 635	EF vs. EF by EM	12.37	3
718	CF - CM	7.60	2	666 x 667	EM vs. EM by EF	13.18	1
719	CM - EM	11.42	2	666 x 667	CM vs. CM by CF	12.00	1
726	CM - EM	9.92	3	699 x 704	EM vs. EM by EF	7.83	2
741	CM - EM	7.97	3	700 x 705	CF vs. CF by CM	18.10	2
741	CF - EF	11.45	2	701 x 706	CF vs. CF by CM	6.58	2
742	CM - EM	6.40	1	702 x 707	EM vs. EM by EF	12.37	1
743	CM - EM	21.42	5	703 x 708	EM vs. EM by EF	17.26	2
747	CF - EF	28.82	6	703 x 708	CM vs. CM by CF	12.26	2
750	CF - EF	7.47	2	703 x 708	CF vs. CF by CM	15.25	2
757	EF - EM	5.78	1	738 x 739	EF vs. EF by EM	8.07	2
764	EF - EM	11.70	2	738 x 739	CM vs. CM by CF	7.10	2
770	EF - EM	10.42	1	766 x 768	CM vs. CM by CF	5.48	1
791	CF - CM	6.16	1	767 x 769	CF vs. CF by CM	6.61	1
793	EF - EM	10.24	2	623 x 642	EF vs. EF	9.37	2
793	CF - CM	15.80	2	630 x 631	EM vs. EF	6.67	2
794	EF - EM	7.58	2	630 x 631	CM vs. CF	7.65	2

*Read: Rating of experimental group mother of herself compared with the rating made of her by her husband. The following 21 entries are to be read in like fashion.